EEG AND BEHAVIOR

EEG AND BEHAVIOR

Edited by GILBERT H. GLASER, M.D

YALE UNIVERSITY SCHOOL OF MEDICINE

BASIC BOOKS, *Inc., Publishers*

NEW YORK   LONDON

Editor's Preface

This volume is based upon a research conference, "Electroencephalographic Correlates of Behavior," held at the Yale University School of Medicine, November 27 and 28, 1961. The conference was sponsored by the Department of Psychiatry, Section of Neurology, Yale University School of Medicine, the Connecticut Post-Graduate Seminar in Psychiatry and Neurology, and the American Psychiatric Association. The organizing committee consisted of Gilbert H. Glaser, Chairman, Thomas Detre, Louis B. Fierman, Daniel X. Freedman, and Burton S. Rosner. The book is not a direct record of the conference. The material presented has been expanded by the contributors. We are grateful to the many discussants, especially to Vernon Rowland and Frank Ervin, who added much to the stimulation of the endeavor. The support and encouragement of Dr. Fredrick C. Redlich, Professor and Chairman of the Department of Psychiatry, Yale University School of Medicine, are greatly appreciated.

This work represents an interdisciplinary endeavor involving neurologists, psychiatrists, psychologists, physiologists, and pharmacologists who have been using the electroencephalogram (EEG) as an indicator of brain function and reactivity. The emphasis on EEG correlates of behavior, both normal and abnormal, is somewhat more focused on the EEG than have been a number of other monographs in recent years concerned with general aspects of the brain and central nervous system and behavior. We hope that this orientation will serve to provide a direct background to these specific applications in clinical neurology and psychiatry, since the EEG is essentially a method of clinical neurophysiology. Its effective use and limitations are presented here.

The general topics considered are EEG activity in sensory responses and learning, including conditioning, neuropharmacological aspects, and epilepsy and behavior disorders. Certain significant problems related to schizophrenic states are discussed. Throughout the book, data, observations, concepts, and reviews are presented from investigations with normal human subjects, patients, and experimental animals. The title of Karl H. Pribram's chapter, "Memory, Novelty, Thought, and Choice," indicates the keynote of the work.

I want to express my gratitude to Miss Mary P. Wheeler for her invaluable assistance in the preparation of the book.

GILBERT H. GLASER

New Haven, Connecticut
September 1962

Contributors

Truett Allison
>*Department of Psychology, Yale University School of Medicine*

José M. R. Delgado
>*Department of Physiology, Yale University School of Medicine*

Thomas Detre
>*Department of Psychiatry, Yale University School of Medicine*

M. David Egger
>*Department of Psychiatry, Yale University School of Medicine*

Eduardo Eidelberg
>*Barrow Neurological Institute, Phoenix*

Robert G. Feldman
>*Section of Neurology, Department of Medicine, Yale University School of Medicine*

Max Fink
>*Missouri Institute of Psychiatry, and Department of Psychiatry and Neurology, Washington University School of Medicine*

John P. Flynn
>*Department of Psychiatry, Yale University School of Medicine*

Daniel X. Freedman
>*Department of Psychiatry, Yale University School of Medicine*

Frederick P. Gault
>*Department of Psychology, Yale University School of Medicine*

Nicholas J. Giarman
>*Department of Pharmacology, Yale University School of Medicine*

Gilbert H. Glaser
>*Section of Neurology, Department of Medicine, Yale University School of Medicine*

William R. Goff
>*Department of Psychiatry, Yale University School of Medicine*

Eli S. Goldensohn
>*Department of Neurology, Columbia University College of Physicians and Surgeons*

Robert G. Heath

Department of Psychiatry and Neurology, Tulane University School of Medicine

Charles E. Henry

Institute of Living, Hartford

Henry Lesse

The Neuropsychiatric Institute, UCLA

Richard J. Newman

Department of Psychiatry, Yale University School of Medicine

Karl H. Pribram

Department of Psychiatry, Stanford University School of Medicine

Burton S. Rosner

Department of Psychiatry, Yale University School of Medicine, and West Haven Veterans Administration Hospital

Roy Schafer

Department of Psychiatry, Yale University School of Medicine

Jerome Sutin

Department of Anatomy, Yale University School of Medicine

Takashi Tsubokawa

Department of Anatomy, Yale University School of Medicine

Lucas Van Orden

Department of Anatomy, Yale University School of Medicine

Marvin Wasman

Department of Psychiatry, Western Reserve University School of Medicine

Charles E. Wells

Division of Neurology, Department of Medicine, Vanderbilt University School of Medicine

Contents

INTRODUCTION

I

The Normal Electroencephalogram and its Reactivity

Gilbert H. Glaser

Basic to considerations of the electroencephalogram and behavior is the background of our knowledge of the EEG under normal circumstances of wakefulness, sleep, and various types of reactivity. This "normal" electroencephalogram is really a statistical concept based on its empirical correlations with physiologically and structurally normal nervous systems in presumably normal subjects.[32, 45, 67] The spontaneous electrical activity of the brain, or the electroencephalogram, was first described by Caton in 1875,[10] who detected this activity with the use of electrodes on the skull or exposed brain of rabbits and monkeys. The next fifty years in the history of this phenomenon have been recorded in a fascinating historical study by Brazier.[6] From 1924 to 1938 Berger[3] laid the groundwork of our present applications of electroencephalography. His hope that these studies would lead to significant information with regard to mental disorders has not been realized in any widespread general sense, but a gradual realization of the limitations of electroencephalography in the application of controlled information has led to significant correlations with regard to brain functioning in certain mental and behavioral states. These will be emphasized in the present work.

The Physiological Basis of the Electroencephalogram[5, 28, 55, 68]

The electroencephalogram is composed of oscillating potentials derived from the scalp surface and originating from the electrical activity of the brain. The potentials may vary in frequency from less than 1 to over 50 cycles per second and achieve amplitudes of be-

3

tween 50 and 200 μV. However, there is a concentration of frequency range in normal individuals and actually a fairly consistent, almost single, frequency dominant in most. This varies from 8 to 13 c./sec., is known as alpha rhythm, usually achieves amplitude of about 50 μV., and matures to a constant rhythmic pattern by late adolescence. The alpha rhythm appears in synchronous fashion mainly from the parietal and occipital regions[54] when the brain is "at rest" but wakeful, is sensitive to visual and sound stimuli, mental activity, drowsiness, and sleep, and exists in a metabolic setting requiring specific levels of oxygen, glucose, vitamins, electrolytes such as sodium and calcium, proteins, amino acids, lipids, and neurohumoral agents such as acetyl-choline.[8, 50, 55, 71] Evoked potentials may be physically induced, such as by photic and sound stimuli, as well as by drugs such as Metrazol. "Abnormal" or changed potentials appear in both faster and slower frequency ranges than do the alpha. Beta potentials, generally the result of activation or desynchronization, are those higher than 13 c./sec., theta rhythms are at 4–7 c./sec., and the slow delta rhythms range between 0.5 and 3.5 c./sec. The "normal" occurrence of these nonalpha rhythms is discussed below. In addition, spike discharges and spike-wave complexes may appear in abnormal states. The deviant potentials may predominate in a focal, lateralized, or generalized way, and occur paroxysmally or asynchronously at random. In addition, periods of suppression of electrical activity or periods of apparent electrical silence may occur in the electroencephalogram, alternating between episodes of abnormal slow waves. There are also correlated, steady, direct current potential differences between the cortical surface and white matter, but these have not been studied in as great detail as the alternating potentials.

Neurophysiological studies in recent years have demonstrated that the cortical projections of intralaminar nuclei, the nonspecific diencephalic relay system, affect control bilaterally over the cortex and influence arousal from sleeping states or alternations between consciousness and unconsciousness. These nuclei have direct connections with the brain stem reticular activating system, which receives collaterals from the specific sensory pathways. There is, therefore, a close correlation between electroencephalographic activity and states of awareness or alertness of the organism,[48, 70] "desynchronization" in the EEG being related to behavioral activation or arousal.

The electroencephalogram records the electrical activity mainly from neuronal units in the outer cortical mantle. Their activity is under control, as indicated above, by the lower nuclear systems, particularly those of the reticular activating system. However, current flows directly from deep units do not cause sufficiently steep voltage gradiants in the scalp or surface electrodes to detect these potential differences. Also, the impedance of cerebral tissue is high—white matter more than gray matter. The initial concept of the electroencephalographic oscillation, an essentially slow rhythm, was that it represented a summated envelope of axon spikes. Implicit in this concept would be the analysis of alpha activity as a derivative of impulse transmission, involved in refractoriness and based on rapid action potential spikes with time durations from less than 1 to 3 milliseconds. There was a gradual realization that this concept did not account for many properties of the electroencephalogram. It is now relegated mainly to the analysis of evoked potentials.

The present dominant concept concerning the major basis of the electroencephalogram is that it represents the electrical activity of dendrites. The dendrites are the most flexible functionally of the three neuronal segments: dendrite, cell body, and axon. The axon gives an all-or-none response, rapidly and with a refractory period. Dendritic responses are graded, slower, and essentially nonrefractory. The dendrites may be over 800 μ long, with ten times the surface of the cell body, up to 10,000 boutons, and contact with up to 4,000 cells. Axodendritic synapses occur all along dendrites. The uniformly radially oriented apical dendrites of pyramidal cells, therefore, could be the major contributors to the electroencephalographic potentials. Dendritic transmission is at axodendritic synapses mainly, probably as postsynaptic potentials. This activity has a long time constant, up to 700 msec. The postsynaptic potentials and the electroencephalogram may both be blocked by d-tubocurarine. Both are chemically mediated and probably are not electrically excitable. Spread is by decrement and is nonpropagated. These potentials are not all-or-nothing and reflect the strength of stimulus input. Graded responses such as these with varying stimuli are similar to analogue modes; these nonlinear responses are typical of biological systems. However, other components, particularly in the neuropil, must play some as yet unknown role. The smaller neurons and their dendrites are probably involved in excitatory-inhibitory activity. Recently interest has developed with regard to the glia, especially the astroglia and the oligoglia, which appear to be mainly metabolic supports of the neuron and are involved in electrolyte transport. However, they may be electrically active and may play a role in gating signals.

Normally, spike discharges can be elicited only with extreme difficulty from dendrites. An electroencephalographic spike, which is really a slow spike induced by epileptic discharge or secondary to a metabolic disturbance such as calcium lack, is a new entity for the system. Dendritic spikes are 15–30 msec. in duration, much slower than axon or cell body discharges. They are membrane phenomena, related to abnormal generations from apical dendrites firing from the cortical surface by effects or irritation, such as those secondary to scarring or pressure as by tumor, metabolic shifts, and triggering from lower centers via nonspecific relay after synapsing onto them in higher cortical levels. They may also be evoked by physical stimuli such as photic or sound stimulation. Microelectrode recordings from epileptic neurons have demonstrated that there is not ordinarily a close relationship between the rapid spike firing from the neuron cell body and the slower dendritic spikes. Spread of epileptiform activity occurs, then, by these neurons firing en masse and producing an overt seizure. Some degree of inhibition may occur by axonal recurrent collaterals to inhibitory interneurons, limiting degrees of depolarization.

The electroencephalogram, therefore, probably represents massed synaptic potentials of apical dendrites of mainly pyramidal cells, becoming synchronous and oscillating as fields of maximal amplitude. This property of the cerebral cortex has an ontogenetic sequence, with slower disorganized rhythms in the newborn period and in infancy gradually developing into the more rigidly defined synchronized alpha rhythms of adult life. Further controls are by impulses from the reticular activating system, varying the amount of depolarization of axodendritic synapses in the superficial cortex. These operate in relation to sensory input and states of awareness, consciousness, and sleep.

The Ontogeny of the EEG in Relation to Developing Behavior[18, 20, 34]

There have been only a few studies of the EEG derived directly from the brain of the human fetus. Low-voltage fast waves ranging from 10 to 30 c./sec. have been found superimposed upon regular low- to medium-voltage slow rhythms ranging from 1 to 3 c./sec. In certain prematures, at 5.5–6 months, 4–5 c./sec. and 9–12 c./sec. low-voltage rhythms appear superimposed upon baseline oscillations of about 0.5 c./sec. At 6 months of fetal age, interhemispheric derivations show intermittent 5 c./sec. waves, especially from the frontal regions, and at 7–8 months, there are regular variations with none of the significant faster waves seen in the younger prematures.

The electroencephalogram of the newborn human is characterized by continuous irregular asymmetric slow waves from all areas. There is no evidence of steady organized rhythms, although brief rhythmic periods may occur, lasting 0.5–4 seconds. The amplitudes range from 50 to 100 μV. and the frequencies between 0.5 and 2 c./sec. Occasionally medium-voltage, 3–4 c./sec., and low-voltage, 7–9 c./sec., waves are present. Fast 20–25 c./sec. activity from the parietal and occipital regions of the newborn usually appears for a few days and disappears, only to return later, gradually, during the first year. The records of newborn infants during the waking and sleeping states are often indistinguishable, but occasionally differentiating rhythms appear, depending upon the depth of sleep. Some infants show low-voltage, 12–14 c./sec. spindles from the central region during sleep within a few days after birth. The spindles are poorly defined and of low amplitude but later become more characteristic of the sleep spindles of older age. During drowsiness regular 2–5 c./sec. slow waves may appear, becoming better modulated with regard to frequency in amplitude as the child becomes older. Occasionally these slower waves assume spindle form during sleep, often alternating with intermittent flattening.

Arousal patterns may be clearly elicited in the newborn. Reactive arousal consists mainly of diphasic slow waves followed by rapid oscillations of about 8–14 c./sec., mainly from vertex electrodes but also from other areas in lower amplitudes. These transient responses to sensory stimulation are similar to the K complexes of older age. They should be differentiated from central sharp wave transients which appear by the age of about five or six months. The Moro reflex tends to disappear at about the time the cerebral cortex responds consistently to these reactions. A more common arousal response in the EEG of the newborn is a flattening, especially during sleep. During the waking state or sleep a loud sound may produce, 2 or 3 sec. later, flattening of the EEG which may last for 7–8 sec. Flattening responses may be preceded by a burst resembling a K complex or a single sharp theta wave. These responses also occur to visual stimulation. Definite sharp waves of 0.1–3 sec. duration in response to visual stimulation have been obtained with both on and off reactions.[21] There is a longer latency than in the adult, between 150 and 220 msec. in the newborn and young infant as compared with 50–60 msec. in the adult. Photic driving and following responses also may be obtainable even in the neonatal period in over 65 per cent of infants to repetitive stimuli, particularly at 2–3 c./sec. This type of photic stimulation may also produce a general activation of the electroencephalogram. Poor EEG responses have been correlated with fetal stress.[34]

In the young infant, correlations have been made between the early maturation of the EEG and its reactivity along with neurological and psychomotor development.[18, 25, 34] The newborn human has archaic reflexes dominated by subcortical mechanisms which also produce the Moro response, automatic walking, creeping, static straightening, grasping responses, and various immature labyrinthine phenomena which poorly control the tonus of the head. These developmental activities persist for two to three months, after which time the EEG becomes better organized, and the child develops better control of head tonus and ocular motor coordination. During the latter half of the first year, the infant develops more control of voluntary prehension, eventual sitting and the beginnings of walking, and repetitions of syllables. Associated with this maturation, the electroencephalogram develops more occipital activity in the 5–6 c./sec. range and the beginnings of organized alpha rhythm.

The EEG of the child is characterized over the early years to adolescence by the slow differentiation of rhythms.[16, 18, 32, 37, 67] Alpha activity eventually appears in the 8–13 c./sec. range from the parietal and occipital regions and becomes more definitive. Theta activity appears dominant from the frontal and temporal regions and remains so for many years into adolescence, achieving then a minimal incidence by adult life. Asymmetric localization of theta, appearing almost focally from a temporal region, may persist into adolescence and early adult life and has been correlated at times with certain personality and behavioral disorders. The dominant delta activity of the early infant rapidly disappears after the first two years, remaining in only very minimal incidence in the electroencephalograms of older individuals.

The electroencephalogram of the child is characterized by certain other reactive differences as compared with the adult. The response to hyperventilation is usually much more marked with the occurrence of bilateral synchronous and asynchronous 2–3 and 3–4 c./sec. slow waves appearing rapidly in response to the alkolosis induced by hyperventilation. By the age of 20, this response to hyperventilation should be relatively minimal with the induction of only a relatively small amount of activity, usually within the theta range. During drowsiness the EEG of the infant and young child may also present some rhythmic 4–5 c./sec. discharges which have a paroxysmal appearance but which occur entirely in response to the drowsy state. These rhythms do not occur in the adolescent or the adult. It should also be noted that it is more characteristic of the electroencephalogram of the young to be manifest, in a seizure state, by spike- and slow-wave complexes appearing synchronously or asynchronously.

In the elderly, the electroencephalogram[53] contains reduced amounts of alpha activity and a higher incidence of both faster (beta) and slower (theta and delta) rhythms. Between the ages of 65 and 79, 18 per cent of normal individuals have been found to have theta-dominant recordings, and over the age of 80 this increases to more than 30 per cent, with up to 5 per cent in the delta range. These shifts in the EEG are related to factors of both the normal aging process of cerebral neurons and the effects of cerebral arteriosclerosis.

Normal EEG Rhythms and Their Variations[7, 32, 45, 47, 67]

ALPHA

The normal alpha frequency varies between 8 and 13 c./sec. with waves of 25–100 μV., appearing mainly from the parietal and occipital regions and reduced or desynchronized by afferent stimulation, especially light, and a conscious effort for vision or mental activity. A small number of people have little or no alpha activity, and others have a persistent alpha activity even during light stimulation. Alpha variants have been designated to be well-defined alpha rhythms within the 8–13 c./sec. frequency range associated with a fast or slow rhythm which is either a multiple or submultiple of this frequency. There have been a number of attempts to relate personality and general behavior to the alpha rhythm in the EEG, but these have not generally been too successful. Short and Walter[61] have attempted to correlate alpha activity with verbal and visual imagery, finding individuals who have minimal alpha in association with marked visual imagery. Also, in the past, passive-dependent individuals have been regarded to be quite alpha-dominant with little reactivity, whereas aggressive personality characteristics were correlated with minimal alpha.[58] It is worthy of note, however, that tension, apprehension, and anxiety lead to a decrease in alpha activity.

PHOTIC STIMULATION

The response of the electroencephalogram to repetitive light (photic) stimulation has been studied in detail in the normal and also as a means of eliciting seizure discharge in predisposed subjects.[48, 52, 66] The evoked potentials appear mainly from the occipital regions, especially from the mid line (in linkage to inion). The responses then may follow the stimulus frequency, so-called "driving," when the waves occur at the same or harmonically related frequency and are locked in phase. The alpha rhythms also may be augmented or "replaced," and interaction can occur between spontaneous alpha and evoked potentials. In addition to the EEG responses, a number of subjective experiences may be elicited,[66] aside from the sensation of flicker, even in normal individuals, such as visual sensations of color, pattern, and movements, other than visual sensations as swaying, vertigo, and anxiety and confusion.

THETA

Theta activity in the 4–7 c./sec. range, as indicated, becomes minimal in adult life but may dominate the electroencephalogram in up to 5–10 per cent of a normal adult population.[51] These waves appear mainly from the temporal and adjacent parietal regions and may be somewhat asymmetrical. Eye-opening has a variable effect but usually tends to abolish or reduce these rhythms. In the child they appear in association with emotional, affective responses.[67]

DELTA

Delta activity, or slow waves in the 0.5–3.5 c./sec. range, is abnormal in the adult. It has been extremely difficult to establish any possible "normal" amount of any of these slow waves, if they ever could be regarded as normally present in alert subjects. Recently, however, occasional waves in the 3–4 c./sec. range have been found posteriorly in 10 per cent of the electroencephalograms of normal adults in the 19–22-year age group.[2] Often, unless great care is taken, it is rather difficult to distinguish between irregular theta and delta discharges appearing abnormally or merely in association with drowsiness and light sleep.

BETA

Beta activity, or rhythms faster than 13 c./sec., appears in the electroencephalograms of all adults, most commonly from the central regions and especially in response to eye-opening, attentiveness, mental activity, and anxiety or apprehension. It may behave independently of alpha activity,[51] representing a "desynchronized" electroencephalogram.[48]

MU

Rhythm rolandique en arceau, mu rhythm, comb or wicket rhythm,[11] has also been described in the normal EEG in about 7 per cent of the instances, gradually diminishing after the age of thirty. These waves appear as runs of 9–11 c./sec., with rounded negative and sharp or pointed positive aspects, appearing bilaterally from the central regions, and diminished by actual movement or intention of moving of the contralateral limbs. It is not affected by the usual stimuli that affect alpha rhythm such as visual or mental efforts.

LAMBDA

Lambda waves also have been described in normal electroencephalograms, appearing usually when the individual is visually attentive to an object of interest.[23] The lambda waves appear mainly from the occipital region, but they may extend into the parietal and occur as random electropositive sharp or saw-tooth waves of about 250 msec. in duration. They are often correlated with marked photic responses, and have been found to occur in many adult subjects, primarily from an electrode placed in the region of the inion.

VERTEX WAVES

These are electronegative waves of 100 μV. amplitude, sharp in appearance, which may appear in fully alert individuals, especially children, in the absence of overt stimulation.[30] At the present time it is not certain whether this is a normal or abnormal phenomenon, but it does appear frequently enough in presumably normal individuals to come into question. A higher incidence of these waves has been noticed in individuals with epilepsy or encephalopathies of various causes.

The Electroencephalogram During Sleep

Much of our knowledge of the electroencephalogram during sleep, particularly in relation to age, is from the work of Gibbs and Gibbs,[32] who have also emphasized the activation, by sleep, of seizure discharges in the EEG of patients with psychomotor-temporal lobe epilepsy. The characteristic features of the EEG of the newborn and young infant during drowsiness and sleep have been commented upon above. In the adult, drowsiness is characterized by a tendency of the electroencephalogram to develop a flattening along with the appearance of irregular theta activity in the 4–7 c./sec. frequency range. This type of reaction occurs after the age of six or seven and continues throughout adult life. After the sixth decade, a common occurrence in drowsiness consists of large slow waves which appear bifrontally. The paroxysmal slow waves occurring in the drowsy states of young children are quite rare after the age of 15.

During light sleep, after the first six months and continuing throughout the first decade of life, biparietal sharp waves appear, often associated with low-voltage fast activity, or 12–14 c./sec. spindles. Positive sharp waves from the occipital regions also occur from early childhood throughout adult life.

During deep sleep, the biparietal sharp waves and spindles are less well formed, and the EEG is characterized by the appearance of irregular asynchronous slow waves, which vary in frequency from 0.5 to 3 c./sec. and achieve an amplitude of 100 or more μV. Irregular faster waves in the theta frequencies may be superimposed. During moderately deep sleep, 10–12 c./sec. spindles may be seen intermittently.

Arousal responses in adults are usually those of a rapid return to the normal patterns of the electroencephalogram during the waking state. In the infant and young child, however, arousal is characterized by the appearance of high-amplitude slow waves in the 4–5 c./sec. range, appearing synchronously and often in paroxysmal fashion quite similar to the pattern previously described in drowsiness.

During drowsiness and light sleep, the EEG remains quite reactive to sensory stimuli, such as light or sound, usually with the occurrence of vertex sharp waves, either occurring singly or followed by synchronous high-amplitude irregular slow-wave activity, the so-called K complex.[57] This complex is more distinctly elicited during moderately deep sleep, when it is often followed by increased 12–14 c./sec. spindle activity.

It should be noted that the sleep induced by sedatives[70] is characterized in the light phase by low-voltage fast or beta activity, often quite sharp and "spiking" in appearance. This type of activity is most prominent with barbiturate administration but may occur also with the nonbarbiturate hypnotics such as chloral hydrate or paraldehyde. The deeper sleep states following drug administration are quite similar to those of natural sleep, with the exception that response to sensory stimulation may be somewhat more difficult to elicit.

Recently Dement and Kleitman[17] attempted to correlate certain cyclic variations in the EEG during sleep in relation to eye movements and dreaming. A correlation was found between pronounced, rapid eye movements, a light sleep stage with low-amplitude beta activity without spindling in the electroencephalogram, and probably dreaming. It was noted that hypnagogic reveries occurring during the stage of falling asleep apparently ceased when the EEG reached a stage of spindling. The visual imagery during dreaming was considered to be related to these phenomena.

The Electroencephalogram and Behavioral Disorders

During the last twenty years there have been many attempts to correlate deviation from normality in the EEG with abnormal behavior.[19, 25, 39, 40, 43, 44, 46] These correlations have been beset by the inherent problems within both of these contexts. Statistical conceptualizations developed which often had questionable validity. Deviation or abnormality in the electroencephalogram has included the following descriptive alterations: an excessive amount of slow-wave activity in both the theta and delta frequencies appearing intermittently, continuously, paroxysmally, or focally; the occurrence of epileptiform discharge either generally or focally in the form of spikes and spike-wave complexes of varying configurations; alterations in responsivity of the EEG to various stimuli induced by light,[52, 66] sounds or drugs such as Metrazol; excessive responsivity of the EEG to hyperventilation, or other stresses such as induced hypoglycemia. Measurements of thresholds of activation have also accompanied the provocation tests, such as with light stimulation and Metrazol (photic-Metrazol myoclonic threshold).[27]

The background of these studies rested upon empirical data accumulated from so-called normal populations, which gave the normal frequency distributions of electroencephalographic waves in various age groups. One striking feature of the electroencephalogram, however, is that there is a great amount of individual variation; although norms may be established, there is still much uncertainty about, for example, how much theta activity might be expected within the population of normal adolescents. There is less doubt concerning the persistence of focal slow-wave discharges and the occurrence of epileptiform discharges, but, even with regard to the appearance of the latter types of discharge, some questions might still be raised in individual instances where recordings may be taken from subjects who are relatives of epileptic patients and who might have transient appearance of such "abnormality" in the EEG, without any other etiologic significance in relation to a behavioral disorder. The data from the various provocation tests have shown such a great variation within so-called normal populations that, despite initial interest and enthusiasm, there has been much less reliance upon such measurements in the last five years.

The same type and degree of reservation may be applied to clinical diagnostic categories within the realm of behavioral disorders. In the most gross way, these might be divided into those disorders secondary to definite "organic" diseases of the brain, or "encephalopathy," such as following head injury, with encephalitis, in association with metabolic disease, or in relation to an epileptic state or disorder; and "functional" disorders of behavior such as those related to defects in personality development due to psychologic disturbances and environmental influences. Over the years there have been many studies of the EEG in "behavior disorders" of childhood as well as of adults. Many of these studies suffer from lack of appropriate etiologic diagnosis of the basic behavioral disturbance. Overall, however, a relatively high incidence of electroencephalographic abnormality has been described, varying from 40 to 75 per cent of instances. In general, this abnormality is that of an excessive amount of theta or delta activity appearing at random or even in paroxysmal fashion, and occasionally focally, mainly from the temporal regions. In many instances, particularly when there does not appear to be an "organic" etiologic factor in the background, the concept of "immaturity" in the electroencephalogram has been invoked. This merely indicates that there has been a persistence of slower wave patterns in the EEG than ordinarily would be present at the particular age of the subject, since in younger individuals there is a higher incidence of slow-wave activity in the theta and delta frequency ranges. However, it is not possible to differentiate these slow-wave discharges from those which might be present as a consequence of an "organic" disturbance of brain function. This type of abnormality or electroencephalographic deviation therefore is essentially quite nonspecific. Also, the problem is compounded by the occurrence of these deviations in such different types of behavioral disturbances as nocturnal enuresis, aggressive antisocial behavior, and stammering.

In 1952 Hill published an intensive study of individuals with psychopathic behavior, particularly the aggressive, and found a high incidence of EEG abnormality indicative of maturational disturbance or lag.[40] Three types appeared: first, bilateral theta activity in excess of normal, particularly from the temporal and central regions (22 per cent as compared with about 10 per cent in a control group); second, alpha rhythm variants with harmonic components, particularly subharmonic (3 per cent as compared with 1 per cent of controls); and third, posterior temporal slow-wave focal discharges appearing episodically in 20 per cent of his cases as compared with 2 per cent of controls. In a similar group of individuals, bilateral occipital slow-wave discharges were correlated with aggressive behavior by Cohn and Nardini.[14] Also a mid-temporal spike focus of abnormality has been correlated with severely aggressive, hypermotile disturbed behavior.[31] Hill emphasized that the appearance of presumed maturational disturbances in the electroencephalogram is a rather alternating one and much more discontinuous than the type of abnormality that might appear following an encephalitis or head injury. However, this is not too clear or valid a distinction.

There have been a number of studies of electroencephalograms from individuals with criminal psychopathic tendencies, particularly those who had committed aggressive acts including murder.[63] A high incidence, up to over 70 per cent, had been found, the EEG abnormalities usually being those indicated above with the excessive slow-wave categories. The association of 14 and 6 c./sec. discharges with these types of behavioral disturbances will be discussed in a later section of this present work.

"Functional" Psychiatric Disorders

The electroencephalogram has been studied in psychoneurotic states including anxiety, hysterical disorders, and obsessive-compulsive disturbances.[19, 29, 39] During anxiety and tension there is a relatively high incidence of low-voltage fast, or beta, activity and a lesser incidence of well-organized alpha activity. Photic stimulation was found to show less driving than normal within the range of 8–10 c./sec., but more with slower and higher frequencies. In addition, an increase in anxiety and other symptoms occurred with photic stimulation, more so in patients with neuroses than in normal individuals.[65]

Much interest has been developed recently in sensory deprivation states and their relation to various mental disorders. Sensory deprivation eventually produces marked distortions in perception with visual-spatial distortions and hallucinations.[38] The EEG during these states has been found to be desynchronized with disappearance of alpha activity and to show increases in beta activity, slowing of alpha frequency, and increased amounts of diffuse theta rhythms.[38]

In affective disorders, such as manic-depressive psychosis, no significant alterations in the electroencephalogram have been found aside from a scatter somewhat greater than "normal" of basic alpha frequencies. Shagass[59] described a technic of determining "sedation threshold" in relation to the induction of fast activity in the EEG by the intravenous administration of amobarbital. A low threshold was found in organic psychotic states and higher thresholds in schizophrenia. A high threshold occurred in neurotic depression, whereas a low threshold was found in endogenous depressive states. These results have been found difficult to confirm.[1]

The Electroencephalogram in Schizophrenia

There have been many studies attempting to correlate electroencephalographic abnormalities with schizophrenia.[19, 39, 41] It is now realized that there may be a number of different personality and behavioral disorders appearing within this concept, but with special characteristics warranting a differentiation between schizophrenia, a specific entity, and schizophrenic-like psychotic reactions which appear in relation to metabolic or structural disease of the brain, as in epileptic states and metabolic disorders. Schizophrenia, as such, is a form of personality disorganization with faulty ego development and aberrant mentation with distorted symbolic processes. These individuals withdraw from reality and alter the world autistically. The electroencephalograms of such individuals usually do not reveal any specific pattern of disorder and may be generally within the normal range. Various investigations, however, of different groups of schizophrenic patients have indicated a frequency of 20–60 per cent abnormality, mainly including excessive amounts of activity within the theta frequency ranges, greater than would be seen within a group of individuals of similar age. The incidence of these alterations appears more in patients with a predominantly catatonic schizophrenia rather than in paranoid states. In addition, the schizophrenic subject has been found to respond to stimulation by electroencephalographic rather than distinct behavioral "arousal."[24]

However, there are certain special instances. In the "periodic catatonias," which are relatively rare and are probably related to a metabolic disturbance, possibly involving thyroid and adrenal functions, the EEG may show a relatively high incidence of slow-wave discharges in the theta and delta ranges during the acute episodes. Abnormal electrical activity with various epileptiform, or seizure, characteristics was recorded by Hill[41] in 20–25 per cent of his schizophrenic subjects. These consisted of fast spike-and-wave complexes in

the 4–5 c./sec. range and bilaterally synchronous slow-wave discharges. A relatively high incidence of these disturbances was found in patients with catatonic schizophrenia. It is necessary to evaluate such patients in great detail clinically because of a possibility that in some of them the "schizophrenic" state might be merely a reflection of an underlying seizure disorder which actually has produced the electroencephalographic abnormality. More recently a number of patients diagnosed as schizophrenic have been found by Sherwood[60] to show paroxysmal spiking and slow-wave activity in the electroencephalograms and in depth recordings from deep, centrally located regions. The relationship between these phenomena and subcortical diencephalic discharges in patients with a clearly defined seizure state is still uncertain and will be discussed later in this volume in relation to psychotic states occurring in patients with psychomotor-temporal lobe epilepsy.

The Electroencephalogram in Encephalopathies

In contrast to the relative paucity of abnormal electroencephalographic findings in the functional disturbances of behavior and personality, the EEG may alter significantly in individuals whose behavior is being changed by disease of brain functioning, be it strictly metabolic or actually producing structural lesions. These EEG abnormalities may be focal or generalized, random or paroxysmal, and consist primarily of alterations in alpha activity and the appearance of a gradually increasing incidence of slow-wave discharges in the theta and eventually delta frequency ranges. There is often a good correlation between the intensity of the behavioral disturbance, the disorder of mental functions, and the EEG abnormality. However, this is not always the case since the electroencephalograph records mainly from brain surface, and the electrical disturbance may be rather deep subcortically or involve the brain stem and remain localized. Recent investigations of the EEG during coma[26, 49] have indicated that although in many cases diffuse high-voltage slow delta wave activity may be present, in some cases "normal" electrocortical activity may appear, as well as more focal alterations. Reactivity to auditory and visual stimuli during coma is quite variable, only occasionally may be correlated with depth of coma, and is more frequent in cases with unilateral or focal EEG changes.[49]

These electroencephalographic alterations, then, are essentially non-specific and reflect only a degree of localized or generalized cerebral dysfunction. A mild encephalopathy might merely slow a basic alpha rhythm from 11 c./sec. to 8 c./sec. and might be associated with the gradual appearance of theta activity first at 6 or 7 c./sec. and then later at 4 c./sec. as a dementia becomes more severe.[69] This type of alpha shift and abnormal theta development has been demonstrated quite graphically in studies of delirium, whatever the cause, by Engel and Romano.[22] Similar changes are recorded in the Alzheimer-Pick presenile dementias, with progressive worsening, focally or generally, and usually but not always correlated with clinical deterioration. Changes that are associated with increases in cerebral excitability and the production of seizures will, in addition, be characterized by the development of epileptiform or paroxysmal discharge in the EEG as in states of tumor, encephalitis, or hypocalcemia.[36] Various metabolic disorders[9, 15, 26, 33, 35, 42, 50, 64] may produce merely nonspecific slow-wave deviations as in hypoglycemia, hyponatremia, uremia, Addison's disease, Cushing's syndrome, myxedema, and hepatic insufficiency. Both oxygen lack and carbon dioxide excess may be associated with similar diffuse slow-wave abnormality in the EEG.

There are a number of states wherein certain special patterns may be seen. While these are not actually pathognomic, they may be suggestive of a certain type of brain disorder. In the encephalopathy associated with acute and chronic liver disease, in the beginning there might be only random theta discharge, but eventually periodic delta waves in the 2–3 c./sec. range occur and occasionally assume a triphasic complex appearance.[4, 62] In subacute encephalitis[12, 56] and cerebral lipidosis[13] a similar periodicity of discharge may occur with such slow waves and associated sharp spiking discharges alternating with periods of almost electrical silence or beta activity. The tendency for the electroencephalogram in states of severe encephalopathy to assume such periodicity[47] has been noted, therefore, in a number of disorders associated with diffuse bilateral brain damage in both cortical and subcortical regions.

References

1. ACKNER, B. and PAMPIGLIONE, G., "An Evaluation of the Sedation Threshold Test," *J. psychosom. Res.*, 3:271, 1959.

2. AIRD, R. B. and GASTAUT, Y., "Occipital and Posterior Electroencephalographic Rhythms," *Electroenceph. clin. Neurophysiol.*, 11:637, 1959.

3. BERGER, H., "Das Elektrenkephalogramm des Menschen," *Acta nova Leopoldina*, 6:173, 1938.

4. BICKFORD, R. G. and BUTT, H. R., "Hepatic Coma: The Electroencephalographic Patterns," *J. clin. Invest.*, 34:790, 1955.

5. BRAZIER, M. A. B., "The Development of Concepts Relating to the Electrical Activity of the Brain," *J. nerv. ment. Dis.*, 126:303–321, 1958.

6. BRAZIER, M. A. B., *A History of the Electrical Activity of the Brain. The First Half Century*, Macmillan, New York, 1961.

7. BRAZIER, M. A. B. *et al.*, "Proposal for an EEG Terminology by the Terminology Committee of the International Federation for Electroencephalography and Clinical Neurophysiology," *Electroenceph. clin. Neurophysiol.*, 13:646–650, 1961.

8. BRAZIER, M. A. B., FINESINGER, J. E., and SCHWAB, R. S., "Characteristics of the Normal Electroencephalogram. II. The Effect of Varying Blood Sugar Levels on the Occipital Cortical Potentials in Adults During Quiet Breathing," *J. clin. Invest.*, 23:313, 1944.

9. CADILHAC, J., RIBSTEIN, M., and LEAN, R., "EEG et Troubles Métaboliques," *Rev. neurol.*, 100:270, 1959.

10. CATON, R., "The Electric Currents of the Brain," *Brit. med. J.*, 2:278, 1875.

11. CHATRIAN, G. E., PETERSEN, M. D., and LAZARTE, J. A., "The Blocking of the Rolandic Wicket Rhythm and Some Central Changes Related to Movement," *Electroenceph. clin. Neurophysiol.*, 11:497, 1959.

12. COBB, W. and HILL, D., "Electroencephalogram in Subacute Progressive Encephalitis," *Brain*, 73:392, 1950.

13. COBB, W., MARTIN, F., and PAMPIGLIONE, G., "Cerebral Lipidosis: An Electroencephalographic Study," *Brain*, 75:343, 1952.

14. COHN, R. and NARDINI, J. E., "The Correlation of Bilateral Occipital Slow Wave Activity in the Human EEG with Certain Disorders of Behavior," *Amer. J. Psychiat.*, *115*:44, 1959.

15. CONDON, J. V., BECKA, D. R., and GIBBS, F. A., "Electroencephalographic Abnormalities in Endocrine Disease," *New Engl. J. Med.*, *251*:638, 1954.

16. CORBIN, H. P. F. and BICKFORD, R. G., "Studies of the Electroencephalogram of Normal Children: Comparison of Visual and Automatic Frequency Analyses," *Electroenceph. clin. Neurophysiol.*, *7*:15, 1955.

17. DEMENT, W. and KLEITMAN, N., "Cyclic Variations in EEG During Sleep and Their Relation to Eye Movements, Body Motility and Dreaming," *Electroenceph. clin. Neurophysiol.*, *9*:673, 1957.

18. DREYFUS-BRISAC, C. and BLANC, C., "Électroencéphalogramme et Maturation Cérébrale," *Encéphale*, *45*:205, 1956.

19. ELLINGSON, R. J., "The Incidence of EEG Abnormality Among Patients with Mental Disorders of Apparently Non-organic Origin: A Critical Review," *Amer. J. Psychiat.*, *111*:263, 1955.

20. ELLINGSON, R. J., "Electroencephalograms of Normal, Full-term Newborns Immediately After Birth with Observations on Arousal and Visual Evoked Responses," *Electroenceph. clin. Neurophysiol.*, *10*:31, 1958.

21. ELLINGSON, R. J., "Cortical Electrical Responses to Visual Stimulations in the Human Infant," *Electroenceph. clin. Neurophysiol.*, *12*:663, 1960.

22. ENGEL, G. L. and ROMANO, J., "Delirium, a Syndrome of Cerebral Insufficiency," *J. chron. Dis.*, *9*:260, 1959.

23. EVANS, C. C., "Spontaneous Excitation of the Visual Cortex and Association Areas—Lambda Waves," *Electroenceph. clin. Neurophysiol.*, *5*:69, 1953.

24. FEDIO, P., MIRSKY, A. F., SMITH, W. J., and PARRY, D., "Reaction Time and EEG Activation in Normal and Schizophrenic Subjects," *Electroenceph. clin. Neurophysiol.*, *13*:923, 1961.

25. FISCHGOLD, H. and GASTAUT, H., *Conditionnement et Réactivité en Électroencéphalographie*, Masson et Cie, Paris, 1957.

26. FISCHGOLD, H. and MATHIS, P., *Obnubilations, Comas et Stupeurs. Études Électroencéphalographiques*, Masson et Cie, Paris, 1959.

27. GASTAUT, H., "Combined Photic and Metrazol Activation of the Brain," *Electroenceph. clin. Neurophysiol.*, *12*:249, 1960.

28. GASTAUT, H., "The Brain Stem and Cerebral Electrogenesis in Relation to Consciousness," in *Brain Mechanisms and Consciousness*, Charles C Thomas, Springfield, Ill., 1954.

29. GASTAUT, H., DONGIER, S., and DONGIER, M., "Electroencephalography and Neuroses: Study of 240 Cases," *Electroenceph. clin. Neurophysiol.* *12*:233, 1960.

30. GASTAUT, Y., "Les Pointes Négatives Évoquées sur le Vertex; Leur Signification Psychophysiologique et Pathologique," *Rev. neurol.*, 89:328, 1953.

31. GIBBS, F. A., "Abnormal Electrical Activity in the Temporal Regions and Its Relationship to Abnormalities of Behavior," *Res. Publ. Ass. nerv. ment. Dis.*, 26:278, 1956.

32. GIBBS, F. A. and GIBBS, E. L., *Atlas of Electroencephalography*, vol. 1, *Methodology and Controls*, Addison-Wesley Press, Cambridge, Mass., 1950.

33. GLASER, G. H., "EEG Activity and Adrenal Cortical Dysfunction," *Electroenceph. clin. Neurophysiol.*, 10:366, 1958.

34. GLASER, G. H., "The Neurological Status of the Newborn: Neuromuscular and Electroencephalographic Activity," *Yale J. Biol. Med.*, 32:173, 1959.

35. GLASER, G. H., "Metabolic Encephalopathy in Hepatic, Renal and Pulmonary Disorders," *Postgrad. Med.*, 27:611, 1960.

36. GLASER, G. H. and LEVY, L. L., "Seizures and Idiopathic Hypoparathyroidism. A Clinical-electroencephalographic Study," *Epilepsia*, 1:454, 1960.

37. HENRY, C. E., "Electroencephalograms of Normal Children," *Monogr. Soc. Child Developm.*, 9, Serial 39, no. 3, 1944.

38. HERON, W., "Cognitive and Physiological Effects of Perceptual Isolation," in *Sensory Deprivation*, Harvard University Press, Cambridge, 1961, pp. 6–33.

39. HILL, D., "Psychiatry," in HILL, D. and PARR, G., *Electroencephalography*, Macdonald and Co., London, 1950, Chap. XI.

40. HILL, D., "EEG in Episodic Psychiatric and Psychopathic Behavior," *Electroenceph. clin. Neurophysiol.*, 4:419, 1952.

41. HILL, D., "The Electroencephalogram in Schizophrenia," in RICHTER, D. (ed.), *Schizophrenia: Somatic Aspects*, Pergamon Press, London, 1957.

42. HOEFER, P. F. A., GUTTMAN, S. A., and SANDS, I. S., "Convulsive States and Coma in Cases of Islet Cell Adenomas of Pancreas." *Amer. J. Psychiat.*, 102:486, 1946.

43. JASPER, H. H., SOLOMON, P., and BRADLEY, C., "Electroencephalographic Analyses of Behavior Problem Children," *Amer. J. Psychiat.*, 95:641, 1938.

44. KENNARD, M. A., RABINOVITCH, M. S., and FISTER, W. P., "The Use of Frequency Analysis in the Interpretation of the EEGs of Patients with Psychological Disorders," *Electroenceph. clin. Neurophysiol.*, 7:29, 1955.

45. KILOH, L. G. and OSSELTON, J. W., *Clinical Electroencephalography*, Butterworths, London, 1961.

46. KNOTT, J. R. and GOTTLIEB, J. S., "Electroencephalographic Evaluation of Psychopathic Personality—Correlations with Age, Sex, Family History

and Antecedent Illness or Injury," *Arch Neurol. Psychiat., Chicago,* 52:515, 1944.

47. LESSE, S., HOEFER, P. F. A., and AUSTIN, J. H., "The Electroencephalogram in Diffuse Encephalopathies," *Arch. Neurol. Psychiat., Chicago,* 79:359, 1958.

48. LINDSLEY, D. B., "Psychological Function and the Electroencephalogram," *Electroenceph. clin. Neurophysiol.,* 4:443, 1952.

49. LOEB, C., "Electroencephalographic Changes During the State of Coma," *Electroenceph. clin. Neurophysiol.,* 10:589, 1958.

50. MEYER, J. S. and GASTAUT, H., *Cerebral Anoxia and the Electroencephalogram,* Charles C Thomas, Springfield, Ill., 1961.

51. MUNDY-CASTLE, A. C., "Theta and Beta Rhythm in the Electroencephalograms of Normal Adults," *Electroenceph. clin. Neurophysiol.,* 3:477, 1951.

52. MUNDY-CASTLE, A. C., "An Analysis of Central Responses to Photic Stimulation in Normal Adults," *Electroenceph. clin. Neurophysiol.,* 5:1, 1953.

53. OBRIST, W. D., "The Electroencephalogram of Normal Aged Adults," *Electroenceph. clin. Neurophysiol.,* 6:235, 1954.

54. PEREZ-BORJA, C., CHATRIAN, G. E., TYCE, F. A., and RIVERS, M. H., "Electrographic Patterns of the Occipital Lobe in Man: a Topographic Study based on Use of Implanted Electrodes," *Electroenceph. clin. Neurophysiol.,* 14:171–182, 1962.

55. PURPURA, D. P., "Nature of Electrocortical Potentials and Synaptic Organizations in Cerebral and Cerebellar Cortex," *Int. Rev. Neurobiol.,* 1:47, 1959.

56. RADERMECKER, J., *Systématique et Électroencéphalographie des Encéphalites et Encéphalopathies,* Masson et Cie, Paris, 1956.

57. ROTH, M., SHAW, J., and GREEN, J., "The Form, Voltage Distribution and Physiological Significance of the K-complex," *Electroenceph. clin. Neurophysiol.,* 8:385, 1956.

58. SAUL, L. J., DAVIS, H., and DAVIS, P. A., "Psychologic Correlations with the Electroencephalogram," *Psychosom. Med.,* 11:361, 1949.

59. SHAGASS, C., "The Sedation Threshold. A Method for Estimating Tension in Psychiatric Patients," *Electroenceph. clin. Neurophysiol.,* 6:221, 1954.

60. SHERWOOD, S. L., "The Relevance of Some Neurophysiological Data to Behavior Disorders," in *Neurological Basis of Behavior, CIBA Symposium,* Little, Brown & Co., Boston, 1958, pp. 359–379.

61. SHORT, P. L. and WALTER, W. G., "The Relationship Between Physiological Variables and Stereognosis," *Electroenceph. clin. Neurophysiol.,* 6:29, 1954.

62. SILVERMAN, D., "Some Observations on the EEG in Hepatic Coma," *Electroenceph. clin. Neurophysiol., 14*:53–59, 1962.

63. STAFFORD-CLARK, D. and TAYLOR, F. H., "Clinical and Electroencephalographic Studies of Prisoners Charged with Murder," *J. Neurol. Psychiat. Neurosurg., 12*:325, 1949.

64. THIEBAUT, F., ROHMER, F., and WACKENHEIM, A., "Contribution à l'Étude Électroencéphalographique des Syndromes Endocriniens," *Electroenceph. clin. Neurophysiol., 10*:1, 1958.

65. ULETT, G. A., GLESER, G., WINOKUR, G., and LAWLER, A., "The EEG and Reaction to Photic Stimulation as an Index of Anxiety-proneness," *Electroenceph. clin. Neurophysiol., 5*:23, 1953.

66. WALTER, V. S. and WALTER, W. G., "The Central Effects of Rhythmic Sensory Stimulation," *Electroenceph. clin. Neurophysiol., 1*:57, 1949.

67. WALTER, W. G., "Normal Rhythms. Their Development, Distribution and Significance," in HILL, D. and PARR, G., *Electroencephalography*, Macdonald and Co., London, 1950, Chap. VII.

68. WALTER, W. G., "Intrinsic Rhythms of the Brain," in FIELD, J., *Handbook of Physiology, Section 1: Neurophysiology*, vol. 1, American Physiological Society, Washington, D. C., 1959, pp. 279–298.

69. WEINER, H. and SCHUSTER, D. B., "The Electroencephalogram in Dementia. Some Preliminary Observations and Correlations," *Electroenceph. clin. Neurophysiol., 8*:479, 1956.

70. WIKLER, A., *The Relation of Psychiatry to Pharmacology, Section III: Neurophysiological Aspects*, Williams & Wilkins, Baltimore, 1957.

71. WOODBURY, D. M., "Effect of Hormones on Brain Excitability and Electrolytes," *Recent Progr. Hormone Res., 10*:65, 1954.

Part One

SENSORY SYSTEMS AND LEARNING

II

Alpha Wave Responsiveness to Light in Man

Charles E. Wells

Berger[3] reported in 1929 that he had recorded electrical activity of the human brain through the intact skull. This pioneer work was largely ignored until similar investigations were carried out in Adrian's laboratory at Cambridge. Then, in 1934, Adrian and Matthews[1] published their classic paper entitled "The Berger Rhythm; Potential Changes from the Occipital Lobes in Man," confirming to a large extent Berger's observations. When a scientist of Adrian's stature demonstrated electrical activity of the brain recorded through the intact skull, even the most skeptical were convinced.

Adrian and Matthews described regular potential oscillations at approximately 10 c./sec. detected by electrodes applied to the scalp. They agreed with Berger's conclusion that these waves were due to electrical activity of the cortex; they demonstrated, however, that these waves arose from the occipital lobes and not from the whole cortex as Berger had contended. Investigating the response of this activity (which became known as alpha activity) to light and other stimuli, they proposed that as the essential condition for the presence of the alpha activity there be no pattern vision. A problem requiring the whole attention of the individual was likewise found to abolish the alpha rhythm even though the eyes were kept closed.* Within a

---

* There is for any author a problem of terminology for the disappearance or attenuation of alpha waves following stimulation. It has been variously entitled activation, desynchronization, arousal, blocking reaction, and so on—terms comprehensible to the neurophysiologist but implying more understanding of the underlying mechanisms than is warranted by fact. The French term *réaction d'arrêt* is perhaps the most accurate descriptive term for the phenomenon, eschewing any implication of the underlying physiological mechanisms.

few months, investigators in Europe and America began to utilize the methods of Berger, Adrian, and Matthews in an attempt to unravel the tangled problems of neural function.

In what Morrell[25] has called "a fine example of serendipity," Durup and Fessard[7] in 1935 discovered that these alpha waves were capable of being conditioned. Durup and Fessard were studying the response of alpha waves to visual stimuli, using a camera to photograph changes in alpha activity after the appearance of a bright light. The click associated with opening the camera shutter had no effect by itself on the alpha activity. When, however, the click was presented in conjunction with the light, they noted that after a few such temporal associations the click began to cause disappearance of alpha activity just as had the light. If the click were then presented several times without visual reinforcement, it ceased to affect the alpha activity. Durup and Fessard interpreted this observation to indicate the development of a conditioned reflex; i.e., an auditory stimulus (the conditioned stimulus), previously having no effect upon the alpha activity, had, by its temporal association with the light (the unconditioned stimulus), which routinely caused disappearance of the alpha waves, acquired the ability to effect disappearance of the alpha activity.

A similar observation was made almost simultaneously by Loomis et al.:[23] "If the subject lies in complete darkness with eyes open, a low tone stimulus lasting five seconds will not stop the alpha waves. If the low tone and also the light stimulus are both presented simultaneously several times in succession at half minute intervals, the waves will of course stop, due to the attempt to see induced by the light, but if now the tone alone is sounded the waves also stop as the attempt is now induced by the sound. However, the effect of the tone alone will not last more than two or three times as the conditioning is not permanent and the sound no longer induces the attempt to see."

Two years later, Travis and Egan[35] reported results of more elaborate experiments designed to investigate conditioning of alpha activity. The response of the subjects' alpha waves to sound alone and to light alone was first tested. The tone alone was followed by disappearance or striking diminution of the amplitude of the alpha activity in 11 per cent of 643 presentations, while light alone was effective in 99 per cent of 344 presentations. The sound and the light stimuli were then presented together, the sound preceding the light by 0.48 to 0.75 sec. During the paired stimulations, disappearance of the alpha activity followed the sound before appearance of the light in 35 per cent of the records. These observations were interpreted to indicate true conditioning of the alpha activity in man.

Knott and Henry[19] re-evaluated the data of Travis and Egan,[35] noting that tone was just as effective in producing alpha blockade in the first one-fifth of the paired presentations as in each of the subsequent four-fifths: that is, there was no curve of increasing effectiveness as pairing of sound and light continued. In their opinion, this did not resemble conditioning, but rather sensitization. In similar studies, Knott and Henry confirmed that sound might be followed by disappearance of alpha activity when it was associated temporally with light. They interpreted this phenomenon, however, as a "conditioned anticipatory response" instead of a conditioned reflex in the Pavlovian sense.

In a detailed study published the same year, Jasper and Shagass[15] demonstrated conditioning of the alpha activity to essentially all forms of Pavlovian conditioning—simple, cyclic, differential, delayed, differential delayed, and backward. More elaborate forms of alpha wave conditioning were developed in this experiment than in others, possibly because these subjects were instructed to press a button whenever light appeared. Even so, Jasper and Shagass found these conditioned responses to be unstable.

Another form of electroencephalographic conditioning, but of an opposite type, was described in 1943 by Beritov and Vorobyev (quoted by Rusinov and Smirnov[32]). They performed an experiment in which darkness was the unconditioned stimulus, disappearance of light causing the *appearance* of alpha activity. When the indifferent stimulus and darkness were combined, the indifferent stimulus acquired the ability to cause the appearance of alpha activity in a previously desynchronized record.

Except for this study, investigation of alpha wave conditioning in man was largely quiescent during World War II, only to be revived with accelerated activity in the postwar era. As early as 1947, Gershuni (quoted by Rusinov and Smirnov[32]) reported the use of subaudible levels of sound as the conditioning stimulus. He demonstrated the development of a conditioned cerebral response when a subaudible sound (conditioned stimulus) was combined with an unconditioned stimulus such as a bright light.

Morrell,[27] with Ross, published in 1958 his first paper on conditioned cerebral responses, initiating a renaissance of interest in the subject in this country. In this paper, he demonstrated again that by pairing a conditioned and an unconditioned cerebral stimulus, the conditioned stimulus acquired the ability to cause obliteration of the alpha activity as did the unconditioned stimulus. In addition, three distinct forms of Pavlovian inhibition were exhibited: extinction of the conditioned reflex, delayed conditioning, and differential inhibition. The interest in cerebral conditioned responses engendered by this paper resulted in many studies, a few carried out in man but most in experimental animals. Only observations relevant to human conditioning will be considered here.

Mayorchik and Spirin (quoted by Rusinov and Smirnov[33]) had already shown that when rhythmic photic stimulation was employed as the unconditioned stimulus, after several combinations the conditioned stimulus sometimes provoked rhythmic activity with a frequency close to that of the photic stimulation. This was subsequently confirmed by Rusinov and Pavlygina,[32] who found that a conditioned response reflecting a rhythmic unconditioned stimulus could be established only in certain subjects and only if reinforced by a photic stimulus at an optimal frequency. This frequency was ordinarily somewhat lower than the rate of the alpha rhythm. In man, conditioning a rhythmic cerebral response is much harder to achieve than conditioning the alpha blocking response, though in animals it has been readily obtained.

B. Pavlov and his collaborators (quoted by Rusinov and Smirnov[33]), utilizing positive and negative conditioned motor responses, demonstrated that the proper response following a positive conditioned stimulus was associated with diminution in alpha activity while that following a negative stimulus was associated with a reinforcement of this rhythm. Jus and Jus[17] have carried out even more elaborate testing procedures, utilizing the method of Ivanoff-Smolenski. This method theoretically promotes the formation of a "temporary cerebral connection" by association of an indifferent stimulus with a simple movement performed by the subject in response to the experimenter's verbal command. They demonstrated formation of conditioned cerebral responses to both positive and negative stimuli of this type, as well as their inhibition.

The awakened interest in cerebral conditioned responses resulted in a cooperative investigation by scientists from the United States, the Netherlands, Poland, and France. These studies[11] revealed that early in the course of conditioning, the electrographic response to the conditioned stimulus developed over wide areas of the cortex (the "startle" response). Later, the response to the conditioned stimulus became localized to the region where the unconditioned response would be expected to appear. Based on these and previous investigations, the authors postulated development of conditioned cerebral responses to be the result of a "temporary link" made in the thalamic reticular formation.

A major question persists as to what to term this phenomenon whereby a previously indifferent stimulus, by temporal association with a stimulus whose effect upon the electroencephalogram is predictable, acquires the ability to provoke this same predictable electrographic response. Early investigators regarded this simply as another form of conditioned reflex, differing from those described by Pavlov in the absence of motivation and of overt response. The alpha blocking response (alpha attenuation, arousal reaction, alpha desynchronization) was regarded by many as the electrographic manifestation of the orientation reflex or, as Pavlov[29] called it, the "What is it?" response. When, by a "conditioning" procedure, a previously indifferent stimulus provoked this alpha attenuation, it was assumed that this represented another form of conditioned reflex. As early as 1941, Knott and Henry[19] questioned this interpretation, suggesting that this might represent a conditioned anticipatory response instead of a true conditioned reflex. The observation of Jasper and Shagass,[15] however, seemed to favor these as representing conditioned reflexes in the Pavlovian sense.

Following publication of Morrell and Ross's paper in 1953, a rebuttal[40] appeared, maintaining that these responses could best be interpreted in non-Pavlovian terms rather than in terms of conditioning and inhibition, a view vigorously opposed by Morrell.[26] Later, Lilly[22] also deprecated the use of standard Pavlovian terms for changes in cerebral function detected by electroencephalographic means. More recently still, Stern *et al.*[34] and W. Grey Walter[39] have advanced further objections to entitling these phenomena "conditioned cerebral responses." This reluctance to employ Pavlovian terms for electrical events has led to their being called "temporary cerebral connections," "electrical correlates of conditioning responses," "contingent alpha blocking," and so on.

This study is concerned predominantly with the development of these phenomena in groups of human subjects, not with the physiological interpretation of this particular response. For this reason and because it is a term readily understood by most scientists familiar with the field, the term "conditioned cerebral response" has been utilized throughout this paper. It is not meant to imply that these "conditioned cerebral responses" necessarily represent true conditioned reflexes in the Pavlovian sense, but alternative terms serve only to expand an already imprecise nomenclature.

Conditioned Cerebral Responses in Normal Subjects and in Patients with Central Nervous System Diseases

One of the continuing problems in electroencephalography is the occurrence of a normal electroencephalogram in certain individuals with patently obvious cerebral disease. Since the early papers of Berger and of Adrian and Matthews, many studies have been devoted to this problem and to means by which an abnormality might be stimulated to appear in the electroencephalogram of patients known to have cerebral disease but whose resting electroencephalograms are normal. Thus a number of activation procedures have been designed to reveal abnormalities where none were observed or to accentuate them where few were found. Hyperventilation, sleep, water loading, stimulation with rhythmically flashing light, injection of cerebral stimulants, injection of sedative drugs—all have been found of some value as activating measures. Hyperventilation, sleep, and rhythmic photic stimulation have proved sufficiently useful to constitute a routine part of the electroencephalographic examination in most laboratories.

It was well known from the studies previously described that by the use of paired sound and light stimuli alpha activity demonstrated conditioned cerebral responses satisfying many of the criteria for Pavlovian conditioning. It was also known that subjects with lesions of the cerebral hemispheres failed to develop conditioned responses of the classic Pavlovian type as well as did normal subjects.[42] The question then arose whether the development of conditioned cerebral responses could be quantitated to evaluate the functional capacity of the cerebrum of man. Since the studies of Travis and Egan[35] and of Knott and Henry,[19] almost no quantitative figures regarding the development of conditioned cerebral responses have been presented. It was therefore necessary to study these conditioned cerebral responses in normal human subjects to determine whether their development could be quantitated. Further investigation of these conditioned cerebral responses in the brain-damaged individual might: (1) demonstrate whether formation of conditioned cerebral responses is impaired in the individual with disease of the cerebral hemispheres, and (2) throw light upon the functional and anatomical substratum necessary for development of these conditioned responses in man.

Some preliminary observations[5] have already been published. These studies, performed in 15 normal subjects and 26 subjects with known cerebral damage, indicated that individuals with gross structural brain damage developed significantly fewer conditioned cerebral responses than did normal subjects. No correlation could be established between the location of the brain lesion and impaired ability to form conditioned cerebral responses. Recently reported studies by Visser,[38] who utilized similar techniques, are in accord with these observations. He noted formation of significantly fewer conditioned cerebral responses in patients with "organic psychosis" than in normal subjects and in patients with other psychiatric diagnoses. He further found a close positive correlation between the alpha frequency and the "intensity" of the conditioned cerebral response. This section reports studies on formation of conditioned cerebral responses in a large number of normal and brain-damaged subjects.

METHODS AND MATERIAL

Studies were carried out in a quiet and semidarkened room with the subject separated by a partition from the examiner, the recording equipment, and the device for triggering sound and light stimuli. Needle scalp electrodes were placed bilaterally in the frontal, parietal, temporal, and occipital areas, and bipolar recordings were made by means of a Grass Model III Electroencephalograph. Auditory stimulation, produced by a Beltone Audiometer, was delivered through earphones to one ear at a frequency of 500 c./sec. at 40 to 50 decibels above the level of audibility. In the earlier experiments, a low masking sound was delivered to the opposite ear, but this was discontinued when better isolation facilities were developed. Visual stimulation was provided by a 150-watt bulb with white reflector placed approximately 12 inches in front of the patient's closed eyes.

Before testing began, the experimental procedure was explained to the subject in general terms to allay apprehensions regarding the study. During the testing period, the subject was seated with eyes closed. He was presented first with the light stimulus, 3 sec. in duration, repeated once or twice to show that light initially suppressed the alpha activity (Figure II–1). Auditory stimuli then followed, 4 sec.

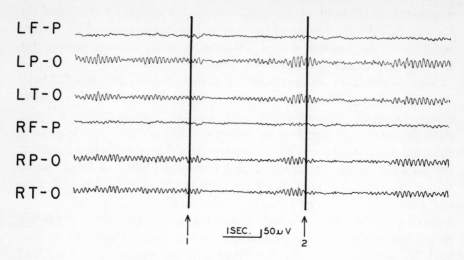

Fig. II—1. *Initial effect of 3-sec. light stimulus on electroencephalogram. Arrow 1 = appearance of light. Arrow 2 = disappearance of light.*

each in duration, repeated until the alpha activity became habituated to the sound—an arbitrarily defined state where five successive presentations of the tone failed to provoke any change in the background activity (Figure II—2). Paired sound and light stimuli were then

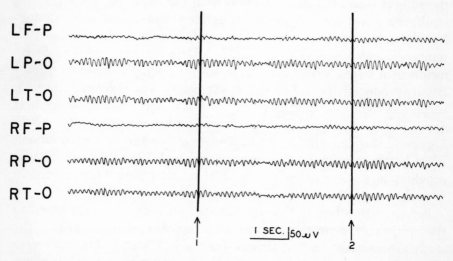

Fig. II—2. *Electroencephalogram of subject habituated to the effect of 4-sec. sound stimulus. Arrow 1 = appearance of sound. Arrow 2 = disappearance of sound.*

presented to the subject, the light appearing 0.8 to 1.0 sec. after the
sound. Both sound and light then continued together for 3 sec.
before stopping simultaneously. The interval separating the appearance of sound and light was timed automatically and remained constant in each subject. The paired sound-light stimuli were presented
to each subject 50 times, at irregular time intervals to avoid cyclic
conditioning. The experimenter tried to present the stimuli when
alpha activity was most prominent. On an average, one sound-light
stimulus was given every 15–20 sec. A total of 50 paired stimuli was
chosen because it was almost impossible to maintain alertness for
any longer period of study.

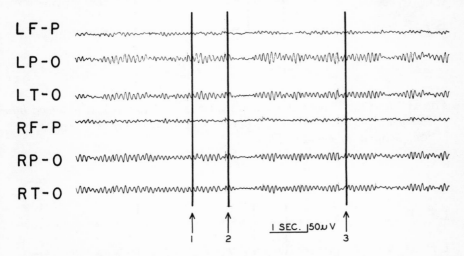

Fig. II—3. *Usual response to paired sound-light stimulus. Arrow 1 = onset
of sound. Arrow 2 = onset of light. Arrow 3 = disappearance of sound
and light. Note that sound alone has no effect upon the electroencephalogram, while light is followed by disappearance of alpha activity.*

The usual response to the paired sound-light stimulus is illustrated
in Figure II—3. Sound generally had no effect upon alpha activity,
but light was usually followed by prompt disappearance or marked
attenuation of the alpha waves. A conditioned cerebral response was
considered to have occurred whenever the alpha rhythm was obliterated or strikingly attenuated following presentation of the auditory
stimulus but before the appearance of the visual stimulus. Figures
II—4 and II—5 demonstrated typical conditioned cerebral responses.
The number of conditioned cerebral responses occurring out of the

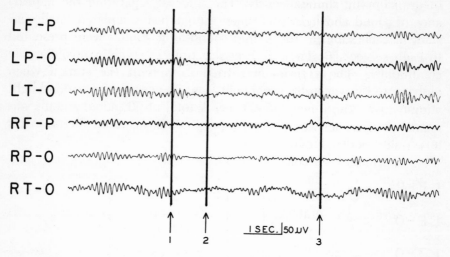

Fig. II—4. *Conditioned cerebral response. Sound, arrow 1, is followed by disappearance of alpha activity before light appears, arrow 2. Arrow 3 = disappearance of sound and light.*

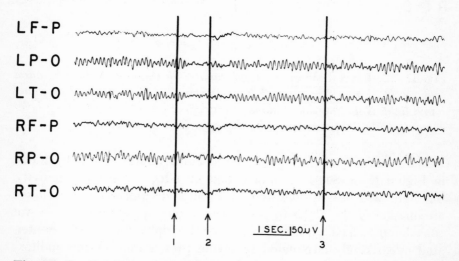

Fig. II—5. *Conditioned cerebral response. Sound, arrow 1, is followed by disappearance of alpha activity before light appears, arrow 2. Arrow 3 = disappearance of sound and light.*

50 paired sound-light presentations was determined for each subject, the author evaluating the records without knowledge of the patient's name or clinical status.

The formation of conditioned cerebral responses has been studied by these methods in 153 subjects. Thirty-eight of these were excluded from statistical evaluation because the poor quality or absence of alpha activity in their electroencephalogram precluded demonstration of these conditioned responses. They are not further considered here. The remaining 115 presented well-developed and well-regulated alpha activity, present for over 50 per cent of the recording in all subjects and over 75 per cent in most subjects. These 115 subjects included 46 control subjects who had no suggestion of any disease involving the cerebral hemispheres or brain stem. These control subjects were predominantly medical students, house-staff physicians, and laboratory personnel but also included some patients admitted to the hospital for diseases not involving the brain stem or cerebral hemispheres.

Sixty-nine patients with diseases of the cerebral hemispheres or brain stem were studied. Their diagnoses are listed in Table II–1. The only criteria for choice were that the patient be capable of sitting for the required period and that he be sufficiently cooperative to permit a satisfactory examination. A number of the "patients" (notably several with seizure disorders and with multiple sclerosis)

Table II-1   *Patients Studied for Conditioned Cerebral Responses*

DIAGNOSIS	NUMBER
Intracranial Neoplasms	20
Meningiomas—6	
Arteriovenous Abnormalities—6	
Primary Intracerebral Neoplasms—4	
Pituitary Adenomas—2	
Carcinoma Metastatic to Cerebrum—2	
Cerebral Vascular Disease	14
Seizure Disorders	10
Disseminated Sclerosis	9
Degenerative Cerebral Diseases	8
Cerebral Emboli	4
Central Nervous System Syphilis	1
Central Nervous System Sarcoidosis	1
Cerebellar Degeneration with Chronic Alcoholism	1
Parkinson's Disease	1
Total	69

had no evidence on clinical neurological examination to suggest a structural lesion of the brain stem or cerebral hemisphere. They were included in the group of patients, however, because their clinical diagnoses made it impossible to exclude such a lesion. The group was thus somewhat weighted in the direction of normal by inclusion of these subjects.

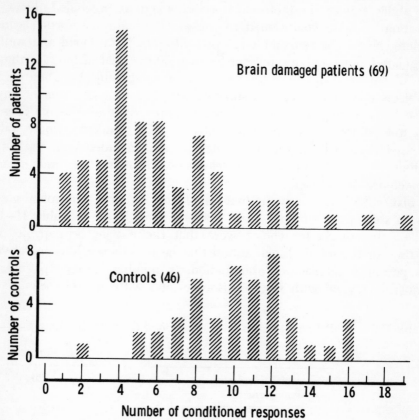

Fig. II—6. *Comparison of number of conditioned cerebral responses formed by the control subjects and the patients with neurological disease.*

RESULTS

The number of conditioned cerebral responses which occurred in the 50 paired sound-light presentations for the control and for the patient group is shown graphically in Figure II—6. The 46 control subjects developed a mean of 10.2 conditioned cerebral responses out of 50 presentations, with a standard deviation of ± 2.9. The

69 patient subjects developed a mean of 6.1 conditioned cerebral responses out of 50 presentations, with a standard deviation of ± 3.8. The difference between the number of conditioned cerebral responses in the control and in the patient group is highly significant, the statistical likelihood of its occurring by chance being less than 1 per cent.

The diagnosis and the result of the routine clinical electroencephalogram in the 21 patients who developed eight or more conditioned cerebral responses are listed in Table II–2. The routine clinical

Table II-2   *Diagnosis and Clinical EEG Findings in Patients Who Had Eight or More Conditioned Cerebral Responses*

DIAGNOSIS	EEG
Disseminated Sclerosis	Rare Spikes
Rt. Frontal Astrocytoma (3 years post surgery)	RF Delta and Theta
Rt. T-O Arteriovenous Malformation (5 years post surgery)	RT-O Theta
Left Cerebral Embolus	Left Hemisphere Delta
Left Cerebral Embolus	Left Hemisphere Delta
Left Hemisphere CVA	Left Hemisphere Delta
Cerebral Degeneration	LF-T Delta
Seizure Disorder	Rare Spikes During Sleep
Seizure Disorder	Normal
Seizure Disorder	Normal
Pituitary Adenoma	Normal
Cerebral Vascular Insufficiency	Normal
Cerebral Vascular Insufficiency	Normal
Brain Stem Vascular Accident	Normal
Brain Stem Vascular Accident	Normal
Ant. Fossa Meningioma	Normal
CNS Sarcoidosis	Normal
Disseminated Sclerosis	Normal
Disseminated Sclerosis	Normal
Disseminated Sclerosis	Normal
Disseminated Sclerosis	Normal

electroencephalogram was normal in 13 of these 21 subjects, while in seven it was abnormal. Six of these patients had normal neurological examinations and normal electroencephalograms. They were included in the patient group because it was impossible to exclude a cerebral lesion in the presence of their clinical diagnosis. Six patients with fewer than eight conditioned cerebral responses had normal clinical electroencephalograms.

Although the average age between the two groups is significantly different (mean age in the control group was 30.8 years; mean age in the patient group, 44.9 years), there was nothing within the groups to suggest that the number of conditioned cerebral responses was correlated with age.

DISCUSSION

The development of conditioned cerebral response has been shown to be a quality which can be quantitated. Although there is a wide variation in response among different subjects, these studies clearly demonstrate that the group of patients suffering from diseases involving the brain stem and the cerebral hemispheres developed significantly fewer conditioned cerebral responses than did the group of normal control subjects. Furthermore, on the basis of evidence obtained in an earlier portion of this study, impairment of the ability to develop conditioned cerebral responses is not related to the location of the cerebral lesion, impairment occurring with lesions of the brain stem as well as with lesions involving any portion of the cerebral hemispheres. Nor can the degree of impairment be correlated with size of the lesion—not a surprising observation when a function manifests such wide variation even among normal subjects.

Although the difference in formation of conditioned cerebral responses in the two groups is statistically very significant, for a variety of reasons the test lacks clinical applicability. Perhaps the most significant factor limiting its clinical use is the wide overlap in results between the control group and the patient group (see Figure II–6). Among the patients who developed as many conditioned cerebral responses as did most of the controls, there were a number whose routine electroencephalogram was within normal limits and whose neurological examination gave no evidence for a focal cerebral lesion (primarily patients with multiple sclerosis or seizure disorders). On the other hand, six patients with known disease of the cerebral hemispheres had normal routine electroencephalographic studies but developed fewer conditioned cerebral responses than did the normal group. Thus, while the test for development of conditioned cerebral responses may occasionally reveal abnormalities of function where none was apparent on the routine electroencephalogram, in general the percentage of abnormality unearthed by this test is no better than that found on the routine electroencephalogram while its interpretation is considerably more difficult and time-consuming.

Several other factors limit the clinical applicability of this test. First, it is hard to administer since the patient must remain alert throughout the paired presentations, a situation frequently difficult to obtain. Further, it is of use only in subjects who have a well-regulated and well-developed alpha activity over at least one hemisphere; thus a significant number of subjects are excluded before the test even begins. Lastly, the records are hard to interpret. The normal fluctuation in alpha activity is such that it may be impossible to judge whether a diminution in alpha wave amplitude is a response to a stimulus or a physiological variation. Even after several years of careful attention to the details of this test, instances continue to arise in some number where the author just cannot be certain whether or not a cerebral conditioned response had occurred. Since all records in the present series have been read by one person without knowledge of the clinical status of the subject at the time of interpretation, it can be assumed that these uncertainties are averaged out over the two groups as a whole.

SUMMARY

Development of the conditioned cerebral response was studied in 153 subjects by the presentation of 50 paired sound-light stimuli, the sound preceding the light by 0.8–1.0 sec. The records of 38 subjects were excluded because of the poor quality or the absence of alpha activity at rest. The remaining 115 subjects included 46 controls and 69 patients with diseases of the cerebral hemispheres or brain stem. The 46 control subjects developed a mean of 10.1 conditioned cerebral responses out of 50 presentations; the 69 patients developed a mean of 6.1 conditioned cerebral responses out of 50 presentations. The difference between the number of conditioned cerebral responses developing in the two groups is highly significant, the likelihood of this difference occurring by chance being less than 1 per cent.

The Effect of Single Flashes of Light on Alpha Activity in Normal Subjects and in Patients with Neurological Diseases

In the course of these studies on conditioned cerebral responses, it became apparent that light, utilized as the unconditioned stimulus, was not a true "unconditioned" stimulus. Its appearance often was followed by no change whatever in the subject's alpha activity (Figures II–7 and II–8). This observation prompted an investigation of

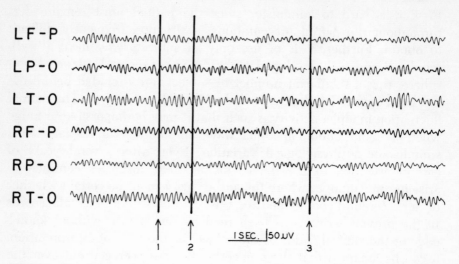

Fig. II—7. *Arrow 1 = onset of sound. Arrow 2 = appearance of light. Arrow 3 = disappearance of sound and light. Neither appearance nor disappearance of these stimuli has any effect here upon the electroencephalogram.*

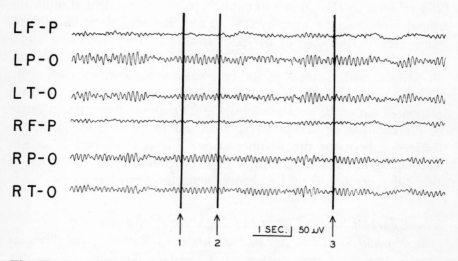

Fig. II—8. *Arrow 1 = onset of sound. Arrow 2 = appearance of light. Arrow 3 = disappearance of sound and light. Neither appearance nor disappearance of these stimuli has any effect here upon the electroencephalogram.*

the effect of visual stimulation alone upon alpha activity, both in normal subjects and in patients with disease involving the brain stem and cerebral hemispheres.

Attenuation of alpha waves on opening the eyes or on shining a light into the closed eyes was one of the first responses of cerebral electrical activity to be discovered. Early studies suggested that light always caused obliteration of the alpha rhythm.[2] The effect of light on alpha activity indeed seemed so constant that visual stimulation was accepted as the unconditioned stimulus in all early investigations of conditioned cerebral responses. Only Travis and Egan[35] appear to have questioned whether light was an unconditioned stimulus, but their studies showed that alpha blocking followed the presentation of light in 99 per cent of 344 presentations. Thus light was accepted as the unconditioned stimulus for most subsequent studies.

The effect of light upon alpha activity was studied in a number of laboratories in the 1930's. These investigations dealt with the effect of variation in stimulus intensity and duration upon the alpha activity,[6, 13] the effect of attention and external stimulation upon the alpha wave response to light,[14] the effect of a motor response to visual stimulation upon the alpha activity,[18] and the perseveration of the alpha blocking response to light alone and to visually presented words and symbols.[12, 36, 37] None of these, however, considered habituation of the alpha wave response to a strong visual stimulus.

In the intervening years, it nevertheless became apparent that suppression of alpha activity with opening the eyes or with the appearance of a bright light in a darkened room was not truly "unconditioned." Thus Redlich *et al.*,[30] in a study of 100 normal subjects, found that eye opening was followed by no change in the alpha activity in 12. Later Gastaut *et al.*[11] and Morrell[24] noted that with repeated paired sound-light presentations, the light might lose its ability to attenuate alpha activity. Studies from this laboratory[41] revealed that a light of 3-sec. duration presented repeatedly to a subject was not invariably followed by attenuation of the alpha activity. Furthermore, a sound preceding this light stimulus by a discrete period modified the response of the alpha waves to the subsequent presentation of light. More recently, Jus and Jus[16] have demonstrated that over the course of six to ten repetitions of a visual stimulus in man, the alpha blocking response is changed from a generalized reaction to a more localized one. If the visual stimuli are repeated further, even the more local reaction tends to disappear after 30–60 presentations.

The attempt to utilize alpha wave responsiveness to light as a measure of cerebral function is not new. A number of years ago, Liberson[21] utilized such "functional electroencephalography" to study a large group of psychiatric patients. The patients whose alpha activity responded least to visual stimulation had arteriosclerotic dementia, catatonia, and toxic psychoses. The most pronounced responses to photic stimulation occurred in patients with psychopathic personality, involutional melancholia, psychoneurosis, anxiety state, and reactive depression. Unfortunately, he did not compare the reactivity in this large group of psychiatric patients with that in normal subjects.

Gastaut et al.[10] in 1951 reported that calm individuals have a slow, high-voltage alpha rhythm at 8–10 c./sec. with hardly any "driving" of the occipital waves to rhythmic photic stimulation. "Nervous" individuals were found to have low-voltage, high-frequency alpha rhythms (10–13 c./sec.) and to show considerable driving to rhythmic photic stimulation. Several investigators have subsequently studied the response to rhythmic photic stimulation of normal subjects and of patients with psychiatric disorders. More pertinent to the present report is that of Kooi and Thomas[20] which demonstrated lower response values to repetitive photic stimulation in patients with brain damage than in normal subjects. Blum[4] showed a significant diminution in alpha wave responsiveness to visual stimulation both in brain-damaged and in schizophrenic subjects.

This section reports the alpha blocking response to single flashes of light in normal control subjects and in patients with neurological diseases affecting the brain stem and cerebral hemispheres. The process of habituation to the flash will be discussed in the next section.

MATERIALS AND METHODS

The first portion of the study consisted of the cerebral conditioning procedure previously described in which 50 paired sound-light stimuli were presented to the subject. At the end of the conditioning procedure, the subject was allowed a few minutes' rest during which time the remainder of the test procedure was explained and the instruments were rearranged.

Photic stimulation for the second portion of the test was provided by a Grass Model PS–3 stimulator, the light source placed approximately 8–10 inches from the eyes. The subject sat in the semidarkened room with his eyes closed while single photic flashes were presented at irregular intervals, averaging once each 10 sec. The examiner tried to present the stimulus when the alpha activity was most prominent.

To evaluate the effect of other stimuli upon the alpha response to light and to study habituation of the alpha response to light, the study was further elaborated as follows. In approximately half the patients in whom this portion of the test was performed, the first 50 photic flashes were presented in a quiet room with extraneous stimuli reduced to a minimum. In the other half, the photic flashes were presented while a loud masking noise, 90 decibels in intensity, was delivered through the earphones to one ear. Following the first 50 flashes, the patient was presented a second 50 flashes, the difference between the two series being that in the patients who experienced the first 50 flashes in quiet, the second 50 flashes were presented along with the loud masking noise. Conversely, the patients who had experienced the first 50 flashes along with the loud masking noise were presented the second 50 flashes in quiet.

Since there was no statistically significant difference in response between the patients tested in quiet and those tested along with the masking noise, results of the two groups have been combined and will not be treated separately in this section. For the sake of simplicity, only results of the first series of 50 flashes will be considered in detail here to document the difference in response between the normal and the brain-damaged subjects. The results of the entire series as they pertain to the habituation response will be discussed in the next section.

Records were evaluated without the author's knowing either the name and status of the subject or whether the flashes were presented with or without the masking noise. The record was studied to determine how many times out of 50 presentations the single photic flash produced obliteration or striking depression in the amplitude of the alpha activity (Figure II–9) and how many times the flash failed to produce any significant change in the alpha waves (Figure II–10).

Responsiveness of the alpha activity to single photic flashes has now been investigated in 85 subjects who had good alpha activity as previously described, including 32 control subjects and 53 patient subjects. The diagnoses of the 53 patients are listed in Table II–3.

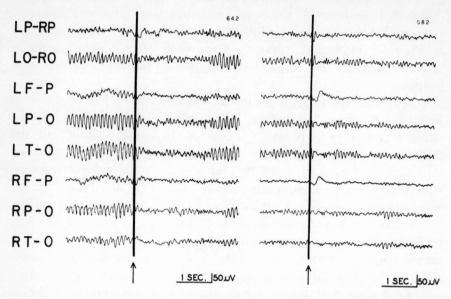

Fig. II—9. *Arrows indicate a single flash of light in different subjects. Flashes here result in prompt disappearance of alpha activity.*

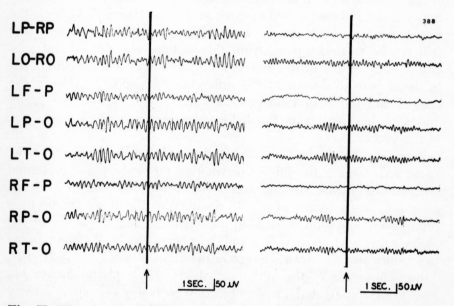

Fig. II—10. *Arrows indicate a single flash of light in different subjects. Neither has any effect upon the subject's electroencephalogram.*

Table II-3　　　*Patients Studied for Response to Single Photic Flashes*

DIAGNOSIS	NUMBER
Cerebral Vascular Disease	12
Seizure Disorders	11
Multiple Sclerosis	8
Degenerative Cerebral Diseases	8
Neoplasms	5
Meningiomas　2	
Pituitary Adenomas　2	
Carcinoma Metastatic to Brain　1	
Cerebral Emboli	4
Central Nervous System Syphilis	1
Central Nervous System Sarcoidosis	1
Parkinson's Disease	1
Cerebellar Degeneration with Alcoholism	1
Hemiballismus	1
Total	53

RESULTS

The number of times out of 50 presentations that the photic stimulus was followed by attenuation of the alpha activity in the patient and control groups is shown graphically in Figure II–11. The 32 control subjects showed alpha attenuation a mean of 23.6 times, with a standard deviation of ± 9.0. The 53 patients with central nervous system dysfunction showed alpha attenuation a mean of 12.8 times, with a standard deviation of ± 9.1. The difference between the control group and the patient group is highly significant, the statistical probability of this difference occurring by chance being less than 1 per cent. Alpha blocking to photic stimulation alone then occurs significantly less frequently in subjects with brain damage than in normal control subjects.

DISCUSSION

Although blocking of alpha activity to photic stimulation occurred significantly less frequently in the group of brain-damaged subjects than in the control subjects, there is considerable overlap in the number of times alpha blocking appeared in the control and in the patient group (see Figure II–11). Sixteen out of 53 patients had alpha blocking occur 16 or more times out of 50 photic presentations, i.e., well within the limits of normal for the control subjects. The diagnosis and evaluation of the routine clinical electroencephalograms

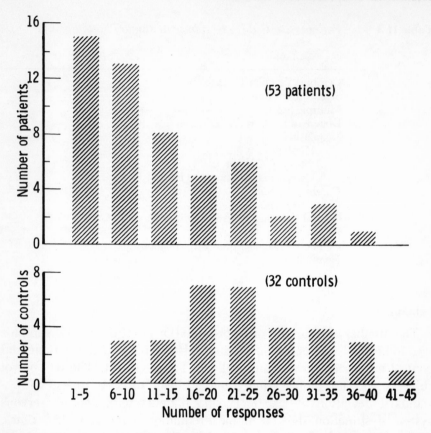

Fig. II—11. *Comparison of number of times flash was followed by alpha blocking in control group and in patient group.*

in these patients is shown in Table II—4. The majority of these patients had normal electroencephalograms; furthermore, because of their basic clinical diagnosis, a number were included within the patient group even though there was no evidence on neurological examination to suggest a focal structural lesion of the cerebral hemispheres or the brain stem. Ten of 32 patients with 15 or fewer positive responses had normal routine clinical electroencephalograms. Quantitative evaluation of alpha wave responsiveness to photic stimulation thus brought out probable abnormalities of function in 10 patients in whom the resting electroencephalogram was normal. While use of a test such as this might uncover some abnormalities of function, in general the overlap between normal and disease groups is too much to give it any wide clinical applicability.

Table II-4   *Diagnosis and Clinical EEG Findings in Patients with Over 16 Positive Responses to Single Flashes*

DIAGNOSIS	EEG
Embolus to Left Hemisphere	LT delta
Carcinoma Metastatic to Cerebrum	Focal delta
Cortico-Spinal Tract Disease, ?etiology	Paroxysmal EEG
Seizure Disorder	Polyspike and Wave Pattern
Seizure Disorder	Spikes in Sleep Record
Degenerative Cerebral Disease	Normal
Degenerative Cerebral Disease	Normal
Hemiballismus	Normal
Pituitary Adenoma	Normal
Cerebral Vascular Disease	Normal
Cerebral Vascular Disease	Normal
Brain Stem Vascular Accident	Normal
Brain Stem Vascular Accident	Normal
Multiple Sclerosis	Normal
Seizure Disorder	Normal
Seizure Disorder	Normal

From the studies reported in the first two sections, it has been demonstrated: first, that subjects with brain damage develop significantly fewer conditioned cerebral responses than do normal subjects; and second, that subjects with brain damage develop significantly fewer instances of attenuation of alpha activity to single photic flashes than do normal subjects. It is therefore logical to inquire whether these two functions are related.

A coefficient of correlation was determined from observations made in the subjects who had both the study of conditioned cerebral responses and the evaluation of alpha blocking to single flashes of light. The coefficient of correlation (r) was found to be 0.77, indicating a high positive correlation between the observations made in these two test situations. Thus there is a marked relationship between the responsiveness of the alpha activity to single photic flashes and the development of conditioned cerebral responses to paired sound-light stimuli.

The following conclusions may then be drawn from these data: (1) A group of subjects with diseases of the cerebral hemispheres and brain stem developed significantly fewer conditioned cerebral responses to paired sound-light stimuli than did a group of normal control subjects. (2) A group of subjects with diseases of the cerebral hemispheres and brain stem responded to single photic flashes with significantly fewer instances of alpha activity attenuation than did the normal group. (3) There is a marked positive correlation (r = 0.77) between the number of times a subject's alpha activity is blocked by single photic flashes and the number of times a cerebral conditioned response develops with paired sound-light stimuli. In other words, under these experimental conditions, the development of conditioned cerebral responses is highly correlated with the responsiveness of the alpha activity to the "unconditioned" or visual stimulus.

Habituation of Alpha Wave Responsiveness to Light

Habituation, as defined by Jus and Jus,[16] is a physiological phenomenon consisting of the specific and lasting extinction of the reaction to a repeated stimulus. The response of the cerebral alpha activity to a visual stimulus has generally been considered an "unconditioned" type of response—that is, a response which is not susceptible to habituation. Thus there have been few studies, at least in man, dealing with the problem of habituation of the alpha wave response to visual stimulation.

Rusinov and Smirnov,[33] in the Marseilles Colloquium of 1955, stated that ". . . extinction of the reaction [alpha attenuation following visual stimulation] is not always obtained even with repeated stimulation," thus suggesting that habituation sometimes occurs with repetition of the stimulus. No figures are given, however, to document the development of any habituation. In 1958, Roger *et al.*[31] published studies on extinction of the orientation reflex in man. They demonstrated rapid habituation of the Rolandic rhythm to proprioceptive stimulation of the opposite arm. When a visual stimulus was employed, however, only with great difficulty could extinction of alpha rhythm blocking in the occipital areas be obtained. If, after the development of habituation to repeated visual and proprioceptive stimuli, a sound 80 decibels above the level of audibility was presented to the subject, the response to the repeated stimulus might temporarily be restored.

Similar studies were carried out by Jus and Jus[16] to investigate cerebral electrical responsiveness to stimulation by sound, light, and tactile stimuli. Rapid extinction of the response to auditory and tactile stimuli was achieved. The response to repeated visual stimulation was quite different. With repeated visual stimulation, the first change in response was shortening of the period of alpha attenuation from several seconds to 200–500 msec. in duration. Extinction of the reaction to light, however, required many more repetitions of the stimulus than did this early change from a tonic to a phasic reaction. While the response to light usually changed in character from tonic to phasic after six to ten repetitions, extinction of the reaction entirely required at least 30–60 repetitions. In some subjects, it was never possible to obtain complete extinction. The application of a new stimulus of high intensity (for example, a painful stimulus) caused a return in the alpha blocking response which had just been habituated (dishabituation).

More recently, Gastaut and Bert[9] have studied habituation of the alpha blocking response to *rhythmically repeated* sensory stimuli. Using as a visual stimulus a 75-watt lamp placed 1.5 m. from the subject's closed eyes, the stimulus being presented rhythmically for 4 sec. every 20 sec., they found rapid habituation of the alpha blocking response, habituation appearing usually between the third and the eighth presentation. The visual stimulus here was weak; it was also presented rhythmically in order to study the induction of sleep.

Other investigators have studied the effect of repeated visual stimulation upon the duration of alpha blocking in man. Wilson and Wilson[43] in 1959 reported that even repeated stimulation with stroboscopic flashes for long periods did not significantly shorten the duration of alpha attenuation (if the first 30 sec. of stimulation were not considered). Response curves were not affected by extraneous sounds nor by changing the subject's level of attention. More recently, they have demonstrated[8] a significant decrease in duration of response when serially decreasing stimulus intensities were presented. If the stimuli were serially increased in intensity, however, duration of the response was the same as if the intensity remained constant. Morrell and Morrell,[28] studying 25 normal subjects, found variations in duration of the alpha blocking response which suggested an intrinsic periodicity, affecting the response duration, superimposed upon the habituation curve.

This study concerns habituation of the alpha blocking response to light in groups of normal subjects and of patients with neurological disease and the effect of modifying the environment upon this habituation.

MATERIALS AND METHODS

The experimental procedure has already been detailed in the previous section. To recapitulate, each subject sat in the semidarkened electroencephalographic examination room while 100 photic stimuli were presented at irregular time intervals from a Grass Model PS–3 stroboscopic unit. The subjects, normal controls and patients, were divided into two groups approximately equal in number. In half of the subjects, the first 50 flashes were presented in quiet, and the last 50 were presented along with a loud masking noise, 90 decibels in intensity, which was delivered through earphones to one ear. In the other subjects, the first 50 flashes were presented along with the loud masking noise, while the last 50 were presented in quiet. The number of times the flash was followed by attenuation of the alpha activity was determined in each subject as previously described.

A total of 82 subjects with good alpha activity were submitted to this examination. This included 33 control subjects who were either entirely healthy or suffered from diseases not affecting the cerebral hemispheres or brain stem and 49 patients affected with disease processes involving the brain stem or cerebral hemispheres.

RESULTS

The mean number of times the flash was followed by attenuation of alpha activity for each group of ten presentations is listed for normal subjects in Table II–5. There is no statistical difference be-

Table II-5   *Normal Subjects: Number of Times Per Ten Presentations Photic Stimulation Produced Alpha Blocking*

Presen-tations	1–10	11–20	21–30	31–40	41–50	51–60	61–70	71–80	81–90	91–100
	Without masking noise					With masking noise				
N = 18	5.3	5.0	4.3	4.3	3.9	5.2	4.8	4.3	4.5	3.7
	With masking noise					Without masking noise				
N = 15	6.3	4.4	4.1	4.2	4.4	5.8	4.3	3.4	4.3	3.3

tween the group whose first 50 flashes were presented in quiet and the group whose first 50 flashes were presented along with the loud masking noise. The pattern of response to the repeated photic stimulus in the two groups is, however, of considerable interest. During the first 50 presentations, whether the flash appeared in quiet or along with the masking noise, there is a decrease in the number of positive responses to flash between the first and the last ten presentations. Then, when the environmental situation is changed, either by the addition of a masking noise to those previously sitting in quiet or by discontinuing the masking noise and allowing the subject to sit in quiet, there is a marked, though temporary, restoration of the response to photic stimulation, the alpha blocking response then again gradually diminishing during the course of the last 50 presentations.

Table II-6 *Patients: Number of Times Per Ten Presentations Photic Stimulation Produced Alpha Blocking*

Presen-tations	1–10	11–20	21–30	31–40	41–50		51–60	61–70	71–80	81–90	91–100
	Without masking noise						With masking noise				
N = 29	3.7	2.4	2.0	1.5	1.6		2.5	1.7	1.8	1.4	1.4
	With masking noise						Without masking noise				
N = 20	3.7	3.1	2.9	2.0	1.8		2.9	2.2	1.7	1.9	1.7

The mean number of times photic stimulation was followed by attenuation of alpha activity for each group of ten presentations in the patients is listed in Table II–6. Again, there is no significant difference in the number of positive responses between the group whose first 50 stimuli were presented in quiet and the group whose first 50 stimuli were presented along with the masking noise. As in normal subjects, both groups of patients showed a gradual decrease in the number of positive responses during the first 50 presentations. With the change in environmental situation, whether this be from quiet to noise or its opposite, there is a temporary restoration of the response

Table II-7 *Number of Times Per Ten Presentations Photic Stimulation Produced Alpha Blocking in Controls and Patients*

Presentations	1–10	11–20	21–30	31–40	41–50	51–60	61–70	71–80	81–90	91–100
Controls (33)	5.8	4.7	4.2	4.3	4.1	5.3	4.5	3.9	4.4	3.5
Patients (49)	3.7	2.7	2.4	1.7	1.7	2.6	1.9	1.7	1.6	1.5

to photic stimulation followed by a gradual diminution in the number
of responses throughout the last 50 presentations.

When the group of normal subjects and the group of patient subjects are considered each as a whole (see Table II–7), the striking
difference in the number of times light was followed by alpha attenuation between the two groups is clearly evident. The difference between these two groups is statistically highly significant, the likelihood of this difference occurring by chance being less than 1 per cent.
This habituation curve for response to photic stimuli for normal and
patient subjects is illustrated graphically in Figure II–12.

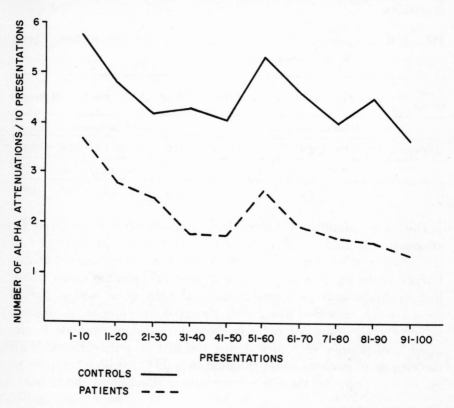

Fig. II—12. *Habituation curves to single flashes of light in normal group
and patient group. Solid line = normal subjects (33); dashed line = patients (49).*

DISCUSSION

These studies clearly demonstrate that repeated stimulation by a
photic flash leads to some habituation of the alpha blocking response.

Even in the course of the first 50 presentations, whether in quiet or in noise and whether in control subjects or in patients, there is a gradual diminution in the number of positive responses to photic stimulation. Even after 100 such presentations though, there is still far from complete habituation to this photic stimulus.

The habituation curve is radically interrupted after the first 50 presentations by the change in the environmental situation. It had been previously shown by Roger *et al.*[31] and by Jus and Jus[16] that the addition of a brief extraneous stimulus was capable of restoring the response which had previously been habituated to a repeated stimulus (that is, the extraneous stimulus was able to cause dishabituation). These studies demonstrate that changing the environmental situation, whether by the addition of a positive stimulus (masking noise) or a negative stimulus (removal of the masking noise), partially restores the responsiveness of alpha activity to the photic stimulation. Thus either a positive or negative stimulus is capable of dishabituating a previously partial habituation to photic stimulation.

The difference in response between the normal and patient groups is also striking. Throughout the course of this experiment, the number of positive responses in the patient group was less than that in the group of normal subjects. This difference in response between these two groups is highly significant. The slope of the habituation curve was also different in the two groups, the habituation curve in the brain-damaged group diminishing at a much more rapid rate than did the habituation curve in the group of normal subjects. Although complete habituation was not obtained in either group, the patient group responded to a photic stimulus significantly fewer times than did the normal group, and the patient group became partially habituated to the photic stimulus much more rapidly than did the normal group.

SUMMARY

The attenuation of alpha activity in response to photic stimulation by single flashes and the development of conditioned cerebral responses to paired sound-light stimulation are functions which can be quantitated. The group of subjects with disease of the central nervous system shows alpha blocking to flashes of light significantly fewer times than does a group of normal subjects. Likewise, the group of subjects with disease of the central nervous system develops significantly fewer conditioned cerebral responses than does the normal group. There is a high positive correlation between the responsiveness of the alpha activity to single photic flashes and the development of conditioned cerebral responses.

The attenuation of alpha activity following the appearance of a visual stimulus is not an "unconditioned" stimulus; indeed, in many instances, light fails to have any effect upon the alpha activity. Partial habituation of the alpha activity to repeated photic stimulation can be demonstrated both in groups of patients with neurological diseases and in normal subjects, the habituation to photic stimulation occurring more rapidly in the patient group than in the normal controls.

Thus, in general terms, it can be said that the patient with disease affecting the cerebral hemisphere or the brain stem demonstrates less responsiveness of the alpha activity to photic stimulation than does the normal subject. In addition, he habituates to photic stimulation more rapidly than does the normal subject. It may well be that this is true for other modalities of stimulation as well, but other stimuli such as noise, touch, and pain have not been investigated extensively in this study. It should be noted, however, that Gastaut and Bert[9] did not find a good correlation between habituation to visual and habituation to auditory stimulation in their large group of normal subjects.

These studies thus constitute a functional approach to electroencephalography such as Jasper and Liberson advocated many years ago. As a clinical tool, the procedures described here are of limited value—while the means of the controls and of the patients are significantly different, there nevertheless is a wide overlap in the results of the two groups which makes their separation by these methods impossible. These observations do, however, support the concept that study of the brain's responsiveness to sensory stimuli by more precise and elegant methods may offer a valuable approach to the evaluation of cerebral function.

Acknowledgments

The author wishes to acknowledge his gratitude to the late Dr. Harold G. Wolff for his advice and encouragement throughout these studies and for making facilities for them available, to Mrs. Lucy Sallick and Mr. Martin Lowy who took the electroencephalograms, and to Miss Katheryn McDaniel who aided in preparation of the manuscript. Some of the illustrations are used with the kind permission of the editor of the *Archives of Neurology*.

References

1. ADRIAN, E. D. and MATTHEWS, B. H. C., "The Berger Rhythm; Potential Changes from the Occipital Lobes in Man," *Brain*, 57:355–385, 1934.

2. BAGCHI, B. K., "The Adaptation and Variability of Response of the Human Brain Rhythm," *J. Psychol.*, 3:463–485, 1937.

3. BERGER, H., "Über das Elektrenkephalogramm des Menschen," *Arch. Psychiat. Nervenkr.*, 87:527–570, 1929.

4. BLUM, R. H., "Alpha-Rhythm Responsiveness in Normal, Schizophrenic and Brain-Damaged Persons," *Science*, 126:749–750, 1957.

5. CHAPMAN, L. F. and WOLFF, H. G., "The Cerebral Hemispheres and the Highest Integrative Functions of Man," *Arch. Neurol., Chicago*, 1:357–424, 1959.

6. CRUIKSHANK, R. M., "Human Occipital Brain Potentials as Affected by Intensity Duration Variables of Visual Stimulation," *J. exp. Psychol.*, 21:625–641, 1937.

7. DURUP, G. and FESSARD, A., "L'Électroencéphalogramme de l'Homme. Observations Psycho-Physiologique Relatives à l'Action des Stimuli Visuels et Auditifs," *Ann. Psychol., Paris*, 36:1–36, 1935.

8. ERWIN, C. W., LERNER, M., WILSON, N. J., and WILSON, W. P., "Some Further Observations on the Photically Elicited Arousal Response," *Electroenceph. clin. Neurophysiol.*, 13:391–394, 1961.

9. GASTAUT, H. and BERT, J., "Electroencephalographic Detection of Sleep Induced by Repetitive Sensory Stimuli," in WOLSTENHOLME, G. E. W. and O'CONNOR, M. (eds.), *CIBA Foundation Symposium on the Nature of Sleep*, Little, Brown & Co., Boston, 1961.

10. GASTAUT, H., GASTAUT, Y., ROGER, A., CORRIOL, J., and NAQUET, R., "Étude Électrographique du Cycle d'Excitabilité Cortical," *Electroenceph. clin. Neurophysiol.*, 3:401–428, 1951.

11. GASTAUT, H., JUS, A., JUS, C., MORRELL, F., STORM VAN LEEUWEN, W., DONGIER, S., NAQUET, R., REGIS, H., ROGER, A., BEKKERING, D., KAMP, A., and WERRE, J., "Étude Topographique des Réactions Électroencéphalographiques Conditionées Chez l'Homme," *Electroenceph. clin. Neurophysiol.*, 9:1–34, 1957.

12. JASPER, H. H. and CRUIKSHANK, R. M., "Electroencephalography: II. Visual Stimulation and After-Image as Affecting the Occipital Alpha Rhythm," *J. gen. Psychol.*, 17:29–48, 1937.

13. JASPER, H. H. and CRUIKSHANK, R. M., "Variations in Blocking Time of Occipital Alpha Potentials in Man as Affected by the Intensity and Duration of Light Stimulation," *Psychol. Bull.*, 33:770–771, 1936.

14. JASPER, H. H., CRUIKSHANK, R. M., and HOWARD, H., "Action Currents from the Occipital Region of the Brain in Man as Affected by Variables of Attention and External Stimulation," *Psychol. Bull.*, 32:565, 1935.

15. JASPER, H. and SHAGASS, C., "Conditioning the Occipital Alpha Rhythm in Man," *J. exp. Psychol.*, 28:373–388, 1941.

16. JUS, A. and JUS, C., "Étude de l'Extinction par Répétition de l'Expression EEG du Réflexe d'Orientation et de l'Action du Frein Externe sur les Réactions EEG aux Différents Stimuli chez l'Homme," *Electroenceph. clin. Neurophysiol.*, Suppl. 13:321–333, 1960.

17. JUS, A. and JUS, C., "Les Méthodes Bioélectriques dans l'Expérience Conditionnelle Clinique," *Electroenceph. clin. Neurophysiol.*, Suppl. 6:25–37, 1957.

18. KNOTT, J. R., "Reduced Latent Time of Blocking of the Berger Rhythm to Light Stimuli," *Proc. Soc. exp. Biol., N. Y.*, 38:216–217, 1938.

19. KNOTT, J. R. and HENRY, C. E., "The Conditioning of the Blocking of the Alpha Rhythm of the Human Electroencephalogram," *J. exp. Psychol.*, 28:134–144, 1941.

20. KOOI, K. A. and THOMAS, M. H., "Electronic Analysis of Cerebral Responses to Photic Stimulation in Patients with Brain Damage," *Electroenceph. clin. Neurophysiol.*, 10:417–424, 1958.

21. LIBERSON, W. T., "Functional Electroencephalography in Mental Disorders," *Dis. nerv. Syst.*, 5:357–364, 1944.

22. LILLY, J. C., "Discussion," in BRAZIER, M. A. B. (ed.), *The Central Nervous System and Behavior*, Trans. First Conference, Josiah Macy, Jr. Foundation, New York, 1958.

23. LOOMIS, A., HARVEY, E. N., and HOBART, G., "Electrical Potentials of the Human Brain," *J. exp. Psychol.*, 19:249–279, 1936.

24. MORRELL, F., "Electroencephalographic Studies of Conditioned Learning," in BRAZIER, M. A. B. (ed.), *The Central Nervous System and Behavior*, Trans. First Conference, Josiah Macy, Jr. Foundation, New York, 1958.

25. MORRELL, F., "Electrophysiological Contributions to the Neural Basis of Learning," *Physiol. Rev.*, 41:443–494, 1961.

26. MORRELL, F., "Further Discussion of A Note on Morrell and Ross's 'Central Inhibition in Cortical Conditioned Reflexes,'" *Arch. Neurol. Psychiat., Chicago*, 75:563–565, 1956.

27. MORRELL, F. and ROSS, M. H., "Central Inhibition in Cortical Conditioned Reflexes," *Arch. Neurol. Psychiat., Chicago*, 70:611–616, 1953.

28. MORRELL, L. K. and MORRELL, F., "Periodic Oscillation in the Habituation Curve of Electrographic Activation," *Electroenceph. clin. Neurophysiol.*, 12:757, 1960.

29. PAVLOV, I. P., *Conditioned Reflexes. An Investigation of the Physiological*

Activity of the Cerebral Cortex, ANREP, G. V. (trans. and ed.), Oxford University Press, London, 1927, 430 pp.

30. REDLICH, F. C., CALLAHAN, A., and MENDELSON, R. H., "Electroencephalographic Changes After Eye Opening and Visual Stimulation," *Yale J. Biol. Med., 18*:367–376, 1946.

31. ROGER, A., VORONIN, L. G., and SOKOLOV, E. N., "An Electroencephalographic Investigation of the Temporary Connexion During Extinction of the Orientation Reflex in Man," *Pavlov J. higher nerv. Activ., 8*:1–13, 1958.

32. RUSINOV, V. S. and SMIRNOV, G. D., "Étude Électroencéphalographique du Conditionnement Chez l'Homme," *Rapport, IV Congr. int. Électroenceph.*, Brussels, 1957.

33. RUSINOV, V. S. and SMIRNOV, G. D., "Quelques Données sur l'Étude Électroencéphalographique de l'Activité Nerveuse Supérieure," *Electroenceph. clin. Neurophysiol.*, Suppl. 6:9–23, 1957.

34. STERN, J. A., DAS, K. C., ANDERSON, J. M., BIDDY, R. L., and SURPHLIS, W., "A Study of 'Conditioned' Alpha Desynchronization," *Science, 134*:388, 1961.

35. TRAVIS, L. E. and EGAN, J. P., "Conditioning of the Electrical Response of the Cortex," *J. exp. Psychol., 22*:524–531, 1938.

36. TRAVIS, L. E. and KNOTT, J. R., "Brain Potential Studies of Perseveration: I. Perseveration Time to Light," *J. Psychol., 3*:97–100, 1936.

37. TRAVIS, L. E. and KNOTT, J. R., "Brain Potential Studies of Perseveration: II. Perseveration Time to Visually Presented Words," *J. exp. Psychol., 21*:353–358, 1937.

38. VISSER, S. L., "Correlations Between the Contingent Alpha Blocking, EEG Characteristics and Clinical Diagnosis," *Electroenceph. clin. Neurophysiol., 13*:438–446, 1961.

39. WALTER, W. GREY, "The Vocabulary of Psycho-Physiology," *Electroenceph. clin. Neurophysiol., 13*:447–448, 1961.

40. WEISS, B., "Morrell and Ross's 'Central Inhibition in Cortical Conditioned Reflexes,'" *Arch. Neurol. Psychiat., Chicago, 74*:171–173, 1955.

41. WELLS, C. E., "Modification of Alpha-Wave Responsiveness to Light by Juxtaposition of Auditory Stimuli," *Arch. Neurol., Chicago, 1*:689–694, 1959.

42. WELLS, C. E. and WOLFF, H. G., "Formation of Temporary Cerebral Connections in Normal and Brain-Damaged Subjects," *Neurology, 10*:335–340, 1960.

43. WILSON, N. J. and WILSON, W. P., "The Duration of Human Electroencephalographic Responses Elicited by Photic Stimulation," *Electroenceph. clin. Neurophysiol., 11*:85–91, 1959.

III

Electroencephalographic Correlates of Conditioned Responses

Charles E. Wells

It has been said that "tools fashion the thinking of the age"[28]—a statement as true for contemporary neurophysiology as for eighteenth-century microscopy or nineteenth-century studies in evolution. Thus, in the early years of the twentieth century, Pavlov studied those factors which could be measured accurately with the tools then available, i.e., the response of animals to various forms and combinations of external stimuli. From these simple but elegant studies, he evolved a theory of neural function based upon "conditioned reflexes." Instrumentation being inadequate for fruitful exploration of central events, a whole theory of central nervous function grew from the minute observation of autonomic and somatic responses. With the development of more adequate means for recording electrical events occurring in the brain, a new age of neurophysiology began. The period since its inception, the last three or four decades, has been devoted largely to an exploration of the electrical events attendant upon neural function, often with scant regard to over-all activity and responsiveness of the animal or human subject.

In the last several years, however, studies of the electrical events occurring within the central nervous system have been combined with studies of behavior and responsiveness. This paper reviews the recent studies in which electrically measured neurophysiological events have been correlated with behavior and response, both in animals and in man. The term "conditioning" is used here in a broad context, including therein many investigational approaches to behavior and responsiveness which are akin to Pavlovian conditioning but do not adhere strictly to patterns set by Pavlov himself. The operational definition offered by Hernández-Peón and Brust-Carmona[63] is apposite: "Conditioning results in the acquisition of a response (conditioned response) to a stimulus (conditional stimulus) which previously was not effective in eliciting that response." Such a terminology seems justified since almost all these studies constitute investigation of a stimulus-response situation (whether the response be electrical or operational) and since Pavlov could hardly have predicted the multiplicity of approaches made available by technological progress.

During the past few years, many symposia considering these subjects have been held throughout the world, leading to an incredible duplication of material published to document the same experimental situations. All-inclusiveness is impossible in a paper of less than monograph length; thus no attempt is made to include here reference to every study which has been carried out in this field—in particular modifications by drugs and results of self-stimulation have been omitted except where particularly relevant.*

The Alpha Blocking Response

Berger's discovery[8] that cerebral electrical potentials could be recorded through man's intact skull led to a revolution of experimental techniques exploring human neural function. Within a few years Adrian and Matthews[2] had confirmed Berger's observations. These electrical potentials, which they called alpha waves, arose predominantly from the occipital lobes. They were abolished when the eyes were opened or even when the eyes were closed, if the subject concentrated on a problem. They also demonstrated photic "driving," showing that the "driving" rhythms were most easily elicited at flicker rates between ten and twenty per second.

Other studies[71] revealed that the blocking time, i.e., the time between the appearance of light and the attenuation of the alpha waves, varied inversely with the intensity of light, the duration of light remaining constant. With the intensity constant, the blocking time was constant for durations of exposure above 200–500 msec. The blocking time increased as exposure time decreased below this value. The blocking time has variously been reported to be unchanged[72] or to be shortened[88] when subjects were instructed to give a motor response as soon as possible after the appearance of light.

---

* For relevant reviews the reader is referred to references 10, 11, 12, 26, 38, 73, 78, 113, 172.

If the first few responses are discounted, the duration of alpha activity attenuation following a flash remains remarkably constant, even over long periods of testing.[171] The duration, furthermore, is not affected by extraneous sound or by changing the subjects' level of attention. If the intensity of the flash stimulus is serially increased, the duration of alpha blocking remains constant.[36] If the intensity is serially decreased, however, a significant decrease in the duration of response follows. Other workers have noted variations in the duration of the alpha blocking response, suggesting an intrinsic periodicity.[123] The appearance of the alpha blocking response to light has been modified by a preceding auditory stimulus.[167] The interval between removal of light and reappearance of alpha rhythm is gradually reduced with repetition.[162]

Light is not alone in provoking the alpha blocking response. As Adrian and Matthews noted,[2] alpha rhythm may disappear with concentration. Sound also may cause alpha blocking,[25] but the response to sound gradually diminishes with repetition; and when the subject is examined on successive days, the reaction to the sound becomes progressively less.[135, 136] Disappearance of alpha activity also occurs whenever any novel or startling stimulus is presented. The observation by Rheinberger and Jasper[139] that arousal or attention in cats results in a low-amplitude fast activity in the electroencephalogram led to this being equated with the alpha blocking response, and to the alpha blocking response being linked with Pavlov's "What is it?" or orienting reflex.[131]

Many workers have noticed that whereas a novel stimulus produces replacement of synchronized activity by low-amplitude fast activity over most of the cranium, repetition of the stimulus leads either to limitation of the cerebral "arousal" reaction to the primary cortical projection region or to its complete disappearance. Roger et al.[140, 165] demonstrated rapid disappearance of the Rolandic rhythm response to proprioceptive stimulation of the opposite arm; but repeated visual stimulation led only at great length to disappearance of the alpha blocking response in the occipital areas. If, then, a sound 80 decibels above the level of audibility was presented, responsiveness was temporarily restored. Jus and Jus[84] likewise showed rapid extinction of the cerebral response to repeated auditory and tactile stimulation. With repeated visual stimulation, however, extinction was a much slower phenomenon, requiring at least 30–60 repetitions and never becoming complete in some subjects. Again, the application of a new stimulus of high intensity caused a return of the alpha blocking response which had just been habituated. Similar studies by Wells[166] have demonstrated a slow lessening of the alpha blocking response to light with repetition and its prompt reappearance with a change in situation, either from a noisy environment to a quiet one or vice versa.

When a light of low intensity is rhythmically repeated, habituation rapidly appears.[47] As the alpha blocking response habituates, the subject usually becomes drowsy. With drowsiness, the response to stimulation may be the appearance of alpha activity rather than its disappearance; with further repetition, even this response usually vanishes as the patient drifts into deeper sleep. Drowsiness and sleep are not, however, necessary for habituation, which may occur without obvious change in the resting electroencephalogram.[166]

Perhaps the most elaborate studies in this field have been done by Sokolov.[153] He distinguished two types of response: a generalized orienting response and a localized orienting reflex. Thus when he measured the response to a tactile stimulus, the first presentation produced a generalized response. After 25 presentations, however, the only effect was a slight depression in the electroencephalographic pattern over the motor region, the other components having disappeared. The generalized form of orienting response had thus changed into a localized form. One of the most important features of this habituation is its selectivity. Thus when a sound is repeatedly presented, response to it disappears, but as soon as the stimulus frequency is changed, the generalized response reappears. This does not represent a drop in sensitivity—for after habituation to a strong stimulus, presentation of a threshold stimulus can still evoke the orienting response. Sokolov believes that habituation depends upon the development of a "neuronal model." When the neuronal model is well developed, presentation of a stimulus causing a cerebral reaction conforming to it does not result in an arousal response; when, however, the stimulus is a new one not conforming to this neuronal model, an arousal response occurs.

In summary, an unexpected or particularly strong sensory stimulus, whatever its nature, causes a generalized desynchronization of the electroencephalogram with appearance of low-amplitude fast activity diffusely over the cranium. Repetition of this stimulus, if it be nontraumatic, is usually followed by disappearance of this generalized response and by appearance of a localized desynchronization, the area of localization depending upon the nature of the stimulus. Further repetition results in disappearance of any desynchronization response if the stimulus be sound or touch. Habituation of the alpha blocking response in the occipital area to light is a much slower phenomenon, one which never develops in a certain percentage of subjects. Habituation is quite specific; thus presentation of a stimulus differing only slightly will usually cause a return of the generalized or localized blocking response. Furthermore, any change in the over-all state of the patient, such as is produced by a painful stimulus or by a change in the environment, causes dishabituation. A major portion of the conditioning studies to be detailed subsequently are based upon these simple observations.

Conditioning in Man

Study of the electroencephalographic response to light led accidentally to the discovery that the alpha blocking response could be conditioned. Durup and Fessard[33] used a camera to photograph the response of man's alpha waves to a visual stimulus. Previous testing had shown that the noise of opening the shutter alone had no effect on the electroencephalogram. After the electroencephalographic response to light had been repeatedly photographed, however, with the attendant noise of opening the camera shutter each time, they noted that the sound stimulus alone sometimes produced attenuation of the alpha activity. A similar observation was made almost simultaneously by Loomis et al.[97] They found that if a tone and a light were presented concurrently to a subject lying in darkness, after a number of combinations the tone alone, which previously had no effect, provoked alpha wave suppression. This acquired response to tone was, however, only transient.

Study of this form of "conditioning" then began in a number of laboratories. Travis and Egan[161] investigated alpha activity responsiveness to tone and light in eight subjects. Tone alone provoked alpha wave suppression in 11 per cent of the presentations and light alone in 99 per cent. When the two stimuli were combined, however, with the sound preceding the light by an average of 0.55 sec., sound was followed by alpha wave attenuation before the appearance of light in 35 per cent of the paired presentations. These observations were interpreted as evidence that the alpha blocking response could be conditioned. Knott and Henry[89] re-evaluated this data, noting that in the paired presentations, tone was just as effective in producing alpha blocking in the first one-fifth of the series as in each of the succeeding four-fifths; that is, there was no curve of increasing effectiveness as the paired presentations were continued. To them this resembled "sensitization" rather than conditioning. They studied six subjects in a similar fashion, increasing the interval between tone and light to 4 sec. The same type of response was observed, but again no curve of increasing effectiveness appeared. They interpreted this response to tone to represent not true "conditioning" but rather "a conditioned anticipatory response."

Jasper and Shagass[76] reported in 1941 more elaborate studies on conditioning the occipital alpha rhythm in man. The conditioned stimulus was a 500 c./sec. sound, which appeared 0.7 sec. before the light, the subject having been instructed previously to press a button whenever light appeared. Under these conditions, simple conditioning was fairly easy to achieve, though the conditioned response was unstable, extinction usually occurring after as few as three unreinforced presentations of the conditioned stimulus. In addition to simple conditioning, they demonstrated cyclic conditioning, delayed conditioning, differential conditioning, trace conditioning, and backward conditioning. They considered "sensitization" to be ruled out by the demonstration of differential conditioning, i.e., the response was frequency-specific and not just any stimulus of equal intensity. More elaborate forms of conditioning were achieved by Jasper and Shagass than by other investigators, probably for two reasons: (1) their experimental design was more complex; and (2) their subjects were instructed to press a button each time that the visual stimulus appeared. It has subsequently been noted that cerebral desynchronization to the conditioned stimulus is easier to obtain and more consistent when the unconditioned stimulus represents a signal for a motor act by the subject.[4, 146]

In the years following the Second World War, investigation of these conditioned cerebral responses burgeoned throughout the world. In 1949, Motokawa and Huzimori[125] reported electroencephalographic and skin galvanic responses to stimulation by sound paired with electric shock. A bell was used as the conditioned stimulus and an electric current, sufficient to cause a paresthetic sensation but no pain, as the unconditioned stimulus. The bell alone had little or no effect on the electroencephalogram or the skin resistance. When it regularly preceded the shock stimulus by a short interval, however, the bell provoked both a depression of the alpha activity and a galvanic skin response. This response became progressively weaker when not reinforced by the unconditioned stimulus. These authors found electroencephalographic conditioning to be easier to establish and more stable than the skin galvanic response. In general, such stability of the conditioned cerebral response has not been observed by other workers, leading one to suspect that the electrical stimulus may have produced more than just a paresthetic sensation.

The interval separating the two stimuli was then prolonged to 10 sec. With this, the authors found the "excitation potentials" (blocking of the alpha activity) considerably delayed, appearing only in the last 2 sec. before the unconditioned stimulus. The figures used to illustrate this delayed conditioning are not entirely convincing, however. In another study,[124] when a metronome as the conditioned stimulus was combined with light as the unconditioned stimulus, the metronome was sometimes followed by alpha blocking, but this response disappeared as the combined stimuli were continued. This unstable response is much like that found by others and suggests that the previously noted amazingly stable response may have been due to some peculiar quality of the unconditioned stimulus.

Iwama,[68] working in Motokawa's laboratory, also studied the effect of long delays. Using a metronome as a conditioned stimulus and a light as an unconditioned stimulus, the metronome was prolonged for 20 sec. before the appearance of the light. In these studies, Iwama found that with the development of the conditioned reflex, the alpha waves increased in amplitude and synchrony at the onset of the metronome. At about the 20th sec. from the start of the metronome beat, alpha activity was suppressed and beta waves appeared. He interpreted the augmentation of alpha waves at the onset of the conditioned stimulus as the expression of internal inhibition due to the delay. Further studies[69, 70] utilized a salivary response and a galvanic skin response as the unconditioned response. Unfortunately the illustrations accompanying both these reports do not permit evaluation of the conclusions reached.

In the United States, Morrell and Ross[122] reawakened interest in conditioned cerebral responses. They employed a tone stimulus followed after 1 or 2 sec. by a fast flickering light, their subjects having been instructed to press a key as soon as the light appeared. By recording on the record when the key was pressed, they were able to measure the latency between appearance of the light and pressing the key. The latency was consistent in both the conditioned and the unconditioned state, being slightly longer in the unconditioned. During extinction (sound not consistently reinforced by light), differential inhibition (one tone constantly reinforced and another never reinforced), and delayed inhibition (reinforcement delayed for 6 sec.), latency was considerably increased. It was proposed that this delay resulted from a central inhibitory process. In view of later work, one of their records is of interest, illustrating differential inhibition in which an unreinforced stimulus brought about clear augmentation in amplitude and rhythmicity of the alpha activity.

These studies, and numerous others in experimental animals (to be detailed subsequently), led to a cooperative study[48] of conditioned cerebral responses in man. In laboratories in France, Poland, the United States, and the Netherlands, sixty subjects having a prominent occipital alpha rhythm and/or a prominent Rolandic rhythm (*en arceau*) were investigated. The conditioned stimulus was a tone; the unconditioned stimulus was either light, light plus active movement of the hand, or passive movement of the wrist. Initial presentation of these "unconditioned" stimuli resulted in a diffuse desynchronization of the cerebral electrical activity; after several presentations, the desynchronization became limited to the specific cortical region involved, i. e., the occipital region for visual stimulation. When the conditioned and unconditioned stimuli were combined and a conditioned cerebral response developed, the conditioned stimulus caused desynchronization of the cerebral electrical activity in the region where the unconditioned stimulus would be expected to cause it. Thus a sound would block the contralateral Rolandic rhythm when it was combined with passive movement of the wrist, and so on. This desynchronization was considered to represent central excitation. The authors looked upon the disappearance of this conditioned cerebral response (and it was not a particularly stable response) as a manifestation of central inhibition. If the paired stimuli were continued, the conditioned stimulus might come to be followed either by increased amplitude of the alpha or Rolandic activity or even by slow waves. This enhancement of the cerebral rhythmicity occupied the same region as that previously occupied by desynchronization. This was considered to represent "conditioned" inhibition, as described by Pavlov. Thus desynchronization (or blocking of the alpha and Rolandic rhythms, or appearance of low-voltage fast activity) was looked upon as a manifestation of central excitation, whereas enhancement of these rhythms or the appearance of slow waves was considered a manifestation of central inhibition.

Further evidence has been amassed for such an interpretation. Alexander[3] studied conditioned reflexes in normal and psychotic subjects, employing sound as the conditioned stimulus and an electric current applied to the hand as the unconditioned stimulus. In normal subjects, there was ready development of conditioned cerebral and psychogalvanic responses, attenuation of the alpha activity being interpreted as central excitation occurring with the conditioned reflex. Also observed, particularly in depressed patients, was central "inhibition" manifested by reduction, delay, or even abolition of the conditioned response. With inhibition, hypersynchrony rather than desynchronization occurred in the electroencephalogram. Similar evidence was presented by Mayorchik et al.[104, 147] They developed a conditioned reflex in man to a sound preceding light by 1.5 to 2 sec., the subject being instructed to perform a certain movement with the appearance of light. In this situation, the sound produced attenuation of the cerebral alpha activity. If, however, the interval were extended to 6.5 sec., the period of delay was marked by the appearance of slow waves. They interpreted these slow waves as an indication of inhibition.

B. Pavlov[130] conditioned man to respond to one stimulus and not to respond to another. In such a situation, the positive stimulus was followed by diminution in the alpha activity, but the negative stimulus was followed by reinforcement of this rhythm. Gastaut[44, 45, 50] has reviewed this subject on several occasions. He is convinced that differentiation, delay, and extinction—all manifestations of inhibition—are manifested electrographically by the same phenomenon, i.e., a slowing of the cerebral rhythms over the region of the unconditioned analyzer.

The studies just outlined, while hardly conforming to classical Pavlovian techniques, were nevertheless in general of a rather specific type, i.e., combination of one stimulus which ordinarily has little effect upon the electroencephalogram with another which predictably affects it. Others have sought to impose upon the brain's normal electrical activity patterns of much greater complexity. Since photic stimulation precipitates epileptiform discharges in susceptible individuals, might not such discharges be conditioned? Gastaut et al.[49] reported two patients in whom such conditioning was possible—one in whom epileptiform activity was conditioned to a sound and another in whom it was conditioned to a word. Stevens[157, 158] studied several patients intensively; she was unable by combination with sound to condition either photically induced spike-and-wave discharges or photically induced driving. Naquet[127] has also tried to condition such activity in 24 patients. He likewise was unable to condition either epileptiform discharges or driving in these subjects. Both Stevens and Naquet were able to facilitate the appearance of some pre-existing discharges, but never were these discharges clearly related to any specific indifferent stimulus. In addition, Stevens and Stevens,[159] by a cyclic conditioning procedure, tried to condition patients who showed high-voltage polyspike or spike-and-wave responses to photic stimulation. Again there was no good evidence of paroxysmal responses to the paired tone signal; however, paroxysmal discharges occurring with the sound, either reinforced or not reinforced, suggested that some cyclic form of excitability might have been engendered. In another approach, Efron[34, 35] demonstrated in one patient that, by means of a conditioning procedure, the spread of an epileptiform discharge from an excitable focus could be aborted.

Adrian and Matthews[2] had noted that a rhythmically flickering light might induce waves of a similar frequency over the occipital regions. Mayorchik and Spirin[105-107] tried to condition this response in man, using sound as the conditioned stimulus and a rhythmic photic stimulus at 20–25 c./sec. as the unconditioned stimulus. They achieved little success, however, with this technique. Somewhat later, Pavlygina and Rusinov[132, 133] noted that occipital following to rhythmic photic stimulation occurred only in certain individuals. Usually the driving was most exact when the frequency of the flicker was low, i.e., 6–8 c./sec. With this in view, they first determined which flicker rate produced the most striking occipital response; they then utilized this as the unconditioned stimulus. This method is said to have given more precise evidence of frequency-specific response in man. Jus and Jus[86] also mention that, rarely, they have noted frequency-specific conditioned responses in man. In general, however, in man these have proved extremely difficult to obtain.

It is well known[170] that certain situations facilitate the emergence of alpha activity, such as changing the environment from light to dark or the general psychological state from attentiveness to relaxation. On this basis, attempts have been made to condition the *appearance* of alpha activity. Beritov and Vorobyev[9] combined sound as the conditioned stimulus with turning off the light (darkness) as the unconditioned stimulus. It is reported that they thereby conditioned the appearance of alpha activity to the sound. Similar paradoxical alpha conditioning is also reported to have been achieved by Kratin.[91] Stern and Lackner,[155] however, have questioned whether this is possible.

Several investigators[23, 85, 146] have explored the electrical changes associated with conditioning of the Ivanoff-Smolenski type, i.e., conditioning in which spoken words serve as the unconditioned stimulus. Conditioned desynchronization of alpha activity has been described under these conditions, and cerebral "inhibition" has been observed with delay, differentiation, or drowsiness. The cerebral electrographic accompaniment of inhibition in these situations is closely analogous to that described previously—the appearance of alpha activity if the background activity is of low amplitude or the appearance of slow waves if the background activity shows a prominent alpha rhythm.

Gershuni et al.[52] have utilized as a conditioned stimulus a tone five to six decibels below the auditory threshold, pairing this with a visual stimulus. Conditioned alpha blocking was thus demonstrated to a tone ordinarily five to six decibels below the level of audibility. It is not stated whether under their experimental conditions the subject remains unaware of the conditioned stimulus or whether the subject now hears the tone due to a lowering of the auditory threshold (such as Sokolov[153] has shown to occur during stimulation by other sensory modalities). Sokolov has also demonstrated that a tone just above threshold audibility is more likely to give a cerebral response than one which is clearly and easily heard.

The effect of cyclic stimulation upon the cerebral electrical activity has also been extensively investigated. As early as 1939, Davis[25] showed that if a tone were omitted after having been presented several times at regular intervals an alpha blocking response occurred. Jasper and Shagass[77] studied this "unconscious" set of the central nervous system in delayed, trace, and cyclic conditioned responses, demonstrating that the response of the occipital alpha rhythm was more accurately timed than was conscious estimation of the same time interval. Lurie and Rusinov[100] presented repeatedly a stereotyped stimulus consisting of click-light-click-switching off the light. After a number of repetitions, the two clicks given successively at the same time intervals, but without any change in the illumination, evoked the whole of the complex electroencephalogram changes which had previously been evoked by the entire stimulus.

Kats,[144, 145] working in Rusinov's laboratory, studied the nonspecific vertex response which appears after many forms of stimulation. It is not very prominent when the stimulus is first presented, becomes more prominent and appears over larger cortical areas with repetition, and may then gradually disappear. Kats presented three sound signals of equal duration separated by identical intervals, the subject having been instructed to press a rubber bulb upon presentation of the third signal only. After a series of combinations in which the third tone signal was delayed or not presented at all, a nonspecific vertex response appeared shortly after the moment when the signal was expected. This non-specific vertex response arose simultaneously with the appearance of a tonic impulse in the electromyogram. Cyclic conditioning of K complexes in man has also been reported.[67]

In summary, a variety of electroencephalographic changes has been described in man both in situations identical to classic Pavlovian conditioning and in situations utilizing a cerebral response as the unconditioned response. Not only simple, but differential, delayed, cyclic, and other forms of conditioned cerebral responses have been elaborated. In general, the conditioned response is manifested by an electroencephalographic response limited to the area overlying that region of cortex subserved by the unconditioned response. The elaboration of a conditioned cerebral response, by whatever means, is usually associated with a reduction of cerebral synchrony and the appearance of low-voltage fast activity over the region of the unconditioned analyzer. With delay, differentiation, or extinction, this desynchronization is replaced by increased synchrony during the conditioned stimulus. The form of the increased synchrony depends upon the background activity, being evidenced by a reappearance of alpha activity if the background activity is of low amplitude or by the appearance of slow waves if the background is manifested by prominent alpha activity.

Conditioning in Animals

The experimental limitations of man soon led to the use of animals for investigation of cerebral conditioning. Morrell and Jasper[112, 118] studied monkeys, using tone, touch, or minimal change in background illumination as the conditioned stimulus and a 500-c./sec. light as the unconditioned stimulus. Repetition of the conditioned stimulus rapidly led to disappearance of the electroencephalographic response. When combined stimuli were first presented, therefore, the conditioned stimulus educed no change in cerebral activity while the unconditioned stimulus produced a clear arousal (or blocking) reaction. The first stage in the development of a conditioned response (as identified by Morrell and Jasper[118]) was marked by the appearance of electroencephalographic arousal in response to the conditioned stimulus before the onset of the light. At this stage, the response appeared more or less diffusely over the cerebral hemispheres. If the associated stimuli were continued, a gradual contraction of this area of blocking occurred until the conditioned stimulus caused blocking only in the occipital regions. This sharply localized blocking response to the conditioned stimulus was the final form of the conditioned cerebral response. They showed that this response could be differentiated.

Sakhiulina[148] made similar studies in the dog, using sound or light as the conditioned stimulus but employing a shock to the foreleg as the unconditioned stimulus. During the first phase—formation of a simple positive conditioned reflex—the electroencephalogram showed a predominance of high-frequency, low-voltage fast activity widely present over the brain. This was observed not only at the moment of stimulation but during the periods separating them as well. As the conditioned reflex was strengthened, the site of these fast waves became more and more limited, gradually becoming localized to the region of the sensory motor cortex. In the rabbit,[95] at the beginning of conditioned reflex formation, changes in electrical activity were clearly seen over the cortical regions both of the conditioned and of the unconditioned stimulus. As the conditioned reflex fixed, however, response over the center of the conditioned stimulus waned while that over the unconditioned stimulus became more intense, i.e., the conditioned stimulus then produced localized low-voltage fast activity only over the region of the unconditioned analyzer. In other studies,[32] the rabbit was presented with sound followed by a light, the light simultaneously being reinforced by a shock to the skin. During the first combinations, "reactivity" was increased in both the optic and the auditory areas; later similar changes appeared in the somatic sensory area. With the development of a good conditioned response, "reactivity" diminished in the auditory and skin areas while it increased in the optic and motor areas.

This gradual localization of the conditioned cerebral response was not substantiated in elegant studies on cats with permanently implanted cortical electrodes done by Beck et al.[7] The animals were drugged with bulbocapnine—a drug, having no readily detectable effect on conditioning, which usually produces slow electroencephalographic patterns, thus making detection of electrocortical arousal easier.

A 2-sec. tone served as conditioned stimulus, and a brief shock to the toes, overlapping its termination, as the unconditioned stimulus. At first the sound was presented repeatedly without reinforcement until it had no effect upon the electroencephalogram. Paired sound and shock were then presented 25–50 times daily on successive days. Almost immediately, the previously habituated animals began to show *some* electrographic arousal to the conditioned stimulus before the onset of the shock. In the first and second training periods, such responses were infrequent and inconsistent; but by the third training session, the cats usually showed electroencephalographic arousal to the conditioned stimulus 80 per cent of the time. Thus there was a gradual increase in the electrographic arousal to the conditioned stimulus over the several successive days (a "learning" curve). In all instances, the electrographic "arousal reaction" to the conditioned stimulus became consistent before any other sign of conditioning appeared. When flexion responses did appear, they were almost invariably accompanied by an electrographic arousal reaction to the conditioned stimulus. These investigators never obtained the clearly localized "arousal response" observed by other workers. The reason for this discrepancy is not readily apparent.

The initial studies of Morrell and Jasper[118] in the monkey used a light flashing at 500 c./sec. as the unconditioned stimulus. Since photic stimulation at slower rates could produce "driving" in the occipital regions, they substituted a slowly flickering light. Photic driving is most prominent when the flicker frequency approaches that of the spontaneous electrical rhythm of the occipital cortex; thus a 6–12-c./sec. frequency was usually utilized as the unconditioned stimulus, being combined with a tone, touch, or change in background illumination as the conditioned stimulus. Again, during early presentations, the conditioned stimulus caused a generalized blocking, the unconditioned stimulus then producing typical driving. With continuation of paired stimuli, an after-discharge to the flickering light appeared, and then, gradually, conditioned repetitive responses began. They first appeared just before the unconditioned stimulus, but in successive presentations began closer to the onset of the conditioned stimulus. This stage was transitory, however, and soon the repetitive discharge to the conditioned stimulus disappeared entirely, the stable conditioned response being manifested by localized blocking in the occipital regions only. Similar observations have been made in the cat and rabbit.[119, 120]

Difficulties arose, however, in interpreting this repetitive response.

In their first studies, Morrell and Jasper noted that the repetitive response was not always uniform nor frequency-specific; indeed, it might vary considerably in form and latency from one presentation to the next. Furthermore, these repetitive responses could be conditioned only within the narrow range of frequencies which appeared spontaneously in the background rhythm of the animal. Although it was possible, in a given animal, to condition several different repetitive rates by using different frequencies, nevertheless the conditioned response was usually not precisely at the flicker frequency but merely tended to approach that frequency with repetitive trials. Thus it was unclear whether this repetitive response reflected the transmission of specific information or whether it was just a nonspecific response.

Even earlier, Livanov and Polyakov[96] had combined rhythmic photic stimuli with rhythmic electric shocks at 3 c./sec. in the rabbit. "Spontaneous activity" at 3 c./sec. was then registered for a "comparatively long time." McAdam et al.[101] used a 20 c./sec. flash for the conditioning stimulus and a delayed shock as the unconditioned stimulus in cats, sampling the electrical response of the reticular formation, hippocampus, thalamus, and several cortical regions. Good frequency-specific responses (at 20 c./sec.) were observed during development of the conditioned reflex only in the hippocampus and in the reticular formation. As the conditioned reflex became more regular, the response disappeared from there as well. Response from thalamic and cortical levels was variable, but the anterior and posterior lateral gyri showed stable driving throughout without change during development of the conditioned reflex.

Stern et al.[156] studied changes in the electrocortical activity of the dog, with the aid of an analyzer of the Walter type, during a rather difficult learning task—a trace-conditioning procedure utilizing either a 5- or 10-sec. delay between the conditioned and the unconditioned stimulus. The conditioned stimulus was photic stimulation at a frequency producing a good driving response at a frequency of relatively low amplitude in the resting record. Using the Walter analyzer, a temporally localized, frequency-specific response was observed in some animals, occurring prior to the conditioned motor reflex and disappearing when the motor reflex was stable. A temporally generalized, frequency-specific response occurred in one animal, i.e., a steady increase in the amount of frequency-specific activity not only during the delay but even when the animal was placed in the testing chamber. A temporally localized, nonfrequency-specific response was noted also in some animals.

Even more intricate studies were designed, one[21] to find whether there could be transference of a conditioned avoidance response. To determine this, a flickering light, which elicited driving, was repeatedly paired with a shock until the light alone stimulated the cat to cross the compartment of a double grill box. A tone was then paired repeatedly with the flickering light, educing the same stages of electrographic conditioning originally described by Morrell and Jasper. In spite of the fact that the development of these two conditioned responses have a common link (rhythmic flicker and its electroencephalographic driving), the tone alone never initiated behavioral crossing.

Chow[21] investigated more complex learning situations, studying the response, in multiple cortical and subcortical areas, to two or three successive two-choice visual discrimination problems. The only recognizable change in the visual area electroencephalogram was the presence or absence of driving when the visual stimulus was presented. A reduced amplitude in the temporal region electrodes was at times observed during the negative stimulus. These changes, however, were never consistent. He found no relation between any electroencephalographic change and the acquisition of learning.

John and Killam[79, 81] trained cats to perform an avoidance response to a 10-c./sec. flickering light. In fully trained animals, appearance of the 10-c./sec. flicker resulted characteristically in a 20-c./sec. discharge in the visual cortex. A 6.8-c./sec. stimulus was then presented as a test for generalization. During the first few presentations, performance of the conditioned avoidance response was the same as to the 10-c./sec. flicker, and the discharge in the visual cortex was clearly at 20 c./sec. rather than at 6.8 c./sec. The animals were then trained to give a differential response, so that pressing a lever during 10-c./sec. stimulation was rewarded with milk, but pressing during the 6.8-c./sec. flicker was not. When the cat responded correctly to the 10-c./sec. flicker, the dorsal hippocampus and the centralis lateralis, in addition to the visual cortex, showed a clear 10-c./sec. discharge. If the animal made a mistake, however, and failed to press the lever during the 10-c./sec. flicker, the dorsal hippocampus and the centralis lateralis showed a shift in frequency toward a slower rate, around 5 or 6 c./sec. With a correct negative response, i.e., failure to press with 6.8-c./sec. stimulation, the dorsal hippocampus and the centralis lateralis also showed a clear 6-c./sec. discharge.

They also evaluated[80] frequency-specific responses to a 10-c./sec. flickering light in the visual cortex, auditory cortex, lateral geniculate, superior colliculus, amygdala, and hippocampus. The frequency-specific response gradually disappeared from these structures during familiarization, but when the flicker was followed by a shock they reappeared in all structures except the amygdala and the hippocampus. When the conditioned avoidance response was fully learned, a 40-c./sec. burst of activity was noted in the amygdala along with multiples of the frequency-specific discharge in the cortex. The significance of these frequency-specific responses, however, remains unknown. Some workers have considered them "a neural memory trace" of the unconditioned stimulus; others, a nonspecific response merely by chance near the frequency of the stimulus.

Morrell et al., [117] using the average response computer at the Massachusetts Institute of Technology, tried to elucidate the nature of this repetitive response. They showed clearly that the repetitive response appeared only during the transient second phase and disappeared during the third phase. They asked, further, whether this response were time- or phase-locked to the conditional signal and whether it were truly frequency-specific. Some of their evidence suggested that the rhythm was phase-locked to the triggering signal; but this was not definite. The question of frequency-specificity was still more difficult. The conditioned rhythmic response usually consisted of a mixture of frequencies, some of which were and some of which were not at the flash rate. The dominant frequency of the repetitive response could be altered by changing the stimulus frequency, but the shift was not directly or linearly related to the alteration in flash frequency.

Because of the frequency range within which the repetitive response appears and because of the nearness of the limbic cortex, it has been suggested that this rhythmic response represents the hippocampal arousal pattern. If it does indeed represent hippocampal arousal patterns, its disappearance in the third phase suggests that there is an early stage in the conditioning procedure which requires the participation of the limbic or hippocampal systems and that later stages no longer require this. Morrell et al. concluded, however, that their evidence was not adequate to prove the frequency-specificity of this response nor its relation to the hippocampal arousal pattern.

The nature of these frequency-specific responses has also been investigated by Yoshii and his associates.[175, 177-180] Using as conditioned stimulus a sound and as unconditioned stimulus rhythmic photic flashes, they confirmed the three stages in the development of a conditioned cerebral response as described by Morrell and Jasper. Using implanted electrodes, they demonstrated, in the second stage, conditioned frequency-specific waves occurring in the hippocampus, reticular formation, red nucleus, septal region, fornix, nucleus of the posterior commissure, and sometimes the internal capsule, in addition to the cortex. These rhythmic waves, at 4–7 c./sec., were earlier in onset, of higher amplitude, and more stable in these subcortical structures than in the cortex. They were first thought to be a "remnant" of memory, i.e., an electrically tagged memory trace, in which a specific memory was reflected by a specific electrical activity. These frequency-specific responses were more likely to occur when the photic stimulation was at 4–5 c./sec. than at 7 c./sec. or more. Since hippocampal arousal is manifested by 4–5-c./sec. waves, Yoshii finally concluded that what had been considered a "remnant" of memory, in the reticular formation and nearby structures, could not be separated from the hippocampal arousal pattern reinforced by an unconditioned stimulus incidentally of the same frequency.

Interest in these rhythmic responses recorded from the reticular formation and neighboring structures arose because these waves might represent frequency-specific memory traces. Such waves are not dependent, however, upon the delivery of a frequency-specific unconditioned stimulus. Shumilina,[152] studying conditioned defensive reflexes in rabbits, found that a synchronized rhythm at 4–6 c./sec. arose in the brain stem reticular formation and in the medial nucleus of the thalamus at the moment when cortical desynchronization appeared in response to the conditioned stimulus. Anokhin[4] also investigated the relation between activity in the reticular formation and in the cerebral cortex. When weak defensive conditioned stimuli were applied, synchronized 4–6-c./sec. activity often appeared in the reticular formation when there was still no desynchronization in the cerebral cortex. He concluded that early in the action of the conditioned stimulus, the reticular formation reacts with a synchronized rhythm while the cerebral cortex has not yet evinced desynchronization. Anokhin obtained such synchronized rhythms regularly with conditioned defensive reflexes but not with conditioned alimentary stimuli.

Much interest has thus developed in whether the responses actually are "frequency-specific" or whether they merely represent nonspecific hippocampal arousal patterns. Green and Arduini[59] had earlier shown in cats that when desynchronization of the neocortical record was induced, it was invariably associated with the appearance of 3–6-c./sec. high-amplitude slow waves in the region of the hippocampus. They interpreted this as a "specialized paleocortical arousal reaction." Grastyán, Lissák and colleagues[56-58, 93] have extensively examined the electrical activity of the hippocampus in cats during conditioning. They observed that the first presentation of a new stimulus produced a startle response, associated with desynchronization in both hippocampal and cortical areas. This was distinguished from the orienting reflex, which appeared only after a stimulus had been presented several times and was associated with searching or turning toward the source of stimulation. During this phase, when the stimulus caused an orienting reflex rather than a startle response, slow 4–7-c./sec. high-amplitude waves appeared in the hippocampal region, associated with deep synchronization in the cortical regions.

In the development of conditioned reflexes, the first presentation usually produced a startle response with desynchronization in both hippocampal and cortical regions. With further pairing of conditioned and unconditioned stimuli, however, the conditioned stimulus began to effect an orienting reflex, associated with 4–7-c./sec. activity in the hippocampal region and with desynchronization in the cortical region. When the animal developed a stable conditioned reflex, both the hippocampal and cortical responses disappeared. They concluded that in the development of a conditioned reflex "something important happens in the hippocampus at the time of the appearance of the orientation reflex."

Adey et al.,[1] studying electrical activity in the hippocampus and entorhinal cortex during approach training, failed to confirm these observations. In cats with chronically implanted electrodes, simultaneous photographic records and electroencephalograms were made to correlate electroencephalographic and behavioral activities. Auto- and cross-correlations were performed so that phase relationships between discharges in various regions could be assayed. The initial hippocampal desynchronization to a stimulus, as reported by Grastyán et al., was not observed. On the contrary, sustained hippocampal slow waves at 4–7 c./sec. appeared in the animals on first exposure to the test situation. With presentation of the conditioning stimuli and during the earliest approach performances, there was rapid stabilization of rhythmic activity at 5–6 c./sec. in the dorsal hippocampus and entorhinal area. This 5–6-c./sec. activity appeared as a sudden transition from the ongoing slower rhythmic activity, without any intervening period of desynchronization. This sudden transition during each approach was the most characteristic electroencephalographic pattern noted in these studies. Specifically, these 5–6-c./sec. waves were not associated with an orientation reflex but were associated with the animal's approach. The discrepancy between the observations of these two groups is not readily explained on the basis of available evidence.

Investigations have not been limited to the development of the conditioned response and its extinction; extensive studies have been devoted to the process which Pavlov entitled "internal inhibition." Rowland and Gluck[53, 142, 143] studied sleeping cats, with the conditioned stimulus being a 2-c./sec. click and the unconditioned stimulus a shock to the skin. After adaptation, the cat was given 10 paired trials a day. At the beginning of the experiment, the interval between the appearance of the conditioned and the unconditioned stimulus was 5 sec.; this was gradually extended to 120 sec. delay by the 16th day, after which it was held constant. As the delay reached 60 sec. and over, the sustained desynchronization characteristic of the shorter delay periods disappeared. The response became characterized by generalized desynchronization at the onset of the conditioned stimulus, followed by a gradually returning synchrony, which was well maintained for 40–60 sec. This was followed by a second period of sustained desynchronization which differed from the initial one in being less generalized and showing marked differences in onset in different areas. In this delay situation, auditory cortex, reticular formation, and hippocampus desynchronized as much as 10 sec. before the association cortex. The authors next presented a differentiating sound which became a signal for canceling the anticipated pain. Within a few trials, all the cats showed the appearance of synchrony in response to the differentiated stimulus.

Thus synchrony was induced by a delayed conditioned stimulus or by a differentiated stimulus signaling withholding pain. In two situations, therefore, where Pavlovian "internal inhibition" would be expected, the electroencephalogram revealed synchrony arising from a background of desynchronization. Rowland[141] had demonstrated earlier, in a study of arousal from sleep to conditioned auditory stimuli, that the conditioned stimulus caused desynchronization, whereas neutral (differentiated) stimuli caused electroencephalographic synchrony.

Similar observations have been made in other laboratories. Yoshii *et al.*[176, 179] demonstrated the development of slow waves during delayed conditioning in cats, and Storm van Leeuwen[160] described increased prominence of the cerebral rhythms as a sign of inhibition in both cats and man. Gastaut[46] quotes the work of Grastyán, Hori, and Roger, who found, in cats trained to a positive and a negative stimulus, that the positive stimulus evoked blocking of spontaneous cerebral electrical activity in the somesthetic region, whereas the negative stimulus caused its reinforcement. Sakhiulina[148] also noted that a negative conditioned stimulus evoked electroencephalographic modifications just contrary to that of a positive conditioned stimulus, i.e., the negative stimulus provoked electrographic synchrony.

Kogan[90] emphasized the importance of desynchronization in external inhibition and synchrony in internal inhibition. He has published examples of extraordinary hypersynchrony in cats occurring in response to differential conditioned stimuli. He pointed out, however, that desynchrony and hypersynchrony do not necessarily represent opposite poles of cortical excitability. As measured by Kogan's method for determining direct cortical excitability, desynchronization is at times associated with increased and at times with decreased cortical excitability.

In recent years, cerebral cortical activity has been studied by newer, and concomitantly more intricate, methods in an effort to elucidate the finer functions of neurons themselves during cerebral conditioning. Jasper et al.[74, 75] investigated the cortex of monkeys with microelectrodes during conditioning, utilizing a flash at 5 c./sec. as the conditioned stimulus and a shock as the unconditioned stimulus. The results of these elegant studies were exceedingly complex. In brief, desynchronization of the electroencephalogram during avoidance conditioning was associated with a predominance of excitation (increased cell firing) in the sensory and motor areas and with a predominance of inhibition (decreased cell firing) in the frontal and parietal areas. Both excitatory and inhibitory processes, however, were apparent in single cells in all areas of the brain. Furthermore, states of excitation or inhibition of the cerebral cortex, as judged by rates of firing of the cortical cells, did not appear related directly to the presence or absence of slow wave in the surface electroencephalogram. No precise sequence of events, as far as firing of individual units was concerned, could be outlined during the development of the conditioned avoidance response.

Morrell[109, 115] used microelectrodes to investigate unit discharges in various subcortical nuclei during development of conditioned cerebral responses. Simultaneous recordings were made from the visual cortex, the nucleus ventralis anterior of the thalamus, the periaqueductal portion of the mesencephalic reticular formation, and the hippocampus. Again, the observations were exceedingly complex, with the unit firing pattern changing regularly in each area studied from habituation through each of the three stages of conditioning. From these studies he concludes: "In different ways it would appear that both hippocampus and mesencephalic reticular formation are concerned in the initial steps which determine what events will or will not become crystalized as engram. In no case where this entire sequence has been observed did the thalamo-cortical linkage appear without prior activity in hippocampal and mesencephalic systems."

Further expanding the methodological approach to this subject, Rusinov[145] studied slow potential changes during development of the conditioned reflex, demonstrating that almost simultaneously with the appearance of the first conditioned reflex movement, a slow negative wave is registered in the occipital area and later in the motor area. With extinction of this conditioned reflex, the slow potential change disappeared. Livanov[94] has also studied conditioned reflexes with a complicated "encephaloscope" of his own design, planned to demonstrate the distribution of bioelectrical activity over multiple areas of the brain. The significance of these observations is not clear at present.

In brief, the electroencephalographic manifestations of conditioning have been investigated in several animal species. The first electrographic evidence of a conditioned cerebral response is the appearance of diffuse desynchronization of the electroencephalogram in response to the conditioned stimulus before the onset of the unconditioned stimulus. Repetition of the combined stimuli leads to gradual narrowing of the zone of desynchronization until it overlies only the region of the unconditioned analyzer. Cortical desynchronization bears no constant relation to the appearance of a behavioral conditioned reflex. Desynchronization is the electrographic manifestation both of the conditioned response and of external inhibition, whereas enhanced synchrony is the manifestation of internal inhibition. If a flickering light at 4–12 c./sec. is used as the unconditioned stimulus, a repetitive response, present widely in the cortical and subcortical structures, appears transiently between the stage of general and of focal desynchronization. There has been much interest in whether these repetitive responses are frequency-specific transmitters of information or whether they are nonspecific responses. The bulk of present evidence points to their being nonspecific responses, identical or closely identified with hippocampal arousal responses. These rhythmic subcortical responses have been linked both to the orientation reflex and to approach behavior. Microelectrode studies have shown wide variation in unit firing from area to area during the development of the conditioned response, but no precise sequence of events for the individual units has been unearthed.

Evoked Responses and Conditioning

Much interest has focused on the transmission of signals through the central nervous system and on the evoked cortical potential signaling transmission there. These studies, behavioral in their orientation, were founded on basic neurophysiological investigations begun by Granit and Kaada.[55] They demonstrated that the efferent gamma system is tonically activated from central regions; thus stimulation of various central neural structures affects discharge from the muscle spindles. Descending pathways then regulate and modify the character and intensity of afferent messages. Therefore, might not synaptic transmission of ascending signals within the central nervous system also be under the influence of higher regulating mechanisms?

Hagbarth and Kerr[60] found that repetitive stimulation of various central structures influenced the size of the dorsal column relayed response and of the dorsal root reflex. The primary afferent spike in the dorsal column was never affected by such stimulation. They concluded that synaptic transmission from the first to the second sensory neuron is under the influence of specific descending pathways. They later demonstrated[87] the effect of central stimulation upon another sensory modality by showing that stimulation of the basal rhinencephalic area depressed electrical activity in the olfactory bulbs. In further studies Granit[54] and Galambos[41] demonstrated that central stimulation affected both the visual and the auditory afferents. Gellhorn, Koella, and others[51, 126] showed that application of mild nociceptive stimuli to anesthetized cats augmented the response to click from the auditory cortex. Thus there is abundant evidence to document the effects of central activity on sensory transmission.

These basic neurophysiological observations led to a study of evoked potentials in various behavioral situations. Hernández-Peón and his associates have investigated these over a number of years. Recording the electrical response to a click along the auditory pathways in the unanesthetized cat, they noted[66] that when the cat paid attention to an outside stimulus, such as a mouse or a fish odor, the amplitude of the response in the second and third order neurons was reduced. Responses returned to the normal amplitude when the outside stimulus was removed. Electrical responses along the visual pathways (the optic tract excepted) also diminished when the cat's attention was fixed upon an acoustic or olfactory stimulus.[65] The depression of the response was roughly proportional to the degree of attention. A reduction in response also occurred when stimulation of the brain stem reticular formation elicited attentive behavior. Studies in an unanesthetized man at surgery[82] revealed that when the patient attended to a flashing light by counting the number of flashes, the amplitude of evoked subcortical visual potentials was augmented. On the other hand, attention to another sensory modality (sound, smell, painful or proprioceptive stimulation, memory recall) resulted in diminished amplitude of the evoked subcortical visual responses. The diminution of amplitude was maximal with painful stimulation. The same is essentially true for responses recorded from the scalp.[43]

Galambos *et al.*[40, 42] investigated these responses in conditioning situations. In cats bearing multiple implanted electrodes, clicks were presented at a rate of one every 3 sec. for long periods of time. Gradually habituation of the click responses developed throughout the auditory pathways from the cochlear nucleus rostrally. After some time, single strong shocks were given across the animal's chest at the same time as randomly selected clicks. Concomitantly, the response to the click, whether associated directly with a shock or not, became greatly augmented in the cochlear nucleus and in the cortical projection area. In further experiments,[61] if a monkey were presented two auditory stimuli, one followed by a shock and the other not, the stimulus followed by shock brought about a rapid increase in amplitude of evoked potentials while that not followed by shock caused no change. In operant conditioning, in which the animal must respond in a definite way either to obtain a positive reinforcement or to avoid a negative reinforcement, evoked responses were reduced in amplitude in either experimental situation.[61, 173]

Later studies[102] examined the response in the cochlear nucleus, superior olive, inferior colliculus, medial geniculate, auditory cortex, caudate nucleus, hippocampus, and field H of Forel during conditioning. In this experiment clicks were randomly reinforced with a puff of air to the eye. Increased amplitude of the evoked response was uniformly observed after reinforcement began; the average increase in nonauditory centers was greater than in the auditory pathway. In general, Hernández-Peón[62] found that nociceptive stimulation had a similar effect upon the evoked response. He also studied the effect of nociceptive stimulation upon the reticular formation response to paired clicks, observing that the association with pain changed the response to both of the paired stimuli.[17]

Jouvet and Hernández-Peón[83] used a tone followed by a shock to develop a conditioned reflex. Whereas previously the evoked cortical potential was limited to the auditory area, after conditioning the tone caused an evoked potential both in the auditory and in the sensory-motor cortex. With extinction by nonreinforcement, the evoked potential disappeared from the sensory-motor region. Russian workers[5] have noted that when a conditioned reflex is firmly established to an auditory stimulus, the primary evoked reaction of the auditory cortex to tone appears more often than before. Segundo et al.[150] observed that, as a consequence of training, the conditioned signal becomes capable of modifying the response to the unconditioned stimulus; that is, the potential in the somatic sensory cortex evoked by a painful stimulus is larger when preceded by its conditioned signal than when not preceded by it. Altered alpha blocking responses under similar situations has also been noted.[167] When a flash stimulus served as signal for a motor conditioned response, evoked potentials became more pronounced, particularly in the region of the motor analyzer in the hemisphere contralateral to the effector limb.[134]

In a number of studies previously described, evoked potentials, i.e., the "on responses" to the conditioned stimuli, were also observed. In Morrell and Jasper's studies[112, 116, 118, 120] the development of this "on response" in general followed rather closely the development of the activation pattern to the conditioned stimulus. These "on responses" were not as stable, however, as these desynchronization patterns. Yoshii et al.[176, 178, 179] noted that, during the development of defensive and salivary conditioned reflexes to light in monkeys, the "on response" spread from the occipital cortex and reticular formation to many other areas, such as the thalamus and hypothalamus and even into the frontal area. When the conditioned reflex became stable, however, the generalized evoked potentials disappeared. Chow et al.[22] observed not only that the "on response" to tone made its appearance during development of the conditioned cerebral response but also that the final conditioned cerebral complex generally included both the evoked potential and the localized blocking response. Beck et al.,[7] on the other hand, found no relationship between the evoked responses and the course of conditioning.

Secondary cortical evoked potentials have been studied as well. Cortical response to peripheral stimulation is manifested not only by a primary response but also by a less discrete secondary response of lower amplitude and more dispersed in space. Thus, for example, a click causes the appearance of an evoked response over both the primary auditory cortex and the parietal region. Pribram *et al.*[138] educed evidence suggesting that the response to click recorded from the parietal cortex is mediated by collaterals which branch from the main geniculo-temporal projection to connect the medial geniculate nucleus with the cortex of the supratemporal plane. Buser and Borenstein[15, 16] studied these "secondary" reactions which appear over wide areas of cerebral cortex which are usually considered "silent." Strong cerebral activation, brought about by stimulation of the reticular substance, was accompanied by almost total disappearance of the secondary responses. As the waking record evolved toward sleep, the secondary responses reappeared. In this state, they had their greatest amplitude and stability.

Fessard[37] has also studied the cortical distribution of electrical responses to various modes of sensory stimulation. He noted that light, sound, and somesthetic stimulation have intricate projections upon the cerebral cortex, and that there are regions where responses to many different modalities of stimulation can be picked up. These regions having heterosensorial projection are not limited to the usual "association" areas but include other areas as well. He concluded that there are no cortical regions which are absolutely specific projections for one modality of stimulus, nor are there cortical regions which are purely associative in nature; rather, all cortical regions are at the same time regions of projection and zones of association.

Buser and Rougeul[18, 19] have investigated these secondary cortical responses in the cat during development of the conditioned reflex, utilizing both classic avoidance responses and purely sensory-sensory associations. Confirming their previous observations, responses were observed outside the primary projection areas of the applied stimulus. These responses, usually polyphasic and very complex, had a longer latency than the primary evoked potential; their form and amplitude varied according to the point considered. Again, an intense and unexpected stimulus abolished them. When the animal's attention was caught by a certain sensory modality, the primary sensory projection area of this modality could show a transient "secondary" response to stimulation by an entirely different sensory modality; if such a "secondary" response already existed, it might be enhanced. Lastly, when one stimulus regularly preceded a second, the first stimulus began to evoke a "secondary" response in the primary projection area of the second stimulus.

Conditioning by Direct Electrical Stimulation of the Cerebrum

Loucks,[98, 99] working in Gantt's laboratory, first substituted direct electrical stimulation of the cerebrum for one part of the reflex arc involved in the conditioned reflex. In the dog, he combined a tone as conditioned stimulus with electrical stimulation of the sigmoid gyrus as unconditioned stimulus. Even after 600 trials, these animals had not developed conditioned reflexes. If each cortical shock were rewarded with food, however, conditioned reflex movement of the limb to tone could be established. Later, he showed that stimulation of the sensory cortex might serve as the conditioned stimulus for a salivary or avoidance reflex. The validity of these observations, however, was questioned because Clark and Ward[24] found that the coil utilized for stimulation in these experiments produced some slight subcutaneous vibration. Since this vibration might itself serve as the conditioned stimulus, further efforts were necessary to prove the correctness of Loucks' hypotheses.

With the discovery that stimulating a portion of the brain could precipitate emotional reactions, an attempt was made to use this as an unconditioned stimulus. Masserman[103] stimulated the hypothalamus to produce "sham rage" as the unconditioned stimulus preceding it by light, sound, and pain as the conditioned stimulus. In his studies, none of these conditioned stimuli ever provoked the emotional reaction produced by direct hypothalamic stimulation.

Delgado et al.[27] elicited a "fear-like" reaction by stimulation of three regions of the cat's brain—the superior part of the tectal area in the neighborhood of the spinothalamic tract, the lateral nuclear mass of the thalamus, and the inferomedial part of the hippocampal gyrus. Cats were trained to turn a wheel at the sound of a buzzer to prevent the application of an electric shock. Stimulation of the fear-producing regions was then substituted for the buzzer; the cats quickly learned to turn the wheel with central stimulation. After this, central stimulation was used as the unconditioned stimulus, preceded by light or tone; turning the wheel in response to the light or the tone would prevent the central stimulation. After 16 to 92 pairings, each light or tone stimulus consistently elicited wheel-turning before application of the central electrical stimulus.

In another approach,[174] animals were taught to put the left foreleg on a food tray, presentation of food serving as reinforcement. After the animals were satiated, weak electrical stimulation of the lateral hypothalamus elicited the same sort of conditioned behavior (placement of the leg on the food tray) as had occurred previously in the hungry animal. Ungher and Steriade[163] used rhythmic flicker as a conditioned stimulus and transcerebral electric shock as an unconditioned one. Prior to these associations, the basic rhythm was only weakly driven by the flicker. Following 20 to 25 associations, however, the flicker produced driving of high amplitude as well as spikes and spike-and-wave complexes. Thus some electroencephalographic manifestations of an epileptiform discharge can be conditioned in the experimental animal, though one would question here whether the cortical response itself might not have been modified by the trauma of repeated electroshocks.

Less dramatic but no less significant are those more subtle changes which have been elicited by cerebral electrical stimulation. Rusinov and Smirnov[128, 147] localized an anodal current on the cerebral projection area of the rabbit's paw. This current was too weak to elicit any movement itself. When sound or light was presented to the rabbit, however, a movement corresponding to the area of polarization appeared. This response to sound and light might last as long as 30 minutes after the current was turned off. Doty *et al.*[28, 31] studied cats with implanted electrodes in various cortical positions. Stimulation for 2 sec. at 50 pulses per sec. were applied to the cerebral cortex, and if at the end of this time the animal still had its paw on a metal plate, the leg was shocked. The cats so studied readily developed conditioned withdrawal response to cortical stimulation. These studies avoided the pitfalls which resulted in criticism of Loucks's earlier work and established stimulation of the cerebral cortex as an effective conditioned stimulus. When the cortical site of the conditioned stimulus was circumsected, the conditioned reflex was maintained, but when the zone was undercut, conditioned reflexes disappeared.

These findings have been further confirmed in an elegant series of experiments carried out by Doty and Giurgea.[30] They have demonstrated without question that conditioned reflexes can be established with cortical stimulation as both the conditioned and unconditioned stimulus in dogs, cats, and monkeys. They could detect no evidence of motivation in these conditioned reflexes formed by the coupling of cortical stimulations.

Other workers have chosen rhythmic electrical stimulation of subcortical nuclear masses as the unconditioned stimulus. Segundo et al.[151] described the development of a conditioned cerebral response and its extinction when tone as a conditioned stimulus was associated with electrical stimulation of the nucleus centre median or the midbrain reticular formation. Yoshii and others confirmed this by stimulation of the nucleus centre median and other thalamic nuclei as well. In addition, Morrell[115] has studied slow potential shifts with central stimulation. A low-intensity tone alone produced no significant slow potential changes. Tone as a conditioned stimulus was then followed by 4–5-c./sec. stimulation of the nucleus centre median in the rabbit. After 30 trials of the conditioned stimulus plus the thalamic stimulus, tone alone caused a negative slow potential shift similar to that usually evoked by thalamic stimulation alone.

Efforts to Interrupt the Conditioned Cerebral Response

Throughout the years, efforts have been made to utilize functional deactivation of one or another portion of the nervous system to delineate further the neural structures necessary for the conditioned reflex. Such methods have also been employed in studying the electroencephalographic aspects of the conditioned reflex.

Loucks[98] utilized this approach in his studies, stimulation of the sigmoid gyrus eliciting a hindleg movement serving as conditioned stimulus and a cutaneous shock to the foreleg as unconditioned stimulus. This conditioned response was not disturbed by narcotization of the spinal cord which blocked all impulses to and from the hind limb. He deduced that stimulation of the sigmoid gyrus itself was an adequate stimulus for the development of a conditioned reaction, neither movement nor proprioceptive stimulation from the hind limb being essential. In related conditioned avoidance tests, Beck and Doty[6] also concluded that movement of the limb was not essential for the development of the conditioned reflex.

Surgical or electrical ablation of specific cerebral structures has been performed to determine its effect upon the development of the conditioned response. Pavlov believed that the cerebral cortex was the requisite organ for the elaboration of a conditioned reflex; and it has been demonstrated many times that decortication seriously interferes with those conditioned reflexes already established and severely impairs the development of new conditioned reflexes. Some extremely simple and basic conditioned reflexes could, however, be established even in the decorticate specimen. Since so many of the electroencephalographic changes noted in the development of conditioned reflexes are akin to those achieved by stimulation of mesencephalic or thalamic structures, it was logical that the effects of lesions in these areas upon the development of conditioned responses should be investigated.

Hernández-Peón *et al.*[63, 64] studied conditioned reflex salivation in cats established either by the inhalation of ether or by the sight and facial contact of a piece of cotton moistened with water. Extensive bilateral lesions were then made involving various structures in different cats. Conditioned salivation was not impaired by widespread decortication nor by extensive subcortical lesions involving the hippocampus, fornix, septal area, amygdaloid complex, medial intralaminar and specific thalamic nuclei, mammillary bodies, posterior hypothalamus, medial mesencephalic reticular formation, pretectal region, or the superior colliculus. In striking contrast, small lesions of the lateral mesencephalic reticular formation, not impairing wakefulness, completely abolished or greatly reduced the conditioned salivary response.

Doty *et al.*[29] studied a conditioned avoidance reflex using a 2-sec. tone as the conditioned stimulus and an unavoidable shock as the unconditioned stimulus. In six cats, large, bilateral electrolitic lesions were then made in the medial diencephalon or mesencephalon. Low-voltage, fast activity consistently reappeared in the electroencephalogram seven to ten days following these procedures. Conditioned defensive reflexes also reappeared after surgery, and the animals were even able to discriminate between tones. It was noted, however, that most conditioned reflexes occurred only when the electroencephalogram showed low-voltage, fast activity—although this was not invariably the case. In other animals extensive lesions essentially transecting the ascending reticular system or destroying the posterior hypothalamus did not preclude conditioning. In one animal, destruction of the region including the nucleus centre median, the posterior hypothalamus, and the mammillary bodies completely abolished conditioning; and in another with lesions in the mammillary area, conditioned reflexes also were unobtainable. In another study, discrete flexion responses could still be conditioned in cats with lesions in the red nucleus and the mammillary bodies. They concluded that the region including the nucleus centre median, posterior hypothalamus, and the mammillary bodies was more important for the type of conditioning studied here than were the medial mesencephalic, the anterior medial thalamic, and the hypothalamic areas.

Kreindler[92] investigated the effect of lesions in the mesencephalic-pontine reticular formation in dogs performing a delayed reaction test. In normal animals, correct responses occurred in 90 per cent of the trials for intervals not over 1 minute; in animals with reticular lesions, correct responses were less frequent. Even for an interval of 10 sec., only 54 per cent of the responses were correct. In contrast, Segundo[149] found that small lesions in the mesencephalic reticular formation and in the amygdaloid complex or large lesions in the lateral nuclear complex of the thalamus did not produce marked abnormalities in learned behavior or learning abilities. At the moment, these discrepancies cannot be readily explained.

Others have sought the effect of more rostral lesions upon the development of conditioned responses. Morrell,[108, 112] working with Chow, made bilateral lesions involving the nucleus reticularis and nucleus ventralis anterior of the thalamus and the anterior limb of the internal capsule. After the symptoms of surgery cleared, they investigated the development of conditioned cerebral responses, using tone as the conditioned stimulus and flickering light as the unconditioned stimulus. The generalized activation pattern characteristic of the first stage was not at all impaired by these lesions. The most striking change involved the early appearance and the abnormal persistence of both the conditioned repetitive response and the prolonged after-discharge to intermittent light. In these animals, though, the conditioned repetitive response was never permanently replaced by the localized activation pattern usually seen in the normal animal. These observations suggested that the discrete localized activation pattern, representing the end point in cerebral conditioning, required the participation of the topographically organized diencephalic reticular formation. The marked enhancement of the repetitive response and of the after-discharge suggested release of cortical structures from lower inhibitory influences. Yoshii and Hockaday[177] observed that unilateral lesions in the nucleus centre median and other nuclei of the thalamus did not prevent the appearance of conditioned electroencephalographic responses, but in one animal with bilateral lesions in the centre median, the characteristic frequency waves failed to appear.

The opposite approach is to establish regions of hyperfunction within the brain and to study their effect upon conditioned reflexes. Excessive neural activity in various regions of the cerebrum (whether induced by direct electrical stimulation or by development of a chronic epileptogenic lesion) impairs learning ability and interferes with the performance of previously learned acts.[20, 129, 137, 154] Morrell *et al.*[110, 111, 121] studied the effect of chronic epileptogenic lesions, induced by alumina cream applied to the cortex, upon conditioned cerebral responses. The development of conditioned cerebral responses was prevented or seriously delayed whenever the chronically firing epileptogenic lesion was situated in the cortical region, which was the primary projection region for the conditioned stimulus; that is, when tone was used as a conditioned stimulus and light as an unconditioned stimulus, an epileptiform lesion in the auditory cortex impaired the development of a conditioned cerebral response, whereas an epileptiform lesion in the visual or somatic receiving areas did not. A lesion in the amygdala might interfere with several forms of conditioned responses. Surgical removal of the epileptiform cortex led to a striking improvement.

These observations were confirmed by Kreindler,[92] who found that cortical epileptiform activity, initiated by electrical stimulation of the projection area of the unconditioned stimulus, exerted no inhibitory effect whatever on natural or elaborated conditioned reflexes. On the other hand, focal cortical epileptiform discharges, produced by electrical stimulation of the projection area of the conditioned stimulus, caused an arrest of conditioned reflexes which might last from 15 to 60 sec. after the epileptiform discharge. He found, further, that if electrical stimulation of the cortex resulted in a generalized seizure rather than merely a focal discharge, during the period of postconvulsive electrical silence conditioned reflexes were abolished. A few seconds following the reappearance of cortical electrical activity, however, conditioned reflexes returned briefly, after which another much longer period of inhibition set in, lasting from 5 to 20 minutes, sometimes even longer. On the other hand, a brain stem convulsive fit resulting from electrical stimulation of the reticular formation caused abolition of conditioned reflexes lasting for 3–10 sec., but afterward the conditioned reflexes reappeared, were more vigorous, and had shorter latencies than prior to the reticular stimulation. Kreindler interpreted these observations as suggesting that the meso-rhomboencephalic reticular neurons are not component links in the elaboration of a conditioned reflex. If they participate directly, there should be a decreased capacity for the development of conditioned reflexes after reticular formation stimulation, as there is after cortical stimulation. These observations of Kreindler have been confirmed in detail by Zuckermann.[181]

It is also apparent that different forms of conditioned responses are affected in different fashions by cerebral stimulation. Thus Galambos[39] quotes the work of Brady and Hunt who elaborated two types of conditioned reflex to a single stimulus in rats. The effect of a convulsive seizure, whether caused by electrical stimulation of the head or by intense sounds, was to abolish one type of conditioned reflex but to leave the other type intact. Gastaut and Roger[50] mention the work of Grastyán in which conditioned reflexes might be either facilitated or inhibited by stimulation of various hypothalamic and reticular structures. Further, Anokhin[4] found that chlorpromazine blocked the activating effect of the reticular formation for a conditioned defensive reaction while its activating effect for an alimentary reaction was retained.

Bureš[13, 14] has very cleverly utilized the spreading depression of Leão to produce functional depression of the cerebral cortex in animals. Depressed cortical function was documented by the depression of the spontaneous electroencephalographic activity, primary responses, direct cortical responses, and strychnine spikes, as well as by an elevation in the electrical threshold in the motor areas. When potassium chloride was applied to the occipital cortex of the rat to induce spreading depression, the incidence of avoidance responses fell to zero, only to show slow improvement after 3 hours. During this same period, an escape response (from an electrified grid) was severely impaired. It was possible, however, to elaborate a very primitive avoidance response though not a more elaborate reaction.

Spreading depression confined to a single hemisphere produced some very interesting results. In one group, spreading depression was elicited in the rat's left hemisphere, and a conditioned reflex was then elaborated. After criterion was reached, the animal was left until next day. At that time, spreading depression was elicited in the right hemisphere. With spreading depression in the right hemisphere, no evidence of retention of the previous day's learning could be detected, i.e., it required the same number of trials to reach criteria on the second day as on the first. When, however, spreading depression on the second day was evoked in the same hemisphere as on the first, there was a very clear-cut retention from the previous day. It was thus demonstrated that learning occurs exclusively in the normal hemisphere and that such retention can be demonstrated only in the intact hemisphere. Dr. Bureš commented on the difference between his results and those achieved by ablation experiments. Since some time must elapse after ablation before testing can even begin, other structures may take over the function of the destroyed part during the obligatory interval of waiting.

He also studied the difference between spreading depression in the neocortex and in the paleocortex. During neocortical spreading depression, some escape reactions remain; but if spreading depression is also evoked in the hippocampal cortex, even the escape reaction may be lost. When cortical spreading depression was elicited just after criterion was reached in the learning procedure, retention could be demonstrated for relearning the same conditional reflex the next day. By contrast, when spreading depression was elicited in the hippocampus just after the criterion was reached in the learning procedure, learning was approximately the same on the following day as in the untrained animal.

Lastly, some work has been done in man in regard to impairment of the ability to form conditioned cerebral responses in patients with neurological dysfunction. These studies are detailed elsewhere,[166] but in summary Morrell[114] has demonstrated that there is a marked impairment in the ability to form a conditioned alpha response to a sound stimulus in patients with sharply localized temporal lobe foci who have temporal lobe-type seizures. In patients with generalized seizure disorders, there was no impairment of conditioning in the interseizure interval, but definite impairment occurred during the seizure discharge itself. Wells and Wolff[169] have shown that the ability to form these conditioned cerebral responses are likewise impaired with a variety of central nervous system lesions and that there is no relationship between the site of the lesion in the central nervous system and the degree of impairment. Other studies have shown the ability to form conditioned alpha wave responses to be impaired in certain mental disorders.[164, 168]

CONCLUSIONS

From this catalogue of extensive investigations pursued during the past several years, attempting to correlate electroencephalographic activity with behavior, what relevant conclusions can be drawn? We have certainly learned something from these widespread investigative efforts; on the other hand, it is fair to assert that these investigations have broadened only slightly our concepts of how the central nervous system actually works to effect normal behavior. These studies have been a disappointment in failing to provide new concepts of central neural function and in failing to provide either a firm scientific basis for the comprehension of behavior or a firm basis upon which a therapeutic approach to central nervous system dysfunction could be constructed.

The examination of electroencephalographic function during conditioning has, however, provided us with much new information and allowed us to prove and disprove many hypotheses concerning such function. It is apparent that the presentation to any subject, animal or human, of various stimuli produces a change in nervous system function involving multiple systems and perhaps even the most distant ramifications of the nervous system. Morrell[115] had stated: "Indeed it seems probable that electrical changes related to the imposed juxtaposition of stimuli may be found almost anywhere in the nervous system that one happens to have placed a recording electrode." When the relationship between the juxtaposed stimuli is constant, a predictable panorama of change in neural activity in various areas of the central nervous system occurs, the type of change dependent upon the resting state of the animal, the nature of the stimuli, the timing of the stimuli, and the area being measured. Thus, juxtaposed stimuli produce changes in nervous activity of a relatively predictable nature almost everywhere within the system. The changes produced by these juxtaposed stimuli, however, are not stable; rather they are transient, evanescent, difficult to detail and to delineate.

With such widespread changes in electrical activity occurring throughout the nervous system, it is human to hope that one particular structure might be most important in promoting normal function and to hope that within one structure the "neural trace" of memory might be found. Detailed study, though, of electrographic activity in the intact animal, as well as of the changes produced by hyperactivity and ablation, suggests that, so far as conditioned reflexes are concerned, there is no "head ganglion." The relative importance of various portions of the central nervous system in conditioning has been debated by various schools of investigation. Thus Russian workers, following in Pavlov's footsteps, have emphasized the importance of the cerebral cortex. Many Western workers, steeped in the new-found importance of the reticular formation, have asserted that this is the site of the "temporary connection"; while later workers have emphasized the significance of the hippocampus and other portions of the limbic system.

It is apparent now that each of these areas plays an important role in the establishment of conditioned reflexes; and it is probable that without normal function in any one of these structures, the development of conditioned reflexes is impaired. These investigations have therefore put to flight the fancies that there might somewhere within the nervous system be a locus for the engram. The position, long held by many workers, has been reemphasized that neural function is a result of complex interrelationships between its diverse parts, the function of the whole being infinitely more subtle than the function of any one of its component parts.

While these investigations have emphasized the involvement of multiple structures within the nervous system in even the simplest sensory associations, they have as yet been unable to associate changes in the electrical activity of the brain with overt behavioral manifestations. Almost no one has asserted that the electroencephalographic changes observed with juxtaposed stimuli bear any direct relation to the behavioral activity of the animal. We are thus still faced with the overriding problem of relating changes in the brain's electrical activity to the subject's behavior.

References

1. ADEY, W. R., DUNLOP, C. W., and HENDRIX, C. E., "Hippocampal Slow Waves. Distribution and Phase Relationships in the Course of Approach Learning," *Arch. Neurol., Chicago*, 3:74–90, 1960.

2. ADRIAN, E. D. and MATTHEWS, B. H. C., "The Berger Rhythm; Potential Changes from the Occipital Lobes in Man," *Brain*, 57:355–385, 1934.

3. ALEXANDER, L., "Apparatus and Method for Study of Conditional Reflexes in Man," *Arch. Neurol. Psychiat., Chicago*, 80:629–648, 1958.

4. ANOKHIN, P., "On the Specific Action of the Reticular Formation on the Cerebral Cortex," *Electroenceph. clin. Neurophysiol.*, Suppl. *13*:257–270, 1960.

5. ARTEMYEV, V. V. and BEZLADNOVA, N. I., quoted by RUSINOV, V. S. and RABINOVICH, M. Y., "Electroencephalographic Researches in the Laboratories and Clinics of the Soviet Union," *Electroenceph. clin. Neurophysiol.*, Suppl. *8*, 1958.

6. BECK, E. C. and DOTY, R. W., "Conditioned Flexion Reflexes Acquired During Combined Catalepsy and De-efferentation," *J. comp. physiol. Psychol.*, *50*:211–216, 1957.

7. BECK, E. C., DOTY, R. W., and KOOI, K. A., "Electrocortical Reactions Associated with Conditioned Flexion Reflexes," *Electroenceph. clin. Neurophysiol.*, *10*:279–289, 1958.

8. BERGER, H., "Über das Elektrenkephalogramm des Menschen," *Arch. Psychiat. Nervenkr.*, *87*:527–570, 1929.

9. BERITOV, I. and VOROBYEV, A., quoted by RUSINOV, V. S. and RABINOVICH, M. Y., "Electroencephalographic Researches in the Laboratories and Clinics of the Soviet Union," *Electroenceph. clin. Neurophysiol.*, Suppl. *8*, 1958.

10. BRAZIER, M. A. B. (ed.), *The Central Nervous Sytem and Behavior*, Trans. First Conference, Josiah Macy, Jr. Foundation, New York, 1958.

11. BRAZIER, M. A. B. (ed.), *The Central Nervous System and Behavior*, Trans. Second Conference, Josiah Macy, Jr. Foundation, New York, 1959.

12. BRAZIER, M. A. B. (ed.), *The Central Nervous System and Behavior*, Trans. Third Conference, Josiah Macy, Jr. Foundation, New York, 1960.

13. BUREŠ, J., "Reversible Decortication and Behavior," in BRAZIER, M. A. B. (ed.), *The Central Nervous System and Behavior*, Trans. Second Conference, Josiah Macy, Jr. Foundation, New York, 1959.

14. BUREŠ, J. and BUREŠOVA, O., "The Use of Leão's Spreading Cortical Depression in Research on Conditioned Reflexes," *Electroenceph. clin. Neurophysiol.*, Suppl. *13*:359–376, 1960.

15. BUSER, P. and BORENSTEIN, P., "Réponses Corticales 'Secondaires' à la Stimulation Sensorielle Chez le Chat Curarisé non Anesthésié," *Electroenceph. clin. Neurophysiol.*, Suppl. *13*:89–108, 1957.

16. BUSER, P. and BORENSTEIN, P., "Variations Caractéristiques des Réponses Sensorielles 'Associatives' du Cortex Cérébral du Chat en Fonction du Degré Général d'Activation Corticale," *C. R. Acad. Sci., Paris*, *243*:93–96, 1956.

17. BUSER, P., JOUVET, M., and HERNÁNDEZ-PEÓN, R., "Modifications, au Cours du Conditionnement Chez le Chat, du Cycle d'Excitabilité au

Niveau de la Reticulée Mésencéphalique," *Acta neurol. latinoamer.,* 4:268–278, 1958.

18. BUSER, P. and ROUGEUL, A., "Cortical Sensory Responses in the Cat (Chronic Preparation). Their Modification During the Establishment of Temporary Connections," *Electroenceph. clin. Neurophysiol.,* 9:362, 1957.

19. BUSER, P. and ROUGEUL, A., "Réponses Sensorielles Corticales Chez le Chat en Préparation Chronique. Leurs Modifications lors de l'Établissement de Liaisons Temporaires," *Rev. neurol.,* 95:501–503, 1956.

20. CHOW, K. L., "Anatomical and Electrographical Analysis of Temporal Neocortex in Relation to Visual Discrimination Learning in Monkeys," in DELAFRESNAYE, J. F., FESSARD, A., GERARD, R. W., and KONORSKI, J. (eds.), *Brain Mechanisms and Learning,* Charles C Thomas, Springfield, Ill., 1961.

21. CHOW, K. L., "Brain Waves and Visual Discrimination Learning in Monkey," *Recent Adv. biol. Psychiat.,* 2:149–157, 1960.

22. CHOW, K. L., DEMENT, W. C., and JOHN, E. R., "Conditioned Electrocorticographic Potentials and Behavioral Avoidance Response in Cat," *J. Neurophysiol.,* 20:482–493, 1957.

23. CHRISTIAN, K., "The EEG Modifications During the Formation of the Conditioned Reflex in Man," *Electroenceph. clin. Neurophysiol.,* 12:755, 1960.

24. CLARK, S. L. and WARD, J. W., "Electrical Stimulation of the Cortex Cerebri of Cats," *Arch. Neurol. Psychiat., Chicago,* 38:926–943, 1937.

25. DAVIS, P. A., "Effects of Acoustic Stimuli on the Waking Human Brain," *J. Neurophysiol.,* 2:494–499, 1939.

26. DELAFRESNAYE, J. F., FESSARD, A., GERARD, R. W., and KONORSKI, J. (eds.), *Brain Mechanisms and Learning,* Charles C Thomas, Springfield, Ill., 1961.

27. DELGADO, J. M. R., ROBERTS, W. W., and MILLER, N. E., "Learning Motivated by Electrical Stimulation of the Brain," *Amer. J. Physiol., 179*: 587–593, 1954.

28. DOTY, R. W., "Brain Stimulation and Conditional Reflexes," in BRAZIER, M. A. B. (ed.), *The Central Nervous System and Behavior,* Trans. First Conference, Josiah Macy, Jr. Foundation, New York, 1958.

29. DOTY, R. W., BECK, E. C., and KOOI, K. A., "Effect of Brain-Stem Lesions on Conditioned Responses of Cats," *Exp. Neurol., 1*:360–385, 1959.

30. DOTY, R. W. and GIURGEA, C., "Conditioned Reflexes Established by Coupling Electrical Excitation of Two Cortical Areas," in DELAFRESNAYE, J. F., FESSARD, A., GERARD, R. W., and KONORSKI, J. (eds.), *Brain Mechanisms and Learning,* Charles C Thomas, Springfield, Ill., 1961.

31. Doty, R. W., Rutledge, L. T., and Larsen, R. M., "Conditioned Reflexes Established to Electrical Stimulation of Cat Cerebral Cortex," *J. Neurophysiol., 19*:401–415, 1956.

32. Dumenko, V. N., quoted in Rusinov, V. S. and Rabinovich, M. Y., "Electroencephalographic Researches in the Laboratories and Clinics of the Soviet Union," *Electroenceph. clin. Neurophysiol.,* Suppl. *8,* 1958.

33. Durup, G. and Fessard, A., "L'Électroencéphalogramme de l'Homme. Observations Psycho-Physiologique Relatives à l'Action des Stimuli Visuels et Auditifs," *Ann. psychol., Paris, 36*:1–36, 1935.

34. Efron, R., "The Conditioned Inhibition of Uncinate Fits," *Brain, 80*: 251–262, 1957.

35. Efron, R., "The Effect of Olfactory Stimuli in Arresting Uncinate Fits," *Brain, 79*:267–281, 1956.

36. Erwin, C. W., Lerner, M., Wilson, N. J., and Wilson, W. P., "Some Further Observations on the Photically Elicited Arousal Response," *Electroenceph. clin. Neurophysiol., 13*:391–394, 1961.

37. Fessard, A., "Le Conditionnement Considéré à l'Échelle du Neurone," *Electroenceph. clin. Neurophysiol.,* Suppl. *13*:157–184, 1960.

38. Fischgold, H. and Gastaut, H., "Conditionnement et Réactivité en Électroencéphalgraphie," *Electroenceph. clin. Neurophysiol.,* Suppl. *6,* 1957.

39. Galambos, R., "Discussion," in *Electroenceph. clin. Neurophysiol.,* Suppl. *13*: 292, 1960.

40. Galambos, R., "Electrical Correlates of Conditioned Learning," in Brazier, M. A. B. (ed.), *The Central Nervous System and Behavior,* Trans. First Conference, Josiah Macy, Jr. Foundation, New York, 1958.

41. Galambos, R., "Suppression of Auditory Nerve Activity by Stimulation of Efferent Fibers to Cochlea," *J. Neurophysiol., 19*:424–437, 1956.

42. Galambos, R., Sheatz, G., and Vernier, V. G., "Electrophysiological Correlates of a Conditioned Response in Cats," *Science, 123*:376–377, 1956.

43. Garcia-Austt, E., Bogacz, J., and Vanzulli, A., "Changes in Photic EEG Responses in Man Due to Attention, Habituation, and Conditioning," *Abstr. int. Congr. physiol. Sci., 21*:103–104, 1959.

44. Gastaut, H., "État Actuel des Connaissances sur l'Électroencéphalographie du Conditionnement," *Electroenceph. clin. Neurophysiol.,* Suppl. *6*:133–160, 1957.

45. Gastaut, H., "The Role of the Reticular Formation in Establishing Conditioned Reactions," in Jasper, H., Proctor, L. D., Knighton, R. S., Noshay, W. C., and Costello, R. J., *Reticular Formation of the Brain,* Little, Brown & Co., Boston, 1958.

46. GASTAUT, H., "Some Aspects of the Neurophysiological Basis of Conditioned Reflexes and Behavior," in WOLSTENHOLME, G. E. W. and O'CONNOR, C. M. (eds.), *Neurological Basis of Behaviour*, Little, Brown & Co., Boston, 1958.

47. GASTAUT, H. and BERT, J., "Electroencephalographic Detection of Sleep Induced by Repetitive Sensory Stimuli," in WOLSTENHOLME, G. E. W. and O'CONNOR, M. (eds.), *CIBA Foundation Symposium on the Nature of Sleep*, Little, Brown & Co., Boston, 1961.

48. GASTAUT, H., JUS, A., JUS, C., MORRELL, F., STORM VAN LEEUWEN, W., DONGIER, S., NAQUET, R., REGIS, H., ROGER, A., BEKKERING, D., KAMP, A., and WERRE, J., "Étude Topographique des Réactions d'Électroencéphalographiques Conditionées Chez l'Homme," *Electroenceph. clin. Neurophysiol.*, 9:1–34, 1957.

49. GASTAUT, H., REGIS, H., DONGIER, S., and ROGER, A., "Conditionnement Électroencéphalographique des Décharges Épileptiques et Notion d'Épilepsie Réflexoconditionnée," *Rev. neurol.*, 94:829–835, 1956.

50. GASTAUT, H. and ROGER, A., "Les Mécanismes de l'Activité Nerveuse Supérieure Envisagés au Niveau des Grandes Structures Fonctionnelles du Cerveau," *Electroenceph. clin. Neurophysiol.*, Suppl. 13:13–38, 1960.

51. GELLHORN, E., KOELLA, W. P., and BALLIN, H. M., "Interaction on Cerebral Cortex of Acoustic or Optic with Nociceptive Impulses: The Problem of Consciousness," *J. Neurophysiol.*, 17:14–21, 1954.

52. GERSHUNI, G. V., KOZHEVNIKOV, V. A., MARUSEVA, A. M., AVAKYAN, R. V., RADIONOVA, E. A., ALTMAN, J. A., and SOROKO, V. I., "Modifications in Electrical Responses of the Auditory System in Different States of the Higher Nervous Activity," *Electroenceph. clin. Neurophysiol.*, Suppl. 13:115–124, 1960.

53. GLUCK, H. and ROWLAND, V., "Defensive Conditioning of Electrographic Arousal with Delayed and Differentiated Auditory Stimuli," *Electroenceph. clin. Neurophysiol.*, 11:485–496, 1959.

54. GRANIT, R., "Centrifugal and Antidromic Effects on Ganglion Cells of Retina," *J. Neurophysiol.*, 18:388–411, 1955.

55. GRANIT, R. and KAADA, B. R., "Influence of Stimulation of Central Nervous Structures on Muscle Spindles in Cat," *Acta physiol. scand.*, 27:130–160, 1953.

56. GRASTYÁN, E., "The Hippocampus and Higher Nervous Activity," in BRAZIER, M. A. B., *The Central Nervous System and Behavior*, Trans. Second Conference, Josiah Macy, Jr. Foundation, New York, 1959.

57. GRASTYÁN, E., "The Significance of the Earliest Manifestations of Conditioning in the Mechanism of Learning," in DELAFRESNAYE *et al.* (eds.), *Brain Mechanisms and Learning*, Charles C Thomas, Springfield, Ill., 1961.

58. GRASTYÁN, E., LISSÁK, K., MADARASZ, I., and DONHOFFER, H., "Hippo-campal Electrical Activity During the Development of Conditioned Reflexes," *Electroenceph. clin. Neurophysiol.*, 11:409–430, 1959.

59. GREEN, J. D. and ARDUINI, A. A., "Hippocampal Electrical Activity in Arousal," *J. Neurophysiol.*, 17:533–557, 1954.

60. HAGBARTH, K.-E. and KERR, D. I. B., "Central Influences on Spinal Afferent Conduction," *J. Neurophysiol.*, 17:295–307, 1954.

61. HEARST, E., BEER, B., SHEATZ, G., and GALAMBOS, R., "Some Electro-physiological Correlates of Conditioning in the Monkey," *Electro-enceph. clin. Neurophysiol.*, 12:137–152, 1960.

62. HERNÁNDEZ-PEÓN, R., "Neurophysiological Correlates of Habituation and Other Manifestations of Plastic Inhibition," *Electroenceph. clin. Neurophysiol.*, Suppl. 13:101–114, 1960.

63. HERNÁNDEZ-PEÓN, R. and BRUST-CARMONA, H., "Functional Role of Subcortical Structures in Habituation and Conditioning," in DELA-FRESNAYE, J. F., FESSARD, A., GERARD, R. W., and KONORSKI, J. (eds.), *Brain Mechanisms and Learning*, Charles C Thomas, Springfield, Ill., 1961.

64. HERNÁNDEZ-PEÓN, R., BRUST-CARMONA, H., ECKHAUS, E., LOPEZ-MENDOZA, E., and ALCOCER-CUARON, C., "Effect of Cortical and Sub-cortical Lesions on Salivary Conditioned Response," *Acta. neurol. latinoamer.*, 4:111–120, 1958.

65. HERNÁNDEZ-PEÓN, R., GUZMAN-FLORES, C., ALCARAZ, M., and FER-NANDEZ-GUARDIOLA, A., "Photic Potentials in the Visual Pathway Dur-ing 'Attention' and Photic 'Habituation,'" *Fed. Proc.*, 15:91–92, 1956.

66. HERNÁNDEZ-PEÓN, R., SCHERRER, H., and JOUVET, M., "Modification of Electric Activity in Cochlear Nucleus During 'Attention' in Unanes-thetized Cats," *Science*, 123:331–332, 1956.

67. HOLUBÁR, J., "EEG Manifestations of the Unconditioned and Condi-tioned Galvanic Skin Response. A Contribution to the Study of the Reticular System in Man by Cutaneous Nociceptive Activation of the EEG," *Electroenceph. clin. Neurophysiol.*, 11:177–178, 1959.

68. IWAMA, K., "Delayed Conditioned Reflex in Man and Brain Waves," *Tohoku J. exp. Med.*, 52:53–62, 1950.

69. IWAMA, K. and ABE, M., "Conditioned Galvanic Reflex and Electro-encephalogram," *Tohoku J. exp. Med.*, 57:327–335, 1953.

70. IWAMA, K. and ABE, M., "Electroencephalographic Study of Condi-tioned Salivary Reflexes in Human Subjects," *Tohoku J. exp. Med.*, 56:345–355, 1952.

71. JASPER, H. H. and CRUIKSHANK, R. M., "Variations in Blocking Time of Occipital Alpha Potentials in Man as Affected by the Intensity and Duration of Light Stimulation," *Psychol. Bull.*, 33:770–771, 1936.

72. JASPER, H. H., CRUIKSHANK, R. M., and HOWARD, H., "Action Currents from the Occipital Region of the Brain in Man as Affected by Variables of Attention and External Stimulation," *Psychol. Bull.*, 32:565, 1935.

73. JASPER, H. H., PROCTOR, L. D., KNIGHTON, R. S., NOSHAY, W. C., and COSTELLO, R. T., *Reticular Formation of the Brain*, Little, Brown & Co., Boston, 1958.

74. JASPER, H., RICCI, G., and DOANE, B., "Microelectrode Analysis of Cortical Cell Discharge During Avoidance Conditioning in the Monkey," *Electroenceph. clin. Neurophysiol.*, Suppl. 13:137–155, 1960.

75. JASPER, H., RICCI, G. F., and DOANE, B., "Patterns of Cortical Neuronal Discharge During Conditioned Responses in Monkeys," in WOLSTENHOLME, G. E. W. and O'CONNOR, C. M. (eds.), *Neurological Basis of Behavior*, Little, Brown & Co., Boston, 1958.

76. JASPER, H. and SHAGASS, C., "Conditioning the Occipital Alpha Rhythm in Man," *J. exp. Psychol.*, 28:373–388, 1941.

77. JASPER, H. and SHAGASS, C., "Conscious Time Judgments Related to Conditioned Time Intervals and Voluntary Control of the Alpha Rhythm," *J. exp. Psychol.*, 28:503–508, 1941.

78. JASPER, H. H. and SMIRNOV, G. D., "The Moscow Colloquium on Encephalography of Higher Nervous Activity," *Electroenceph. clin. Neurophysiol.*, Suppl. 13, 1960.

79. JOHN, E. R., "Discussion," in BRAZIER, M. A. B. (ed.), *The Central Nervous System and Behavior*, Trans. First Conference, Josiah Macy, Jr. Foundation, New York, 1958.

80. JOHN, E. R. and KILLAM, K. F., "Electrophysiological Correlates of Avoidance Conditioning in the Cat," *J. Pharmacol. exp. Ther.*, 125:252–274, 1959.

81. JOHN, E. R. and KILLAM, K. F., "Studies of Electrical Activity of Brain During Differential Conditioning in Cats," *Recent Adv. biol. Psychiat.*, 2:138–148, 1960.

82. JOUVET, M. and COURJON, J., "Variation of the Subcortical Visual Responses During Attention in Man," *Electroenceph. clin. Neurophysiol.*, 10:344, 1958.

83. JOUVET, M. and HERNÁNDEZ-PEÓN, R., "Mécanismes Neurophysiologiques Concernant l'Habituation, l'Attention et le Conditionnement," *Electroenceph. clin. Neurophysiol.*, Suppl. 6:39–49, 1957.

84. JUS, A. and JUS, C., "Étude de l'Extinction par Répétition de l'Expression EEG du Réflexe d'Orientation et de l'Action du Frein Externe sur les Réactions EEG aux Différents Stimuli Chez l'Homme," *Electroenceph. clin. Neurophysiol.*, Suppl. 13:321–333, 1960.

85. JUS, A. and JUS, C., "Les Méthodes Bioélectriques dans l'Expérience Conditionnelle Clinique," *Electroenceph. clin. Neurophysiol.*, Suppl. 6:25–37, 1957.

86. JUS, A. and JUS, C., "Studies on Photic Driving Conditioning in Man," *Electroenceph. clin. Neurophysiol.*, 11:178, 1959.

87. KERR, D. I. B. and HAGBARTH, K.-E., "An Investigation of Olfactory Centrifugal Fiber System," *J. Neurophysiol.*, 18:362–374, 1955.

88. KNOTT, J. R., "Reduced Latent Time of Blocking of the Berger Rhythm to Light Stimuli," *Proc. Soc. exp. Biol., N.Y.*, 38:216–217, 1938.

89. KNOTT, J. R. and HENRY, C. E., "The Conditioning of the Blocking of the Alpha Rhythm of the Human Electroencephalogram," *J. exp. Psychol.*, 28:134–144, 1941.

90. KOGAN, A. B., "The Manifestations of Processes of Higher Nervous Activity in the Electrical Potentials of the Cortex During Free Behavior of Animals," *Electroenceph. clin. Neurophysiol.*, Suppl. 13:51–64, 1960.

91. KRATIN, I. G., quoted by WORDEN, F. G., in BRAZIER, M. A. B. (ed.), *The Central Nervous System and Behavior*, Trans. Second Conference, Josiah Macy, Jr. Foundation, New York, 1959, pp. 162–163.

92. KREINDLER, A., "The Role of the Reticular Formation in the Conditioning Process," *Electroenceph. clin. Neurophysiol.*, Suppl. 13:281–293, 1960.

93. LISSÁK, K. and GRASTYÁN, E., "The Changes of Hippocampal Electrical Activity During Conditioning," *Electroenceph. clin. Neurophysiol.*, Suppl. 13:271–279, 1960.

94. LIVANOV, M. N., "Concerning the Establishment of Temporary Connections," *Electroenceph. clin. Neurophysiol.*, Suppl. 13:185–198, 1960.

95. LIVANOV, M. N., KOROLKOVA, T. A., and FRENKEL, G. M., quoted by RUSINOV, V. S. and RABINOVICH, M. Y., "Electroencephalographic Researches in the Laboratories and Clinics of the Soviet Union," *Electroenceph. clin. Neurophysiol.*, Suppl. 8, 1958.

96. LIVANOV, M. N. and POLYAKOV, K. L., quoted by RUSINOV, V. S. and RABINOVICH, M. Y., "Electrographic Researches in the Laboratories and Clinics of the Soviet Union," *Electroenceph. clin. Neurophysiol.*, Suppl. 8, 1958.

97. LOOMIS, A., HARVEY, E. N., and HOBART, G., "Electrical Potentials of the Human Brain," *J. exp. Psychol.*, 19:249–279, 1936.

98. LOUCKS, R. B., "The Experimental Delimitation of Neural Structures Essential for Learning: The Attempt to Condition Striped Muscle Responses with Faradization of the Sigmoid Gyri," *J. Psychol.*, 1:5–43, 1935.

99. LOUCKS, R. B., "Studies of Neural Structures Essential for Learning: II. Conditioning of Salivary and Striped Muscle Responses to Faradization of Cortical Sensory Element and the Action of Sleep Upon Such Mechanisms," *J. comp. Psychol.*, 25:315–332, 1938.

100. LURIE, R. N. and RUSINOV, V. S., quoted by RUSINOV, V. S. and RABINO-VICH, M. Y., "Electroencephalographic Researches in the Laboratories and Clinics of the Soviet Union," *Electroenceph. clin. Neurophysiol.*, Suppl. 8, 1958.

101. MCADAM, D., SNODGRASS, L., KNOTT, J. R., and INGRAM, W. R., "Some Preliminary Observations of Electrical Changes in Deep Brain Structures During Acquisition of a Classical Conditioned Response," *Electroenceph. clin. Neurophysiol.*, 13:146, 1961.

102. MARSH, J. T., McCARTHY, D. A., SHEATZ, G., and GALAMBOS, R., "Amplitude Changes in Evoked Auditory Potentials During Habituation and Conditioning," *Electroenceph. clin. Neurophysiol.*, 13:224–234, 1961.

103. MASSERMAN, J. H., "Is the Hypothalamus a Center of Emotion?" *Psychosom. Med.*, 3:3–25, 1941.

104. MAYORCHIK, V. E., RUSINOV, V. S., and KUZNETSOVA, G. D., quoted by RUSINOV, V. S. and RABINOVICH, M. Y., "Electroencephalographic Researches in the Laboratories and Clinics of the Soviet Union," *Electroenceph. clin. Neurophysiol.*, Suppl. 8, 1958.

105. MAYORCHIK, V. E. and SPIRIN, B. G., quoted by RUSINOV, V. S. and RABINOVICH, M. Y., "Electroencephalographic Researches in the Laboratories and Clinics of the Soviet Union," *Electroenceph. clin. Neurophysiol.*, Suppl. 8, 1958.

106. MAYORCHIK, V. E. and SPIRIN, B. G., quoted by RUSINOV, V. S. and SMIRNOV, G. E., "Étude Électroencéphalographique du Conditionnement Chez l'Homme," *Rapport, IV Congr. int. Electroenceph.*, Brussels, 1957.

107. MAYORCHIK, V. E. and SPIRIN, B. G., quoted by RUSINOV, V. S. and SMIRNOV, G. D., "Quelques Données sur l'Étude Électroencéphalographique de l'Activité Nerveuse Supérieure," *Electroenceph. clin. Neurophysiol.*, Suppl. 6:9–23, 1957.

108. MORRELL, F., "An Anatomical and Physiological Analysis of Electrocortical Conditioning," *Proc. IV Congr. int. Electroenceph.*, Brussels, 1957, pp. 377–391.

109. MORRELL, F., "Discussion," in DELAFRESNAYE, J. F., FESSARD, A., GERARD, R. W., and KONORSKI, J. (eds.), *Brain Mechanisms and Learning*, Charles C Thomas, Springfield, Ill., 1961.

110. MORRELL, F., "Effects of Experimental Epilepsy on Conditioned Electrical Potentials," *Univ. Minn. med. Bull.*, 29:82–102, 1957.

111. MORRELL, F., "Effets de Lésions Épileptiques Focales sur la Formation de Connexions Temporaires Chez le Singe," *Electroenceph. clin. Neurophysiol.*, Suppl. 6:51–74, 1957.

112. MORRELL, F., "Electroencephalographic Studies of Conditioned Learning," in BRAZIER, M. A. B. (ed.), *The Central Nervous System and*

Behavior, Trans. First Conference, Josiah Macy, Jr. Foundation, New York, 1958.

113. MORRELL, F., "Electrophysiological Contributions to the Neural Basis of Learning," *Physiol. Rev.*, *41*:443–494, 1961.

114. MORRELL, F., "Interseizure Disturbances in Focal Epilepsy," *Neurology*, *6*:327–334, 1956.

115. MORRELL, F., "Microelectrode and Steady Potential Studies Suggesting a Dendritic Locus of Closure," *Electroenceph. clin. Neurophysiol.*, Suppl. *13*:65–79, 1960.

116. MORRELL, F., "Some Electrical Events Involved in the Formation of Temporary Connections," in JASPER, H. H. *et al.* (eds.), *Reticular Formation of the Brain*, Little, Brown & Co., Boston, 1958.

117. MORRELL, F., BARLOW, J., and BRAZIER, M. A. B., "Analysis of Conditioned Repetitive Response by Means of the Average Response Computor," *Recent Adv. biol. Psychiat.*, *2*:123–137, 1960.

118. MORRELL, F. and JASPER, H. H., "Electrographic Studies of the Formation of Temporary Connections in the Brain," *Electroenceph. clin. Neurophysiol.*, *8*:201–215, 1956.

119. MORRELL, F. and NAQUET, R., "Conditioning of an Abnormal Hypersynchronous Discharge," *Electroenceph. clin. Neurophysiol.*, *9*:161, 1957.

120. MORRELL, F., NAQUET, R., and GASTAUT, H., "Evolution of Some Electrical Signs of Conditioning. Part I. Normal Cat and Rabbit," *J. Neurophysiol.*, *20*:574–587, 1957.

121. MORRELL, F., ROBERTS, L., and JASPER, H. H., "Effect of Focal Epileptogenic Lesions and Their Ablation Upon Conditioned Electrical Responses of the Brain in the Monkey," *Electroenceph. clin. Neurophysiol.*, *8*:217–236, 1956.

122. MORRELL, F. and Ross, M. H., "Central Inhibition in Cortical Conditioned Reflexes," *Arch. Neurol. Psychiat.*, *Chicago, 70*:611–616, 1953.

123. MORRELL, L. K. and MORRELL, F., "Periodic Oscillation in the Habituation Curve of Electrographic Activation," *Electroenceph. clin. Neurophysiol.*, *12*:757, 1960.

124. MOTOKAWA, K., "Electroencephalograms of Man in the Generalization and Differentiation of Conditioned Reflexes," *Tohoku J. exp. Med.*, *50*:225–234, 1949.

125. MOTOKAWA, K. and HUZIMORI, B. "Electroencephalograms and Conditioned Reflexes," *Tohoku J. exp. Med.*, *50*:215–223, 1949.

126. NAKAO, H. and KOELLA, W. P., "Influence of Nociceptive Stimuli on Evoked Subcortical and Cortical Potentials in Cat," *J. Neurophysiol.*, *19*:187–195, 1956.

127. NAQUET, R., "Conditionnement de Décharges Hypersynchrones Épileptiques Chez l'Homme et l'Animal," in DELAFRESNAYE, J. F. *et al.* (eds.), *Brain Mechanisms and Learning*, Charles C Thomas, Springfield, Ill., 1961.

128. NOVIKOVA, L. A., RUSINOV, V. S., and SEMIOKHINA, A. F., quoted by RUSINOV, V. S. and RABINOVICH, M. Y., "Electroencephalographic Researches in the Laboratories and Clinics of the Soviet Union," *Electroenceph. clin. Neurophysiol.*, Suppl. 8, 1958.

129. OLDS, J., "Discussion," in BRAZIER, M. A. B. (ed.), *The Central Nervous System and Behavior*, Trans. Second Conference, Josiah Macy, Jr. Foundation, New York, 1959.

130. PAVLOV, B., quoted by RUSINOV, V. S. and SMIRNOV, G. D., "Quelques Données sur l'Étude d'Électroencéphalographie de l'Activité Nerveuse Supérieure," *Electroenceph. clin. Neurophysiol.*, Suppl. 6:9–23, 1957.

131. PAVLOV, I. P., *Conditioned Reflexes. An Investigation of the Physiological Activity of the Cerebral Cortex*, ANREP, G. V. (trans. and ed.), Oxford University Press, London, 1927, 430 pp.

132. PAVLYGINA, R. A. and RUSINOV, V. S., quoted by RUSINOV, V. S. and RABINOVICH, M. Y., "Electroencephalographic Researches in the Laboratories and Clinics of the Soviet Union," *Electroenceph. clin. Neurophysiol.*, Suppl. 8, 1958.

133. PAVLYGINA, R. A. and RUSINOV, V. S., quoted by RUSINOV, V. S. and SMIRNOV, G. E., "Étude Électroencéphalographique du Conditionnement Chez l'Homme," *Rapport, IV Congr. int. Électroenceph.*, Brussels, 1957.

134. PEIMER, I. A., "Local Electrical Responses in the Cerebral Cortex of Man and Their Relationship to Generalized Reactions in the Process of Conditioned Reflex Activity," in BRAZIER, M. A. B. (ed.), *The Central Nervous System and Behavior*, Trans. Second Conference, Josiah Macy, Jr. Foundation, New York, 1959. (Translations from the Russian medical literature, U.S. Dept. Health, Education, and Welfare, Dec. 1, 1959, pp. 771–784.)

135. POPOV, N. A., "Contribution à l'Étude de la Réaction d'Arrêt du Rhythme Alpha Chez l'Homme," *C.R. Soc. Biol., Paris, 144*:1667–1669, 1950.

136. POPOV, N. A., "Observations Électroencéphalographiques sur les Réactions Corticales Chez l'Homme," *Ann. Psychol., 53*:415–429, 1953.

137. PRIBRAM, K. H., "Discussion," in BRAZIER, M. A. B. (ed.), *The Central Nervous System and Behavior*, Trans. First Conference, Josiah Macy, Jr. Foundation, New York, 1958.

138. PRIBRAM, K. H., ROSNER, B. S., and ROSENBLITH, W. A., "Electrical Responses to Acoustic Clicks in Monkey: Extent of Neocortex Activated," *J. Neurophysiol., 17*:336–344, 1954.

139. RHEINBERGER, M. B. and JASPER, H. H., "Electrical Activity of the Cerebral Cortex in the Unanesthetized Cat," *Amer. J. Physiol.*, *119*:186–195, 1937.

140. ROGER, A., VORONIN, L. G., and SOKOLOV, E. N., "An Electroencephalographic Investigation of the Temporary Connexion During Extinction of the Orientation Reflex in Man," *Pavlov J. higher nerv. Activ.*, 8:1–13, 1958.

141. ROWLAND, V., "Differential Encephalographic Response to Conditioned Auditory Stimuli in Arousal from Sleep," *Electroenceph. clin. Neurophysiol.*, 9:585–594, 1957.

142. ROWLAND, V., "Discussion," in BRAZIER, M. A. B. (ed.), *The Central Nervous System and Behavior*, Trans. First Conference, Josiah Macy, Jr. Foundation, New York, 1958.

143. ROWLAND, V. and GLUCK, H., "Electrographic Arousal and its Inhibition as Studied by Auditory Conditioning," *Recent Adv. biol. Psychiat.*, 2:96–105, 1960.

144. RUSINOV, V. S., "Electroencephalographic Studies in Conditioned Reflex Formation in Man," in BRAZIER, M. A. B. (ed.), *The Central Nervous System and Behavior*, Trans. Second Conference, Josiah Macy, Jr. Foundation, New York, 1959.

145. RUSINOV, V. S., "General and Localized Alterations in the Electroencephalogram During the Formation of Conditioned Reflexes in Man," *Electroenceph. clin. Neurophysiol.*, Suppl. *13*:309–319, 1960.

146. RUSINOV, V. S. and SMIRNOV, G. D., "Étude Électroencéphalographique du Conditionnement Chez l'Homme," *Rapport, IV Congr. int. Électroenceph.*, Brussels, 1957.

147. RUSINOV, V. S. and SMIRNOV, G. D., "Quelques Données sur l'Étude Électroencéphalographique de l'Activité Nerveuse Supérieure," *Electroenceph. clin. Neurophysiol.*, Suppl. 6:9–23, 1957.

148. SAKHIULINA, G. T., "Electroencephalograms of Dogs in Some Complex Forms of Conditioned Reflex Activity," *Electroenceph. clin. Neurophysiol.*, Suppl. *13*:211–220, 1960.

149. SEGUNDO, J. P., "Discussion," in DELAFRESNAYE, J. F. *et al.* (eds.), *Brain Mechanisms and Learning*, Charles C Thomas, Springfield, Ill., 1961.

150. SEGUNDO, J. P., GALEANO, C., SOMMER-SMITH, J. A., and ROIG, J. A., "Behavioural and EEG Effects of Tones 'Reinforced' by Cessation of Painful Stimuli," in DELAFRESNAYE, J. F. *et al.* (eds.), *Brain Mechanisms and Learning*, Charles C Thomas, Springfield, Ill., 1961.

151. SEGUNDO, J. P., ROIG, J. A., and SOMMER-SMITH, J. A., "Conditioning of Reticular Formation Stimulation Effects," *Electroenceph. clin. Neurophysiol.*, *11*:471–484, 1959.

152. SHUMILINA, A., quoted by ANOKHIN, P., "On the Specific Action of the Reticular Formation on the Cerebral Cortex," *Electroenceph. clin. Neurophysiol.*, Suppl. *13*:257–270, 1960.

153. SOKOLOV, E. N., "Neuronal Models and the Orienting Reflex," in BRAZIER, M. A. B. (ed.), *The Central Nervous System and Behavior*, Trans. Second Conference, Josiah Macy, Jr. Foundation, New York, 1959.

154. STAMM, J. S., PRIBRAM, K. H., and OBRIST, W., "The Effect of Cortical Implants of Aluminum Hydroxide on Remembering and Learning," *Electroenceph. clin. Neurophysiol.*, *10*:766, 1958.

155. STERN, J. A. and LACKNER, H., "On Conditioned Alpha Enhancement," *Electroenceph. clin. Neurophysiol.*, *11*:843, 1959.

156. STERN, J. A., ULETT, G. A., and SINES, J. O., "Electrocortical Changes During Conditioning," *Recent Adv. biol. Psychiat.*, *2*:106–122, 1960.

157. STEVENS, J. R., "Electroencephalographic Studies of Conditioned Cerebral Response in Epileptic Subjects," *Electroenceph. clin. Neurophysiol.*, *12*:238, 1960.

158. STEVENS, J. R., "Electroencephalographic Studies of Conditional Cerebral Response in Epileptic Subjects," *Electroenceph. clin. Neurophysiol.*, *12*:431–444, 1960.

159. STEVENS, J. R. and STEVENS, C. M., "Cyclic Conditioning of Epileptic Discharges," *Electroenceph. clin. Neurophysiol.*, *12*:705–714, 1960.

160. STORM VAN LEEUWEN, W., "The So-Called 'Frequency Specific Conditioned Response,'" *Electroenceph. clin. Neurophysiol.*, *11*:611, 1959.

161. TRAVIS, L. E. and EGAN, J. P., "Conditioning of the Electrical Response of the Cortex," *J. exp. Psychol.*, 22:524–531, 1938.

162. TRAVIS, L. E. and KNOTT, J. R., "Brain Potential Studies of Perseveration: I. Perseveration Time to Light," *J. Psychol.*, 3:97–100, 1936.

163. UNGHER, J. and STERIADE, M., "Electrographic Analysis of Conditioned Epileptic Seizures," *Electroenceph. clin. Neurophysiol.*, *12*:752, 1960.

164. VISSER, S. L., "Correlations Between the Contingent Alpha Blocking, EEG Characteristics and Clinical Diagnosis," *Electroenceph. clin. Neurophysiol.*, *13*:438–446, 1961.

165. VORONIN, L. G. and SOKOLOV, E. N., "Cortical Mechanisms of the Orienting Reflex and its Relation to the Conditioned Reflex," *Electroenceph. clin. Neurophysiol.*, Suppl. *13*:335–346, 1960.

166. WELLS, C. E., "Alpha Wave Responsiveness to Light in Man," Chapter 2, this volume.

167. WELLS, C. E., "Modification of Alpha-Wave Responsiveness to Light by Juxtaposition of Auditory Stimuli," *Arch. Neurol., Chicago*, *1*:689–694, 1959.

168. WELLS, C. E. and WOLFF, H. G., "Electrographic Evidence of Impaired Brain Function in Chronically Anxious Patients," *Science, 131*:1671–1672, 1960.

169. WELLS, C. E. and WOLFF, H. G., "Formation of Temporary Cerebral Connections in Normal and Brain-Damaged Subjects," *Neurology, 10*:335–340, 1960.

170. WILLIAMS, A. C., JR., "Facilitation of the Alpha Rhythm of the Electroencephalogram," *J. exp. Psychol., 26*:413–422, 1940.

171. WILSON, N. J. and WILSON, W. P., "The Duration of Human Electroencephalographic Responses Elicited by Photic Stimulation," *Electroenceph. clin. Neurophysiol., 11*:85–91, 1959.

172. WOLSTENHOLME, G. E. W. and O'CONNOR, C. M. (eds.), *Ciba Foundation Symposium on the Neurological Basis of Behaviour*, Little, Brown & Co., Boston, 1958.

173. WORDEN, F. G., "Discussion," in BRAZIER, M. A. B. (ed.), *The Central Nervous System and Behavior*, Trans. Second Conference, Josiah Macy, Jr. Foundation, New York, 1959.

174. WYRWICKA, W., DOBRZECKA, C., and TARNECKI, R., "On the Instrumental Conditioned Reaction Evoked by Electrical Stimulation of the Hypothalamus," *Science, 130*:336–337, 1959.

175. YOSHII, N., "Discussion of Paper by MORRELL and NAQUET," *Electroenceph. clin. Neurophysiol., 9*:161, 1957.

176. YOSHII, N., "Principes Méthodologiques de l'Investigation Électroencéphalographique du Comportement Conditionné," *Electroenceph. clin. Neurophysiol.*, Suppl. *6*:75–88, 1957.

177. YOSHII, N. and HOCKADAY, W. J., "Conditioning of Frequency-Characteristic Repetitive Electroencephalographic Response with Intermittent Photic Stimulation," *Electroenceph. clin. Neurophysiol., 10*:487–502, 1958.

178. YOSHII, N., MATSUMOTO, J., MAENO, S., HASEGAWA, Y., YAMAGUCHI, Y., SHIMOKOCHI, M., HORI, Y., and YAMAZAKI, H., "Conditioned Reflex and Electroencephalography," *Med. J. Osaka Univ., 9*:353–375, 1958.

179. YOSHII, N., MATSUMOTO, J., OGURA, H., SHIMOKOCHI, M., YAMAGUCHI, Y., and YAMASAKI, H., "Conditioned Reflex and Electroencephalography," *Electroenceph. clin. Neurophysiol.*, Suppl. *13*:199–210, 1960.

180. YOSHII, N., PRUVOT, P., and GASTAUT, H., "Electrographic Activity of the Mesencephalic Reticular Formation During Conditioning in the Cat," *Electroenceph. clin. Neurophysiol., 9*:595–608, 1957.

181. ZUCKERMANN, E., "Effect of Cortical and Reticular Stimulation on Conditioned Reflex Activity," *J. Neurophysiol., 22*:633–643, 1959.

IV

Cerebral Electrical Responses to External Stimuli

Burton S. Rosner
William R. Goff
Truett Allison

Cerebral cortical mechanisms which participate in our perception of external reality form a major topic in neurophysiology. Numerous experiments have focused upon electrical responses of the brain to external stimuli. The earliest studies employed anesthetized, acute preparations. More recent investigations on unanesthetized animals have uncovered neuroelectric responses which are longer and more complex in wave form than those in anesthetized preparations. Furthermore, through automatic averaging devices, neurophysiologists now record even more intricate cerebral-evoked potentials from normal man.

The goal of research on human neuroelectric responses is to understand their physiological mechanisms and psychological significance. Experiments on animals, however, provide essential data which are unobtainable from normal man. Proper integration of animal data with human electrophysiological findings requires identification of homologous components in the two classes of evoked activity. Since human and animal responses show many disparities, systematic experimental study is necessary to establish such homologies. The present paper summarizes our work over the last two years on this problem.

This work was supported in part by grant M–1530 from the National Institute of Mental Health, United States Public Health Service.

Methods

Our general procedure has involved recording average evoked responses from man and monkey (*Cebus albifrons*) under parallel sets of experimental manipulations. Stimuli were 100 microsecond (μsec.) constant current electrical pulses applied percutaneously to the median nerve at the left wrist. Intensity always was made sufficient to evoke a thumb twitch. Subdermal needle electrodes led off the responses from the scalp; placement of the indifferent electrode at the bridge of the nose made the records monopolar. The subject, human or monkey, was placed in a dimly illuminated, sound-deadened recording chamber. Two blowers ventilated the chamber and provided 75 db SPL of masking noise.

Human subjects (medical and graduate students at Yale University) sat in a comfortable chair and faced an oscilloscope which displayed their EEGs. We instructed the subjects to "keep the tracing as quiet as possible." This minimized electromyographic interference and helped the subject maintain alertness. To determine the scalp location lying above the hand area of human post-Rolandic gyrus, we drew an interaural coronal circle and placed the electrode on this circle at a point 7 cm. lateral to the midline. In many subjects, we checked this determination against the location of the Rolandic sulcus as estimated by Krönlein's[30] method. The two procedures agreed within 1 cm.

Monkeys sat in a standard Foringer primate chair to which we added devices for restraining the arms and limiting head movements. We used a scaled-down version of the interaural circle method to locate electrodes over postcentral cortex in monkey. Gross dissections on three animals brought to autopsy confirmed the accuracy of this procedure.

A special-purpose dual channel analogue computer[45] averaged responses as they came from the subject. Averaging brings into clear display a recurring signal which otherwise would remain hidden in noise.[12, 13] This method is necessary for experiments on man or unanesthetized animals, where spontaneous activity of the brain obscures cerebral evoked potentials. For those who may be unacquainted with averaging, Figure IV-1 shows how the process operates. In Al, a square wave is locked in time to the start of the oscilloscope trace at t_0. This pulse constitutes a signal. Random noise added to the square wave in A2 obscures the signal. Now imagine a column of 20 samples of signal plus noise like that in A2, with each trace starting at a single

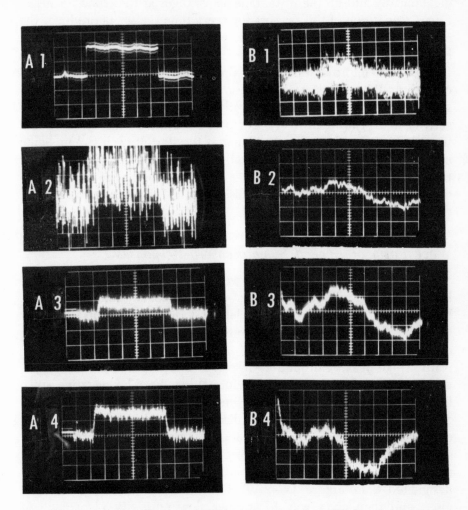

Fig. IV—1. **A.** *A pulse signal (A1) is obscured by added audio-frequency random noise (A2). Twenty samples (A3) and forty (A4) of signal plus noise are summated. Calibrations: 10 msec./cm. for all traces; 0.5 mV./cm. for A1 and A2 and 25 mV./cm. for A3 and A4.* **B.** *Twenty responses evoked at a contralateral post-Rolandic lead in man following brief shocks to left index finger are superimposed photographically (B1). Twenty (B2) and forty (B3) individual responses are summated. First 100 msec. of B3 is expanded (B4). Calibrations: 50 msec./cm. for B1 through B3 and 10 msec./cm. for B4; 2.5 μV./cm. for B1 and 25 μV./cm. for B2 through B4. From Rosner, Allison, Swanson, and Goff (1960).*

vertical line representing t_0. Select any particular time t_i after t_0 and algebraically add up the instantaneous voltages at that time for all 20 traces. Repetition of this process for every time t_j after t_0 produces the result in A3. Algebraic summation, which is equivalent to averaging, brings the pulse signal out of the noise. Doubling the sample size from 20 to 40 improves resolution even further, as A4 shows. Column B of Figure IV—1 illustrates detection of small, obscure evoked responses. B1 shows 20 photographically superimposed sweeps of evoked activity at a scalp lead over right post-Rolandic cortex. Brief shocks were delivered to the left index finger at the start of each sweep. Some evoked activity is vaguely discernible. B2 and B3 respectively show the results of summating 20 and 40 evoked responses. The sweep durations in B1 through B3 are 500 milliseconds; B4 shows in greater detail the first 100 msec. of B3.

Wave Form of Evoked Somatosensory Responses

Figure IV—2 shows tracings of average evoked potentials at contralateral post-Rolandic scalp leads in man and monkey following stimulation of left median nerve. The left and right records in each row represent respectively sweep durations of 100 and 500 msec. The earliest obvious activity in records from man is a sharp negative (downward) spike peaking around 19 msec.; a smaller positive wave beginning at 17 msec. often appears before the spike. The negative spike leads into a sharp positive wave which reaches maximum around 23 or 24 msec. For purposes of later discussion, we have designated this entire triphasic complex as component 1. This complex occasionally is small or even undetectable; in subjects who show it, the final positive portion may coalesce into the leading edge of the slow positivity designated 2 in Figure IV—2. This latter wave peaks at about 30 msec. and then gives way to another slow positivity (labeled 3 in Figure IV—1) which peaks around 50 msec. A large negative deflection follows component 3; furthermore, one to three positivities of various amplitudes may appear at different points along this negative deflection. In most subjects, the negative wave reaches a maximum at about 135 msec. after stimulation and then leads into a large positive deflection which peaks at about 220 msec. A slow negativity often follows this last large positivity. Gumnit and Grossman[23] have adduced evidence that the final slow negativity may be an artifact of capacity-coupled recording, which we have used throughout.

In the average evoked response at a contralateral postcentral scalp lead in monkey, the first obvious deflection is the positivity designated *a* which peaks at about 12 msec. This leads into a second, slower positivity marked *b*, peaking around 30 msec. A negative wave then follows *b;* a highly labile positive deflection rides on the leading or trailing edge of the negativity. Depending on the position and size of the labile positivity, the negative wave reaches an apparent maximum at 50 to 100 msec. The final part of the monkey's response is a positive wave peaking at about 150 msec. and ending at about 200 msec.

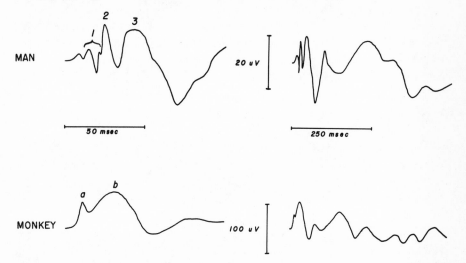

Fig. IV—2. *Average evoked responses at a contralateral post-Rolandic lead in man and in monkey following percutaneous electrical stimulation of left median nerve. N = 40 for man and 30 for monkey. Positivity upward in these and all succeeding records.*

The obvious differences in wave form between somatic evoked responses in man and monkey concretely pose the problem of identifying physiologically homologous components. To approach this problem, we have studied three properties of evoked potentials: recovery cycles, spatial distribution, and effects of anesthesia. Our results so far establish tentative homologies in the first 50 msec. or so of evoked activity. The succeeding portions of the responses present a most intriguing challenge for physiological analysis. Unfortunately, we cannot yet offer an initial account of homologies in this late activity. We also must emphasize that the designations in Figure IV—2 do not imply that each wave necessarily reflects the

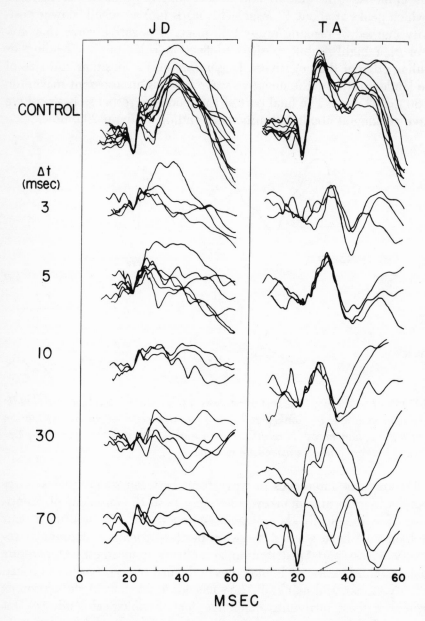

Fig. IV—3. *Recovery of early components of response at con-tralateral post-Rolandic lead in man. N = 40 for each trace. From Allison (1962).*

operation of a single, unitary physiological process. In fact, we will present evidence somewhat to the contrary.

Recovery Cycles of Human Somatosensory Responses

When a conditioning stimulus precedes a test stimulus at a sufficiently short interval, the response to the first stimulus alters the response to the second. The amplitude of a given component of the test response plotted against interstimulus interval is a recovery function for that wave. Physiologically distinct portions of a complex neuro-electric response often have different recovery functions.[14, 32, 37, 42] To aid the analysis of human cerebral evoked potentials, one of us[3] therefore studied the recovery cycle of these responses under equally intense paired shocks to left median nerve. Since the human cerebral somatosensory evoked response lasts some 500 msec., the conditioning response would obscure the test response at interstimulus intervals of less than 500 msec. Measurement of either response would accordingly be difficult. To avoid this problem, the computer was programmed to subtract out the conditioning response.

Figure IV—3 shows the recovery of short-latency waves recorded from a contralateral post-Rolandic location in two subjects. The earliest portions of the response seem better recovered at interstimulus intervals of 3 to 5 msec. than at 10 msec. Furthermore, particularly in T.A., a negative wave peaking at 30 to 40 msec. after stimulation appears at interstimulus intervals of 10 msec. or less.

Recovery functions of component *1* for several subjects appear in Figure IV—4. Amplitude of this wave was measured from the peak of the negative deflection around 19 msec. to the peak of the succeeding positivity around 24 msec. The amplitude of *1* for control responses to a single stimulus was then equated to 100; proportionate adjustment of amplitudes for the test responses yielded the data points in Figure IV—4. The functions in Figure IV—4 (A) represent responses recorded at a contralateral post-Rolandic location. Those in IV—4 (B) derive from potentials at a posterior midline electrode, where early deflections also are prominent. (See Figure IV—7.) In both cases, the recovery functions are U-shaped. Recovery seems complete at interstimulus intervals between 30 and about 200 msec., depending on the subject and electrode location.

Figure IV—5 shows recovery functions for component *2* at a contralateral post-Rolandic locus in three subjects. The amplitude of the wave was measured from base line to peak and again is expressed as a percentage of the amplitude of a control response. The recovery of 2 also follows a U-shaped time course. This wave, however, shows

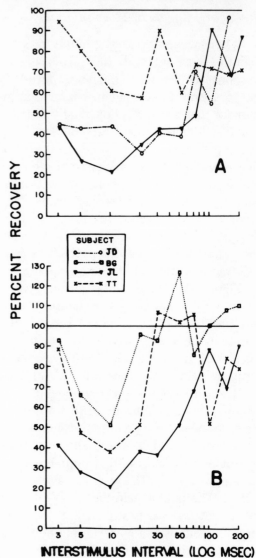

Fig. IV—4. *Recovery of component 1 in man at contralateral post-Rolandic (A) and posterior mid-line (B) loci. From Allison (1962).*

statistically greater subnormality than does 1 (p < .001 by analysis of variance). The functions for different subjects show the greatest variation during the first 50 msec. The appearance of a negativity after 2 at short interstimulus intervals contributed to difficulties encountered in attempts to measure component 3. Inspection of records indicates that 3 probably recovers at least as slowly as 2.

In preliminary experiments on monkeys, we have observed a shallow negativity after component *a* at short interstimulus intervals during the recovery cycle. Components *a* and *b* of the monkey's response may have somewhat different recovery functions. Again, however, measurement of component *b* proved troublesome.

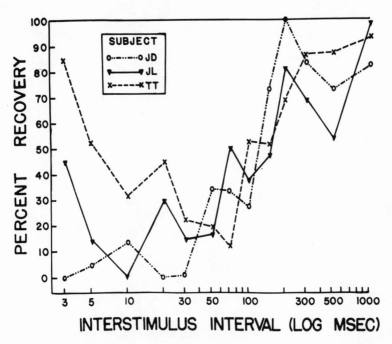

Fig. IV—5. *Recovery of human component 2 at a post-Rolandic locus. From Allison (1962).*

Spatial Distribution

A total of 16 subjects has yielded data on the distribution over the scalp of human somatosensory evoked potentials. Six subjects underwent extensive study, involving recording from 21 different electrodes. We have reported these results in detail elsewhere.[22] Generally, we obtained average responses from each electrode twice during a session for a total of three sessions. (We used 7 electrodes within any one session.) To reduce the resulting data to manageable proportions for analysis and illustration, we traced the records from a given locus in a given subject on the same sheet of paper and visually constructed an average curve through them. Figure IV—6 shows two examples of this procedure.

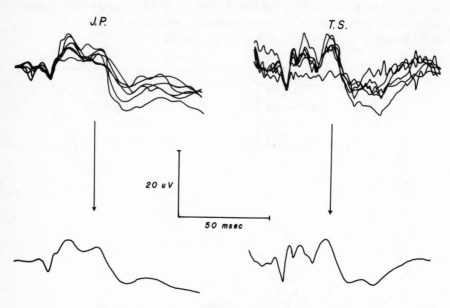

Fig. IV—6. *Examples for two subjects of conversion of overlapped tracings of average responses into single, visually determined average curves. Each overlapped trace is the sum of 40 individual responses.*

Figure IV—7 shows the distribution across the scalp of such visually averaged responses for one subject. The figure presents responses along ipsilateral, midline, contralateral, and coronal arcs. Each tracing represents only the first 100 msec. of activity following stimulation. The two heavy lines diverging from the midline on the schema of the head show the position of the Rolandic sulci reconstructed by Krönlein's method. Points on the schema represent recording locations. The encircled point behind each sulcus identifies the probable location of the post-Rolandic hand area. Inspection of records along the contralateral and coronal arcs shows that components 1 and 2 have comparable distributions. They appear in a band stretching from the contralateral post-Rolandic locus back to the occiput. Although these deflections are present at the two most posterior midline locations, they are absent at the vertex and more anterior midline loci.

Thus, their distribution is more extensive along the anteroposterior axis than along the coronal. Smaller early responses also appear at ipsilateral posterior parietal locations. All these results are representative of our findings on other subjects.

Component 3 appears over the entire contralateral half of the skull, including anterior electrode locations which do not yield the two

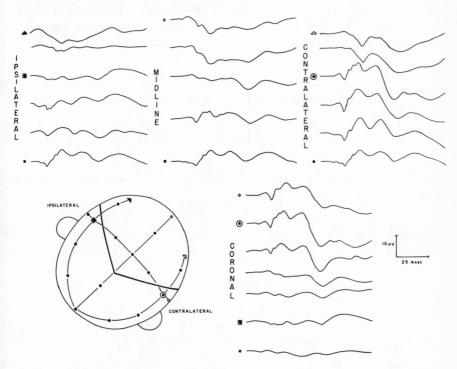

Fig. IV—7. *Distribution across the scalp of early evoked potentials in man following percutaneous electrical stimulation of left median nerve. Each trace constructed from overlapped averages as shown in Fig. IV—6. Schematic of scalp drawn from dorso-occipital photograph of head.*

earlier deflections. Ipsilateral loci infrequently yield signs of 3. The largest records of *1* and *2* consistently come from electrodes *posterior* to the estimated position of contralateral post-Rolandic hand area. The point of maximal response for *3*, however, is more variable; this wave generally seems largest in the vicinity of the Rolandic sulcus. A negative deflection peaking at about 30 msec. appears at anterior contralateral and midline loci; this negativity blurs the picture of component 3 even further.

The distribution of early evoked activity across the monkey's scalp appears in Figure IV—8. Component *a*, a positivity peaking around 12 msec., arises at contralateral electrode locations extending back to the occiput. The focus of this deflection is around the central sulcus. Component *b*, peaking at 30 msec., is bilaterally distributed over the anterior half of the cranium. On the ipsilateral side, the leading edge of *b* apparently starts at about 10 msec. and displays a two-limbed form. We will show later that two separate responses contribute to the leading edge of the ipsilateral record.

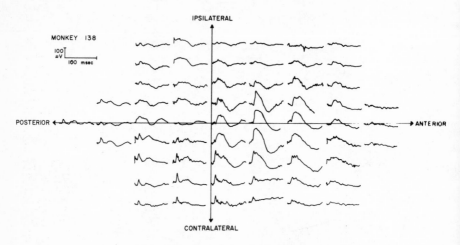

Fig. IV—8. *Distribution across the scalp of average early evoked responses in monkey following percutaneous electrical stimulation of left median nerve. N = 20 for each trace. From Rosner, Goff, and Allison (in press).*

Effects of Pentothal Anesthesia

Application of neuropharmacological agents frequently aids the analysis of a complex electrophysiological response. Barbiturate anesthetics have been a particular favorite for this type of work. Figure IV—9, adapted from previous work,[46] shows the effects of Pentothal anesthesia on somatosensory evoked responses in monkey. The upper and lower traces in each pair show respectively responses at contralateral and ipsilateral pericentral electrodes. Notice again the slowly

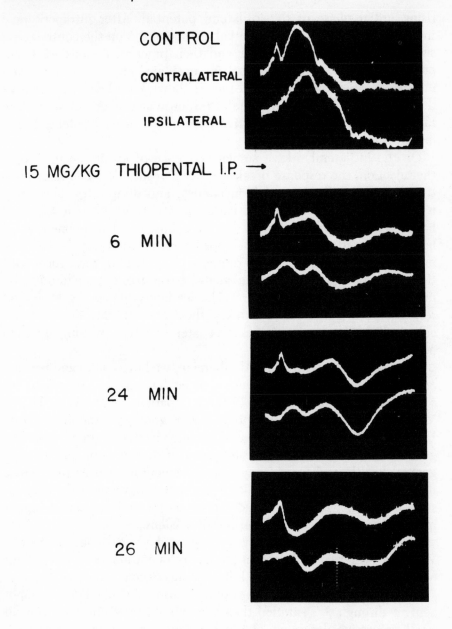

CONTROL

CONTRALATERAL

IPSILATERAL

15 MG/KG THIOPENTAL I.P. →

6 MIN

24 MIN

26 MIN

100 msec

Fig. IV—9. *Effects of Pentothal anesthesia on contralateral and ipsilateral peri-Rolandic average evoked responses in monkey. Monkey 139. N = 20 for each trace. Adapted from Rosner, Goff, and Allison (in press).*

rising initial phase of the ipsilateral potential. After intraperitoneal injection of 15 mg./kg. of Pentothal, component *b* on the contralateral side becomes smaller and later and then practically vanishes. Component *a* remains unaffected or, in most animals, shows a marked increase in amplitude. The final record shows a well-defined negative deflection after *a*. The contralateral response at this time assumes the familiar diphasic, positive-negative form of the evoked potential seen in barbiturized animals.

On the ipsilateral side, a similar sequence of events occurs. After the injection, the response breaks into two positivities. The later positivity grows smaller, increases in latency, and disappears. This wave is apparently ipsilateral *b*. The earlier positivity which is left behind has a peak latency exceeding that of contralateral component *a*. A larger negativity follows the early ipsilateral positivity in the last record. At this time, the ipsilateral response is identical in wave form with that seen at exposed cortex in acute, barbiturized preparations by numerous workers.[15, 18, 20, 21, 40, 41] The leading edge of the ipsilateral response in unanesthetized monkey therefore contains two pharmacologically different positivities, the later of which is companion to contralateral *b*.

In collaboration with H. A. Abrahamian, we have conducted parallel experiments on the effect of Pentothal on human evoked somatosensory responses.[4] Subjects were 10 surgical patients at the West Haven Veterans Administration Hospital and a graduate student at Yale University. All patients were undergoing elective surgery involving general anesthesia. They were 50 years of age or younger, in good general health, and free of any history of neurological or psychiatric illness. We performed the studies in an operating room in the surgical suite in which we had installed the computer and associated equipment. EEGs were recorded during all sessions.

On a day prior to operation, we obtained normal control records. We took further control data on the day of operation, after the patient had received premedication (100–150 mg. Seconal and 0.4–0.6 mg. atropine intramuscularly). The premedication did not affect components *1* through *3*. Pentothal then was administered intravenously in small successive doses; we obtained an average response after each dose. Administration of anesthetic ceased when the patient manifested vital signs characteristic of the clinically desired depth of anesthesia. The EEG in all patients never showed depression beyond light "pattern 3" as defined by Kiersey *et al.*[28]

Figure IV—10 illustrates the effects of Pentothal on subjects with large early responses. In L.G.1 and H.M., component 3 becomes later and ultimately smaller, after passing through a stage of temporary potentiation. This wave is not easily isolated in the control record of T.A.; the anesthetic, however, sufficiently increased the latency of 3 to make it clearly differentiable from 2. Concomitant with the changes in 3 in these subjects, a negativity develops after 2. Pentothal does not suppress components 1 and 2 in contrast to its effects on 3. If anything,

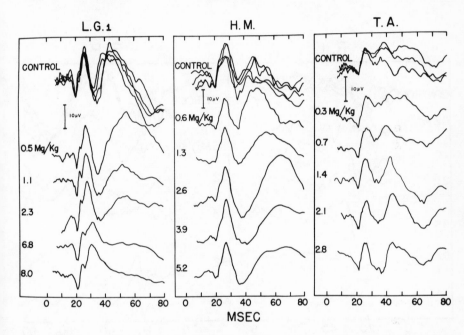

Fig. IV—10. *Effects of Pentothal anesthesia on early components of evoked somatosensory response at contralateral post-Rolandic locus in three human subjects. N = 40 for each trace. From Allison, Goff, Abrahamian, and Rosner (in press).*

2 may become somewhat larger during anesthesia while manifesting a slight increase in latency of 3 or 4 msec. Component 1 remains essentially unaffected. The less dramatic effect of Pentothal on the response of T.A. is attributable to the small dose of anesthetic given this subject. He showed only mild drowsiness after the final injection.

In five of the 11 subjects, control records contained few traces of components 1 and 2. The effects of Pentothal were more complicated in these subjects. Figure IV—11 shows records from two such cases.

In subject R.L., Pentothal ultimately potentiated some early activity which seems just visible in his control tracings. This potentiated activity has a latency and wave form comparable to that of 2 in control records of other subjects. Subject E.P. showed a large component 3 in his control records. This deflection became later and smaller as anesthesia deepened. At the final level of anesthesia, early activity which apparently includes at least component 1 suddenly appeared. Other subjects with no obvious evoked activity before component 3 in their

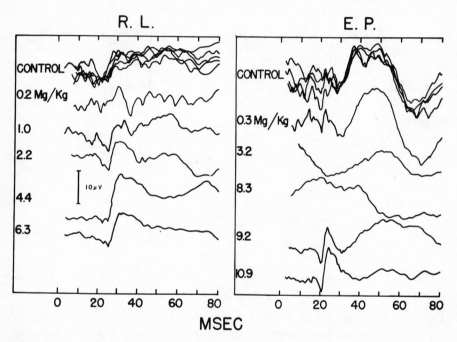

Fig. IV—11. *Same as Fig. IV—10 for two subjects who showed small early components before anesthesia. N = 40 for each trace. From Allison, Goff, Abrahamian, and Rosner (in press).*

control records showed no early potentiated deflections after induction of anesthesia. Component 3, however, vanished in these subjects. These results are not contradictory to those which Figure IV—10 illustrates. Figure IV—11 does demonstrate, however, that the wave form and pharmacological properties of human evoked somatosensory responses vary quantitatively between subjects.

Figure IV—12 allows an explicit comparison of the effects of Pentothal on evoked responses in man and monkey. In monkey, component *a* potentiates while *b* grows smaller and later, unmasking a negativity after *a*. In man, *3* grows smaller and later, unmasking a negativity after component 2. Component *1* remains essentially intact and *2* becomes somewhat larger and slightly later. The human records in this figure derive from a second study on patient L.G. several weeks after the session yielding those marked "L.G.1" in Figure IV—10. This patient had a bilateral hernia requiring two-stage surgery. Comparison of his records in Figures IV—10 and IV—12 illustrates the reproducibility of results within individual subjects.

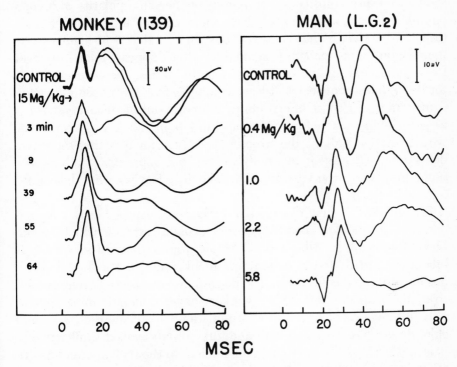

Fig. IV—12. *Comparison of effects of Pentothal on somatosensory evoked responses in monkey and man. N = 20 and 40 respectively for monkey and man. From Allison, Goff, Abrahamian, and Rosner (in press).*

Tentative Identification of Components

Any comparison of somatosensory evoked potentials from man and monkey must consider differences in the length of the conduction pathway from the site of stimulation to the outer portions of the cerebrum.

The onset latency of the human cerebral response to stimulation at the wrist is about 17 msec., while that in monkey is about 7 msec. This difference fits the fact that the conduction pathway in man is more than twice as long as that in monkey. Accordingly, we may anticipate that components of the human response will be at least 8 to 10 msec. later than their homologues in monkey.

The easiest way to approach identification of homologies is to start with component 3 in man. This deflection is a positivity peaking around 50 msec. and appearing prominently over the anterior and middle contralateral scalp. At least one of our subjects, however, shows widespread ipsilateral responses of the same polarity and comparable latency; other subjects have yielded some indications of such ipsilateral activity. These observations suggest that 3 in man may be homologous to component *b* in monkey, which appears bilaterally over the anterior half of the cranium. In both species, the recovery cycle for these deflections seems at least as long as that for preceding waves. Furthermore, at short interstimulus intervals during recovery tests, a negativity appears before 3 in man and *b* in monkey. Experiments with Pentothal provide the strongest evidence for equating these two deflections. This agent markedly delays and suppresses both waves, unmasking a negativity before each. The drug leaves earlier deflections relatively intact.

French *et al.*[19] first recorded directly from exposed cortex in unanesthetized monkey a somatosensory evoked response which resembles component *b*. Albe-Fessard *et al.*[1] found that this response is bilaterally distributed in chloralosed monkey and has a frontal and a posterior parietal concentration. The response disappears after administration of barbiturates. Other workers have observed similar potentials following somatosensory stimulation in unanesthetized[9] and chloralosed[2, 35] cats. Visual and auditory stimuli evoked similar potentials in cat.[6, 10, 48] The centre median nucleus of the thalamus along with other extralemniscal structures mediates this activity, variously named the "association area," "ascending reticular formation," "secondary" and "irradiation" response. This rich profusion of labels deters us from using any of them at present.

If we identify components *b* in monkey and 3 in man as homologous, an obvious problem arises. Human subjects generally have a markedly contralateral distribution of 3, whereas *b* in monkey is clearly bilateral. In addition, relative to deflections which precede them, these two potentials may differ in their recovery cycles and in their amplitudes.

Assuming the homology, these discrepancies may indicate a rapid evolution between monkey and man of the mechanisms mediating this activity.

We turn now to component 2 in man, which our present data indicate is homologous to *a* in monkey. Both waves are positivities of comparable latency and wave form, considering relative lengths of conduction pathways. Both appear in the contralateral posterior quadrant of the scalp, although *a* in monkey extends anteriorly as well. The amplitude of both deflections is either unaffected or potentiated by Pentothal.

Component *a* clearly seems identical with the initial surface-positive portion of the diphasic evoked potential which Hirsch and Coxe[25] mapped over the exposed cortex of barbiturized Cebus. The U-shaped recovery function of 2 in man is reminiscent of the U-shaped recovery function of the "primary" positivity at visual cortex of unanesthetized cat.[17, 47] This response at visual cortex shares many properties with component *a* in monkey's somatosensory response.

The anisotropy of the distribution of 2 in man suggests that posterior parietal cortex receives rapid afferent input like that already known for the post-Rolandic somatic projection area. This suggestion receives reinforcement from the fact that most subjects show their largest early responses at posterior parieto-occipital locations. Hirsch *et al.*[26] recently have provided further support for this idea by recording similar large responses at exposed posterior parietal cortex in neurosurgical patients. Our data also hint that component *a* in unanesthetized monkey extends more posteriorly than Hirsch and Coxe[25] found in anesthetized preparations. These impressions, together with the obviously related problem of passive spread of potentials through cerebrospinal fluid and bone, require further study. Finally, if component *a* in monkey is homologous to 2 in man, the latter may be generated around layers II and III of cerebral cortex. Mountcastle *et al.*[39] have reported evidence that the homologue of *a* in cat arises in this region. Various authors[11, 16, 31, 43] have offered hypotheses about the cellular mechanisms responsible for the "primary" evoked surface positivity in animals. Our findings indicate that component 2 in man may come within the purview of these theories.

As Figures IV—9 and IV—12 show, the anesthetized animal displays a "primary" diphasic evoked response which is surface-positive and then surface-negative. On the basis of latency and wave form, the surface-negative component following 2 in anesthetized man seems homologous to the surface negativity in anesthetized monkey. Although neither species when unanesthetized commonly shows this wave, it does appear under one condition in both. This condition is during the early stages of recovery cycles at short interstimulus intervals (10 to 20 msec.). (See Figure IV—2.) A small minority of human subjects also show in their response to a single shock a negative deflection which goes below base line between waves 2 and 3. Thus, this negative wave may be normally present in unanesthetized man and monkey but masked by components 3 and *b* respectively. If this suspicion proves correct, component 3 in man would contain a mixture of at least two different processes. This could account in part for the difficulties which we have generally encountered in attempts to measure 3 quantitatively. Contemporary neurophysiological opinion ascribes the surface negativity seen in anesthetized animals to activity in apical dendrites. Our data shed no light on this opinion.

Neurophysiologists generally consider the large surface-positive wave of the evoked potential in anesthetized animals as a postsynaptic event. This hypothesis, applied to human component 2 under its homology with *a* in monkey, suggests that 2 represents summated postsynaptic potentials. If this is so, then component 1 in man might reflect activity in presynaptic thalamocortical afferent fibers. Several facts support this suggestion. First, the brief duration and triphasic wave form of 1 resembles the response of synchronized, parallel axons in a volume conductor.[33, 38] Second, the recovery function of 1 is shorter than that of 2 and also is U-shaped. Marshall [34-36] found a similar U-shaped function for recovery of thalamic visual and somatic relay nuclei. Component 1 shows considerable recovery at interstimulus intervals of 30 to 50 msec.; King *et al.*[29] observed a comparable recovery time for the thalamocortical radiation response in unanesthetized rabbit. Third, the distribution of 1 follows that of 2. This should be the case if 1 represents the process which triggers 2. Finally, along the same lines, Pentothal anesthesia does not affect 1. In fact, this drug may separate 1 and 2 even further; it increases the latency of 2 by about 4 msec. while lengthening that of 1 by only a msec. or so. King *et al.* also observed a 1.0 to 1.5 msec. increase in the latency of the thalamic radiation response following administration of barbiturates to the preparation.

If component 1 in man is the thalamocortical radiation response, it is odd that its homologue seems undetectable in the monkey. Direct stimulation of thalamic relay nuclei in animals does give a radiation response recorded easily at cortex.[8] Furthermore, responses from auditory cortex to acoustic clicks sometimes show a brief nega- tivity before the first evoked surface-positive wave.[24, 44] Hawkins[24] found that this brief negativity does not reverse polarity as the record- ing electrode is driven through cortex down to white matter; in con- trast, the succeeding surface positivity reverses polarity. This finding indicates that the negative spike is generated in white matter. Our frequent observation of *1* in man is not a peculiarity of our conditions of recording. Jasper *et al.*[27] and Hirsch *et al.*[26] have obtained similar records directly from the pial surface of the brains of neurosurgical patients. Jasper and his colleagues refer to this early rapid complex as the "primary evoked potential." Our present interpretation of com- ponent *1* is at variance with their terminology.

In summary, we suggest that component *1* in man is a presynaptic radiation response. Component *2* seems homologous to *a* in monkey and apparently reflects cortical postsynaptic activity in answer to the radiation volley. Component *3* seems homologous to *b* in monkey; the latter wave involves extralemniscal pathways. A surface negativity intervening between *2* and *3* in man normally lies hidden under the latter and, incidentally, contributes to the complex behavior of *3* under several experimental conditions. A similar process seems to occur between *a* and *b* in monkey.

This argument is tentative and, as we have emphasized, leaves open many questions. Besides those already discussed, a final problem re- quires attention. We pointed out an early ipsilateral response which rides on the leading edge of *b* in monkey (Figure IV–9). We have not indicated any possible homologue in man for this initial ipsilateral response. The reason for this is simple: We have not seen any ipsi- lateral activity in man which is clearly comparable to the first ipsi- lateral response in monkey. Human subjects do show ipsilateral re- sponses at posterior parietal and occipital leads. These potentials resemble *1* and *2* in latency and wave form. Brazier[7] also describes such ipsilateral activity. The properties of these ipsilateral responses raises the question of whether passive spread of potentials through cerebrospinal fluid and bone contaminates or even accounts entirely for their appearance. Another observation on monkey, however, sug- gests that we may not have employed appropriate conditions for evoking early post-Rolandic ipsilateral responses. In monkey, the first ipsilateral response has a threshold much higher than that of the first contralateral one.[46] Further studies in man with intense stimuli and with anesthetics may help to clarify this problem of early ipsilateral evoked activity.

SUMMARY

Average evoked cerebral responses to percutaneous electrical stimulation of median nerve in man and monkey have been studied by spatial mapping, by the recovery cycle technique, and by following the effects of Pentothal anesthesia. We tentatively conclude that the first rapid triphasic complex of the human contralateral post-Rolandic response represents activity in thalamocortical afferent axons. A slower positivity which then follows seems homologous to the first large deflection in the monkey's response. These deflections apparently represent postsynaptic cortical activity. Another still slower positivity then ensues in both species and seems homologous between them. This last response in monkey apparently arises through extralemniscal pathways. Under restricted conditions, a negative wave appears between the two relatively slow positivities in both species. This negative wave may be present normally but masked by the second slow positivity. Finally, the monkey shows an early ipsilateral response for which we have not yet found a similar process, if one exists, in man.

References

1. ALBE-FESSARD, D., ROCHA-MIRANDA, C., and OSWALDO-CRUZ, E., "Activités d'Origine Somesthésique Évoquées au Niveau du Cortex Non-Spécifique et du Centre Médian du Thalamus Chez le Singe Anesthésié au Chloralose," *Electroenceph. clin. Neurophysiol.*, 11:777–787, 1959.

2. ALBE-FESSARD, D. and ROUGEUL, A., "Activités d'Origine Somesthésique Évoquées sur le Cortex Non-Spécifique du Chat Anesthésié au Chloralose; Rôle du Centre Médian du Thalamus," *Electroenceph. clin. Neurophysiol.*, 10:131–152, 1958.

3. ALLISON, T., "Recovery Functions of Somatosensory Evoked Responses in Man," *Electroenceph. clin. Neurophysiol.*, 14:331–343, 1962.

4. ALLISON, T., GOFF, W. R., ABRAHAMIAN, H. A., and ROSNER, B. S., "The Effects of Barbiturate Anesthesia upon Human Somatosensory Evoked Responses," in HERNÁNDEZ-PEÓN, R. (ed.), *The Physiological Basis of Mental Activity.* In press.

5. AMASSIAN, V. E., "Studies on the Organization of a Somesthetic Associaciation Area, Including a Single Unit Analysis," *J. Neurophysiol.*, 17:39–58, 1954.

6. BRAZIER, M. A. B., "Long-Persisting Electrical Traces in the Brain of Man and their Possible Relationship to Higher Nervous Activity," *Electroenceph. clin. Neurophysiol.*, Suppl. *13*:347–358, 1960.

7. BRAZIER, M. A. B., "Some Uses of Computers in Experimental Neurology," *Exp. Neurol.*, *2*:123–143, 1960.

8. BREMER, F., "Cerebral and Cerebellar Potentials," *Physiol. Rev.*, *38*:357–388, 1958.

9. BUSER, P. and BORENSTEIN, P., "Réponses Somesthésiques, Visuelles et Auditives, Recueillies au Niveau du Cortex Associatif Suprasylvien Chez le Chat Curarisé Non Anesthésié," *Electroenceph. clin. Neurophysiol.*, *11*:285–304, 1959.

10. BUSER, P., BORENSTEIN, P., and BRUNER, J., "Étude des Systèmes 'Associatifs' Visuels et Auditifs Chez le Chat Anesthésié au Chloralose," *Electroenceph. clin. Neurophysiol.*, *11*:305–324, 1959.

11. CHANG, H.-T., "The Evoked Potentials," in FIELD, J., MAGOUN, H. W., and HALL, V. (eds.), *Handbook of Physiology*, vol. I, Amer. Physiological Soc., Washington, D.C., 1959.

12. COMMUNICATION BIOPHYSICS GROUP and SIEBERT, W. H., *Processing Neuroelectric Data*, Research Lab. of Electronics, Mass. Inst. of Technology, Tech. Report 351. Technology Press, Cambridge, 1959.

13. DAWSON, G. D., "A Summation Technique for the Detection of Small Evoked Potentials," *Electroenceph. clin. Neurophysiol.*, *6*:65–84, 1954.

14. DEMPSEY, E. W. and MORISON, R. S., "The Electrical Activity of a Thalamo-Cortical Relay System," *Amer. J. Physiol.*, *138*:283–296, 1943.

15. DERBYSHIRE, A. J., REMPEL, B., FORBES, A., and LAMBERT, E. F., "The Effects of Anesthetics on Action Potentials in the Cerebral Cortex of the Cat," *Amer. J. Physiol.*, *116*:577–596, 1936.

16. ECCLES, J. C., "Interpretation of Action Potentials Evoked in the Cerebral Cortex," *Electroenceph. clin. Neurophysiol.*, *3*:449–464, 1951.

17. EVARTS, E. V., FLEMING, T. C., and HUTTENLOCHER, P. R., "Recovery Cycle of Visual Cortex of the Awake and Sleeping Cat," *Amer. J. Physiol.*, *199*:373–376, 1960.

18. FORBES, A. and MORISON, B. R., "Cortical Response to Sensory Stimulation under Deep Barbiturate Narcosis," *J. Neurophysiol.*, *2*:112–128, 1939.

19. FRENCH, J. D. VERZEANO, M., and MAGOUN, H. W., "An Extralemniscal Sensory System in the Brain," *Arch. Neurol. Psychiat.*, *Chicago*, *69*:505–518, 1953.

20. GARDNER, E. D. and HADDAD, B., "Pathways to the Cerebral Cortex for Afferent Fibers from the Hindlimb of the Cat," *Amer. J. Physiol.*, *172*:475–482, 1953.

21. GARDNER, E. D. and MORIN, F., "Spinal Pathways for Projection of Cuta-

neous and Muscular Afferents to the Sensory and Motor Cortex of Monkey (*Macaca mulatta*)," *Amer. J. Physiol., 174*:149–154, 1953.

22. GOFF, W. R., ROSNER, B. S., and ALLISON, T., "Distribution of Cerebral Somatosensory Evoked Responses in Normal Man," *Electroenceph. clin. Neurophysiol, 14*:697–713, 1962.

23. GUMNIT, R. J. and GROSSMAN, R. G., "Potentials Evoked by Sound in the Auditory Cortex of the Cat," *Amer. J. Physiol., 200*:1219–1225, 1961.

24. HAWKINS, J. E., *Electrophysiology of the Auditory Cortex*, Ph.D. dissertation, Harvard University, 1941.

25. HIRSCH, J. F. and COXE, W. S., "Representation of Cutaneous Tactile Sensibility in the Cerebral Cortex of *Cebus*," *J. Neurophysiol. 21*:481–498, 1958.

26. HIRSCH, J. F., PERTUISET, B., CALVET, J., BUISSON-FREY, J., FISCHGOLD, H., and SCHERRER, J., "Étude des Réponses Électrocorticales Obtenues Chez l'Homme par des Stimulations Somesthésiquées et Visuelles," *Electroenceph. clin. Neurophysiol., 13*:411–424, 1961.

27. JASPER, H., LENDE, R., and RASMUSSEN, T., "Evoked Potentials from the Exposed Somatosensory Cortex in Man," *J. nerv. ment. Dis., 130*:526–537, 1960.

28. KIERSEY, D. B., BICKFORD, R. G., and FAULCONER, A., Jr., "Electro-encephalographic Patterns Produced by Thiopental Sodium During Surgical Operations: Description and Classification," *Brit. J. Anaesth., 23*:141–152, 1951.

29. KING, E. E., NAQUET, R., and MAGOUN, H. W., "Alterations in Somatic Afferent Transmission Through the Thalamus by Central Mechanisms and Barbiturates," *J. Pharmacol. exp. Ther., 119*:48–63, 1957.

30. KRÖNLEIN, R. U., "Zur Cranio-cerebralen Topographie," *Brun's Beitr. klin. Chir., 22*:364–370, 1898.

31. LANDAU, W. M., BISHOP, G. H., and CLARE, M. H., "The Interactions of Several Varieties of Evoked Response in Visual and Association Cortex of the Cat," *Electroenceph. clin. Neurophysiol., 13*:43–53, 1961.

32. LANDAU, W. M. and CLARE, M., "A Note on the Characteristic Response Pattern in the Primary Sensory Projection Cortex of the Cat Following a Synchronous Afferent Volley," *Electroenceph. clin. Neurophysiol., 8*:457–464, 1956.

33. LORENTE DE NÓ, R., "A Study of Nerve Physiology," *Stud. Rockefeller Inst. med. Res., 132*, 1947, Chap. 16.

34. MARSHALL, W. H., "Observations on Subcortical Somatic Sensory Mechanism of Cats under Nembutal Anesthesia," *J. Neurophysiol., 4*:25–43, 1941.

35. MARSHALL, W. H., "Excitability Cycle and Interaction in the Geniculate-Striate System of Cat," *J. Neurophysiol., 12*:277–288, 1949.

36. MARSHALL, W. H., "Temporal Periodicities in the Primary Projection System," in FUORTES, M. G. F. (ed.), *Electrophysiology of the Visual System, Amer. J. Ophthalmol., 46,* no. 3, Part II, 1958.

37. MARSHALL, W. H., TALBOT, S. A., and ADES, H. W., "Cortical Response of the Anesthetized Cat to Gross Photic and Electrical Afferent Stimulation," *J. Neurophysiol., 6:*1–15, 1943.

38. MAURO, A., "Properties of Thin Generators Pertaining to Electrophysiological Potentials in Volume Conductors," *J. Neurophysiol., 23:*132–143, 1960.

39. MOUNTCASTLE, V. B., DAVIES, P. W., and BERMAN, A. L., "Response Properties of Neurons of the Cat's Somatic Sensory Cortex to Peripheral Stimulation," *J. Neurophysiol., 20:*374–407, 1957.

40. NAKAHAMA, H., "Contralateral and Ipsilateral Cortical Responses from Somatic Afferent Nerves," *J. Neurophysiol., 21:*611–632, 1958.

41. NAKAHAMA, H. and SAITO, M., "Interconnections of the Somatic Areas I and II (Limb) of the Cats," *Jap. J. Physiol., 6:*200–205, 1956.

42. PERL, E. R. and WHITLOCK, D. G., "Potentials Evoked in Cerebral Somatosensory Region," *J. Neurophysiol., 18:*486–501, 1955.

43. PURPURA, D. P., "Nature of the Electrocortical Potentials and synaptic Organization in Cerebral and Cerebellar Cortex," *Int. Rev. Neurobiol., 1:*47–163, 1959.

44. ROSENZWEIG, M. R. and ROSENBLITH, W. A., "Responses to Auditory Stimuli at the Cochlea and the Auditory Cortex," *Psychol. Monogr., 67,* no. 363, 1953.

45. ROSNER, B. S., ALLISON, T., SWANSON, E., and GOFF, W. R., "A New Instrument for the Summation of Evoked Responses from the Nervous System," *Electroenceph. clin. Neurophysiol., 12:*745–747, 1960.

46. ROSNER, B. S., GOFF, W. R., and ALLISON, T., "Properties of Cerebral Somatic Evoked Responses in Unanesthetized *Cebus* Monkey," in HERNÁNDEZ-PEÓN, R. (ed.), *The Physiological Basis of Mental Activity.* In press.

47. SCHOOLMAN, A. and EVARTS, E. V., "Responses to Lateral Geniculate Radiation Stimulation in Cats with Implanted Electrodes," *J. Neurophysiol., 22:*112–129, 1959.

48. THOMPSON, R. F. and SINDBERG, R. M., "Auditory Response Fields in Association and Motor Cortex of the Cat," *J. Neurophysiol., 23:*87–105, 1960.

V

Behavior During Propagated Hippocampal After-Discharges

John P. Flynn
Marvin Wasman
M. David Egger

The experiments to be described deal with forms of behavior observed during hippocampal after-discharges. The forms of behavior studied were suggested by current notions about the function of the hippocampus or by our own findings in the course of this work.

Intense propagated hippocampal after-discharges have been used in these studies. After-discharges are the experimental counterpart of epileptic seizures. They are large electrical potentials, which when present in the neocortex are ordinarily accompanied by gross convulsions. In this respect, hippocampal after-discharges differ radically from neocortical ones, for no marked change in the animal's appearance occurs during hippocampal after-discharges. This is despite the fact that the potentials exceed the normal potentials by twenty times or more. Partly because of this absence of overt change, they have been suggested as the counterpart of psychomotor epilepsy, in which the most marked symptom is an amnesia for the events taking place during the seizure.

An after-discharge provides a means of seriously disrupting the normal transmission of neural impulses. The factors which appear to influence normal transmission are the number of neurones active, their firing rate, and the pattern of firing. What evidence is available relative to these factors during an electrically initiated hippocampal after-discharge?

During normal activity, there appears to be little or no relation between the activity of individual cells and the EEG. However, particularly during after-discharges initiated by electrical stimulation or by the application of strychnine or penicillin, there is a very high correlation between EEG and activity of individual nerve cells.[3, 7] In general, this correlation may be either a negative one, as in the case of the deafferented fornix preparation, or more often a positive one, as in the case of the intact hippocampal preparation. The general picture during an electrically initiated after-discharge in the intact hippocampus is largely one of synchronous membrane potentials on which spikes are imposed until depolarization inactivates the spike generator.[10, 14] The membrane potentials are synchronized with the EEG in the absence of spikes, but as polarization returns, spikes again appear. This marked synchronous activity during an after-discharge, particularly in view of the absence of synchrony during most normal states, implies a disruption of the pattern of firing.

With respect to the rate of firing, one ordinarily observes during neocortical after-discharges that the nerve cells fire at a markedly increased rate. However, Sawa[14] has pointed out that this phenomenon does not occur in the hippocampus during the seizure state. In view of this absence of high-frequency unitary discharges, one wonders what distinguishes an after-discharge from the effects of electrical stimulation. In the first place, the frequency of the after-discharge varies, whereas stimulation frequency is usually fixed. A second difference, one noted in intracellular recordings, is that the depolarization potential can reach a level great enough to inactivate the spike generator during an after-discharge, whereas during stimulation this does not ordinarily occur. Inactivation of the spike generator occurs readily in hippocampal neurones. Sawa has suggested that this tendency toward depolarization in the hippocampus may be closely related to its low seizure threshold.

The number of neurones involved in the seizure is probably related to the intensity of the seizure and its physical extent inside the hippocampus. Though no direct evidence is available, this seems to be the most reasonable assumption in view of the correlation existing during a seizure at a single site. By way of analogy, an after-discharge might be compared to bursts of static reaching a radio receiver. When the static is sufficiently intense, reception of music or speech becomes impossible. Similarly, the effects of hippocampal after-discharges are dependent upon their intensity. The after-discharges used in these studies have ordinarily been in excess of 1 mV. intensity; furthermore, they have involved both hippocampi, even though they may have been initiated in only one. These conditions are important for the appearance of the results to be described. With less intense and localized after-discharges, little or no effect is observed.[1]

The first study was done jointly with MacLean and Kim.[11] It in-

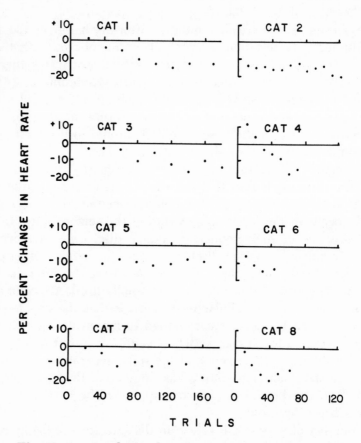

Fig. V—1. *Conditioned cardiac response in cats. Sound paired with shock. Change in heart rate based on comparison of rate before sound to rate after sound but before shock occurred.*

volved a test of the hypothesis that visceral reactions were mediated by the visceral brain or the limbic system and that skeletal responses were mediated by neocortex. This hypothesis predicts that a response such as a learned respiratory or cardiac response would be disrupted by hippocampal after-discharges, whereas a learned skeletal response would not be. With difficulty, cats were trained to show a change in respiration and heart rate.[4] Clicks were paired with an electrical shock. The time between the clicks and the shock was ordinarily 6 sec. The cat could not escape the shock. The conditioned responses

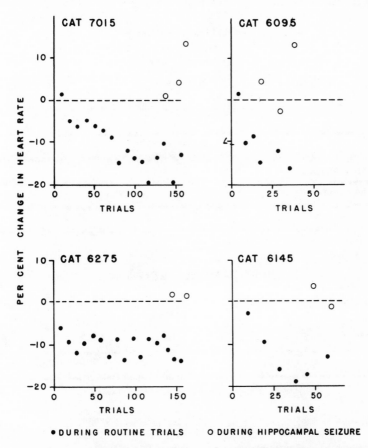

Fig. V—2. *Disappearance of conditioned cardiac response during after-discharge. No difference or increase in heart rate during after-discharges, whereas bradycardia present during routine trials.*

were shallow, rapid respiration and slowing of the heart. An example of the learning and the magnitude of the change is given in Figure V—1. This response should disappear during hippocampal after-discharges, if the assumptions made were correct. In fact they do, as shown in Figure V—2, in which there is no indication of the previously acquired learned response during the hippocampal after-discharge.[5]

The second prediction from the hypothesis was that the skeletal responses would not be disrupted. Contrary to assumption, the skeletal response did not continue in the presence of the hippocampal after-discharge. An illustration of this is given in Figure V—3. A cat trained

ROUTINE TRIAL

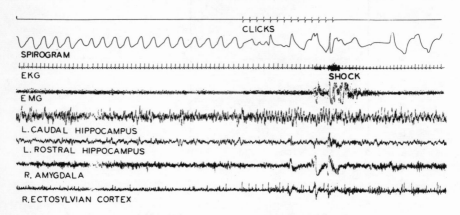

HIPPOCAMPAL SEIZURE

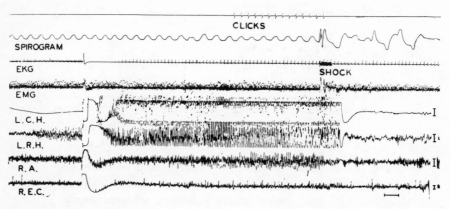

Fig. V—3. *Illustration of the absence of conditioned leg lifting to a sound during after-discharge. Calibration.*

to lift his leg at the sound of clicks which preceded a shock did not do so during hippocampal after-discharges. The general disruption that occurs during hippocampal after-discharges does not affect the visceral and skeletal systems differentially.

The question remains regarding the nature of the behavioral disruption that occurs during the hippocampal after-discharges. Was the lack of response due to a motor deficiency? This did not seem highly probable because in the previous experiment when shock was applied to the animal's leg, he lifted his paw during the after-discharge. Was the lack of the conditioned response traceable to a sensory deficiency? The potentials evoked by clicks which preceded the shock continued to arrive at the cortex during the seizure. At least the sensory pathways were not occluded. Was it possible that the animal no longer associated the clicks with the change in heart rate or lifting of the leg? The hippocampus has been implicated in such functions as memory and recall, and drive states which are considered by some to be essential for learning. The hypothesis that the hippocampal after-discharges disrupted the coupling between the clicks and the lifting of the leg was taken as the most likely and was investigated by training cats only during after-discharges. If the hypothesis were true, no evidence of learning would be secured with such training.

The results of this experiment[6] are shown in Figure V—4. Cats 1, 2, and 3 seldom showed a lifting of the leg at the sound of the clicks during the after-discharges. When the animals were tested for learning in the absence of after-discharges, they regularly avoided the shock by lifting their legs at the sound of the clicks. The frequency with which this occurred was far in excess of that observed in five cats trained not for 60 but for 100 trials according to the same procedure but without after-discharges. No control animal showed more than 35 per cent response for any block of 20 trials within the first hundred, whereas the experimental animals all showed more than 60 per cent response in the first 20 trials after the training period.

In view of the evidence for learning during after-discharges, our earlier ideas about motor detriment had to be re-examined. Animals had electrodes implanted not only in the hippocampus but also in motor cortex, and movements were elicited by direct stimulation of the motor cortex. After-discharges were then induced, and the effect of these upon the cortically elicited movement was ascertained. Table V—1 contains the results of this experiment. The latency of the cortically elicited response was increased, and the magnitude of the movement was decreased. The motor system is impaired in its functioning during hippocampal after-discharges.

The fact that the cats learned during the after-discharges implies that the sensory deficit, if it exists, was not such as to render them incapable of learning. However, the findings of this experiment do not rule out some partial impairment of the auditory system.

The sensory function of the hippocampus is particularly stressed in those theories[13] in which the hippocampus is regarded as mediating the perception of affective stimuli or alerting to potentially affective stimuli. The basis for this is the form of alerting shown in the hippocampal EEG. (See Figure V—3, left caudal hippocampus 5/sec. rhythms at clicks.)

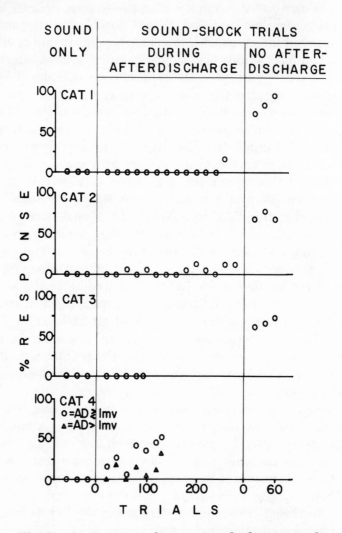

Fig. V—4. *Learning during after-discharges in the relative absence of performance (Cats 1, 2, and 3). Performance may also take place if after-discharges are not intense and occasionally even during intense after-discharges (Cat 4).*

To assess these theories, an experimental situation was needed in which sensory control was clearly exercised over an emotional response. There were hints in the literature that directed attack could be elicited by stimulation of the hypothalamus. Hess and Brügger[8] and Hunsperger[9] had reported that a cat stimulated in the hypothalamus would sometimes attack the experimenter. Nakao[12] had stated that such cats would also bite sticks held in front of them. We introduced a rat into the situation and found that few cats, in our sample only nine in 50, normally attacked rats, but when they were electrically stimulated in the hypothalamus the cats who did not normally attack made a clearly directed attack upon the rat. This situation met our requirements for an emotional response under sensory control.

Table V-1   *Increase in Latency and Decrease in Magnitude of Cortically Elicited Movements During After-Discharges as Compared to Movements Elicited in Their Absence. All Differences Significant at $P < .001$.*

INCREASE IN LATENCY (sec.)

Cat	Mean	SD Mean	N
A	0.37	0.07	24
B	0.18	0.04	23
C	2.16	0.25	29

DECREASE IN MAGNITUDE (mm.)*

Cat	Mean	SD Mean	N
A	6.06	0.49	24
B	1.77	0.19	26
C	3.30	0.45	38

* 1 mm. recorded response =12.5 mm. actual movement.

Two forms of attack were observed.[15, 16] One corresponds in great part to the classical picture of the enraged cat, particularly to the affective defense of Hess and Brügger. The cat's tail becomes bushy, the hair down the middle of his back stands on end, the ears go back, the cat hisses and approaches the rat and strikes him with his unsheathed claws. In contrast to this, there is a form of attack in which the cat appears to be stalking his prey. He is quiet, his head is low, his nose twitches slightly as if he were sniffing, and his hair is only slightly raised. He approaches the rat quietly and viciously bites its head and neck. Mixed forms are also seen. The sites from which the different forms of attack are elicited are shown in Figure V–5. The

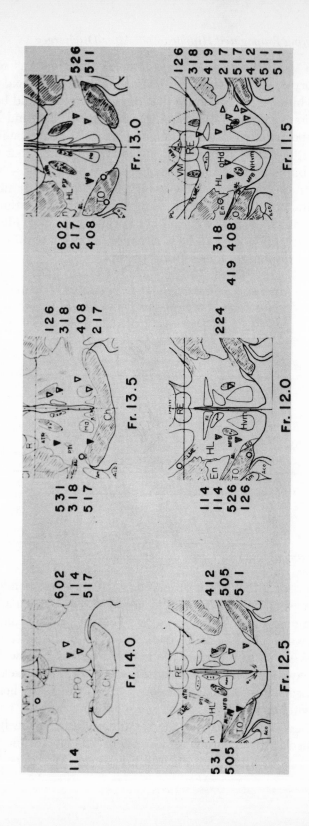

Fig. V—5. *Location of electrode tips from which indicated forms of behavior were elicited. Stalking attack points have been placed on the left side, and affective attack points on the right side for purposes of illustration only.*

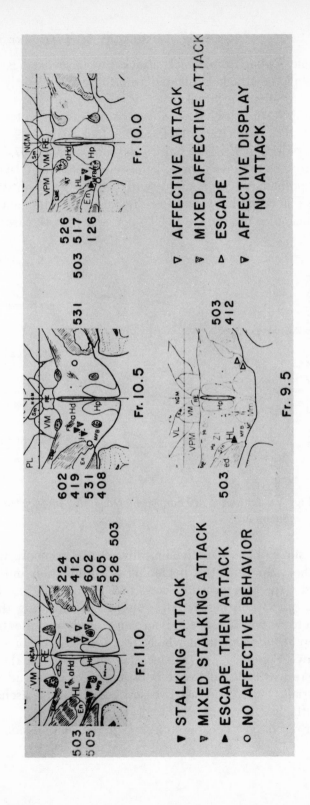

hypothalamic region from which attack can be evoked is extensive; however, stalking attack is elicited from a region slightly lateral to that proper to affective attack.

Hippocampal after-discharges did not seriously disrupt either form of hypothalamically elicited attack. Attack took place in 94.2 per cent of the trials during after-discharges as compared to 97.4 per cent under control conditions. These values were obtained with a low level of hypothalamic stimulation; with a high level of stimulation, there is no difference between after-discharge and the control condition. The incidence of attack was 99.6 per cent in both cases.

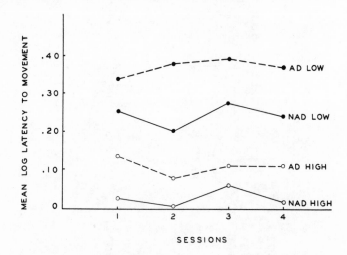

Fig. V—6. *After-discharges increase the latency to movement.*

Two measures of the hypothalamically elicited response were used. One was the time from the beginning of stimulation until the cat took his first step. This measure shows that the cats did not take their first step as quickly during the after-discharges as during the control trials (Figure V–6). The second measure used was the time from the first step to the moment at which the cat bit the rat or struck him with his paw (Figure V–7). This measure shows that in the first two sessions there was little difference between the control and the after-discharge trials, but in the last two sessions the after-discharges delayed the attack.

The after-discharges became longer over the four sessions (Figure

V–8) and spread to other structures. We therefore thought that the delay in attack was due possibly to spread of the after-discharges to the other structures, for example, the amygdala.

To test this notion, electrodes were inserted in the amygdala as well as the hypothalamus of cats, and the amygdala was electrically

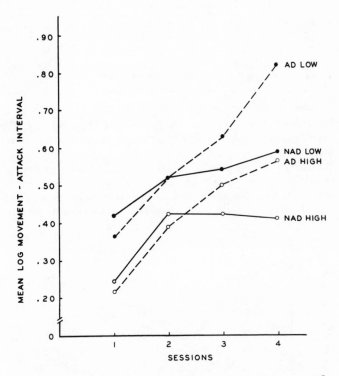

Fig. V—7. *The time from first movement to attack is not affected by after-discharges in the first two sessions but is definitely in the last two.*

stimulated at the same time as the hypothalamus. After-discharges were not induced; in fact, we intentionally used a level of amygdaloid stimulation low enough to avoid them. Simultaneous stimulation of the amygdala and the hypothalamus resulted in the attack being delayed or completely inhibited, whereas movement was not affected in any consistent fashion. The effects of amygdaloid stimulation upon attack are shown for five cats in Table V—2.

Table V-2   *Mean Attack Latency for Hypothalamic Stimulation and Mean Increase When Amygdaloid Stimulation Is Added to Hypothalamic Stimulation.*

CAT	N*	MEAN ATTACK LATENCY (sec.)	MEAN ±SDм INCREASE IN ATTACK LATENCY (sec.)	P**	P_B***
515	48	7.48	+2.32 ± 0.11	83	48
519	22	8.10	+3.46 ± 0.54	91	41
606	36	5.33	+3.58 ± 0.54	94	28
623	54	8.98	+7.10 ± 0.62	93	57
701	14	8.29	+3.49 ± 1.37	64	0

N* = Number of trial pairs on which means are based.

P** = Percentage of trial pairs on which amygdaloid stimulation added to the hypothalamic resulted either in increased attack latency or in no attack at all.

P_B*** = Percentage of trial pairs on which attack did not occur during the combined hypothalamic and amygdaloid stimulation. Such trials were included in the computation of the mean increase in attack latency as though attack actually occurred at time of stimulus termination.

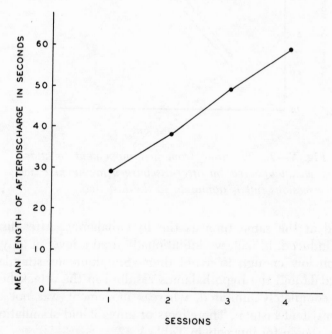

Fig. V—8. *After-discharges increase in duration from session to session.*

SUMMARY

The simplest explanation for the various experimental results observed is that the hippocampus, rather than playing a role specific to learning or emotional behavior, exerts an inhibitory influence upon motor behavior. This would account not only for the loss of the learned response, but also for the effects upon the hypothalamically elicited attack, as well as the direct effect upon cortically elicited movement. The last experiment provides data to substantiate the role of the amygdala in emotion and, moreover, provides direct evidence for its exerting a modulating effect upon the hypothalamus.

References

1. CHOW, K. L., "Effect of Local Electrographic After-Discharges on Visual Learning and Retention in Monkey," *J. Neurophysiol.*, *24*:391–400, 1960.

2. EGGER, M. D. and FLYNN, J. P., "Amygdaloid Suppression of Hypothalamically Elicited Attack Behavior," *Science, 136*:43–44, 1962.

3. ENAMOTO, T. F. and AJMONE-MARSAN, C., "Epileptic Activation of Single Cortical Neurons and Their Relationship with Electroencephalographic Discharges," *Electroenceph. clin. Neurophysiol.*, *11*:199–218, 1959.

4. FLYNN, J. P., "Discussion," (*Proc. Symp. Central Nervous System: Control of Circulation*. Washington, D.C., Nov. 1–3, 1959), *Physiol. Rev.*, *40*, Suppl. 4:292–293, 1960.

5. FLYNN, J. P., MACLEAN, P. D., and KIM, C., "Effects of Hippocampal Afterdischarges on Conditioned Responses," Chap. 27 in SHEER, D. E. (ed.), *Electrical Stimulation of the Brain*, Austin, Texas, University of Texas Press, 1961.

6. FLYNN, J. P. and WASMAN, M., "Learning and Cortically Evoked Movement During Propagated Hippocampal Afterdischarges," *Science, 131*:- 1607–1608, 1960.

7. GERIN, P., "Microelectrode Investigations on the Mechanisms of the Electrically Induced Epileptiform Seizure ('Afterdischarge')," *Arch. ital. Biol.*, *98*:21–40, 1960.

8. HESS, W. R. and BRÜGGER, M., "Das subcorticale Zentrum der affektiven Abwehrreaktion," *Helv. physiol. pharmacol. Acta, 1*:33–52, 1943.

9. HUNSPERGER, R. W., "Affektreaktionen auf electrische Reizung im Hirnstamm der Katze," *Helv. physiol. pharmacol. Acta*, 14:70–92, 1956.

10. KANDEL, E. R. and SPENCER, W. A., "Excitation and Inhibition of Single Pyramidal Cells During Hippocampal Seizure," *Exp. Neurol.*, *4*:162–179, 1961.

11. MacLean, P. D., Flynn, J. P., and Kim, C., "Experiments Bearing on the Role of the Limbic System in Cardiovascular Function: Conditioning and Reserpine Studies," *Proc. ann. Meeting, Amer. Heart Ass.*, 4:107–126, 1955.

12. Nakao, H., "Emotional Behavior Produced by Hypothalamic Stimulation," *Amer. J. Physiol.*, 194:411–418, 1958.

13. Passouant, P., Cadilhac, J., and Passouant-Fontaine, Th., "Influence en Cours de Sommeil Spontane de la Stimulation Électrique Reticulaire et des Stimuli Sensoriels sur les Rhythmes Hippocampique de Chat," *J. Physiol. Path. gén.*, 47:715–718, 1955.

14. Sawa, M., (Personal communication).

15. Wasman, M., *Effects of Hippocampal Afterdischarges on Attack Behavior Elicited by Hypothalamic Stimulation in Cats,* Unpublished Doctoral Dissertation, Yale University, 1961.

16. Wasman, M. and Flynn, J. P., "Directed Attack Induced by Hypothalamic Stimulation," *Arch. Neurol., Chicago,* 6:220–227, 1962.

17. Wasman, M. and Flynn, J. P., "Effects of Hippocampal Afterdischarges upon Hypothalamic Elicited Attack" (In preparation).

VI

The New Neurology: Memory, Novelty, Thought, and Choice

Karl H. Pribram

> Thus judgment is a . . . process . . . which is brought about by the difference between the . . . cathexis of a memory and a similar perceptual cathexis. It follows from this that when these two cathexes coincide, the fact will be a biological signal for ending the activity of thinking and for initiating discharge. When they do *not* coincide, an impetus is given to the activity of thinking which will be brought to a close when they *do* coincide.
>
> . . . One of the chief characteristics of nervous tissue is that of "memory": that is, speaking generally, a susceptibility to permanent alteration by a single process. This offers a striking contrast to the behaviour of a material that allows a wave-movement to pass through it and then returns to its former condition. Any psychological theory deserving consideration must provide an explanation of memory. Now any such explanation comes up against the difficulty that . . . after an excitation neurones are permanently different from what they were before, while, on the other hand, it cannot be denied that, in general, fresh excitations meet with the same conditions of reception as did the earlier ones. Thus the neurones would appear to be both influenced and also unaltered. . . . We cannot off-hand imagine an apparatus capable of such complicated functioning.
>
> SIGMUND FREUD[10, 11]

Biological scientists the world over have recently turned their heavy laboratory artillery on an age-old problem: the nature of memory

149

mechanisms; event storage and retrieval; learning through novel experience. This interest has, of course, been shared by their colleagues in the behavioral sciences; these investigators have, in addition, readmitted to investigation a field of experimental inquiry that had gone out of fashion for half a century: an analysis of thought processes and of decision-making.

I shall report some of these exciting efforts to you; as academic lecturer I shall take license to weave a tapestry with the data. Bear in mind that other designs, even other fabrics, could be constructed from the same thread—I present my version to demonstrate the rich textures made possible by the new materials with the hope that the particular patterns chosen represent more than mere fantasy. My version of this fabric will evolve from the following four basic threads.

By "memory" I will mean any set of events that makes available to an organism something of a situation after that situation no longer obtains. "Novel" I will define as any aspects of a situation which differ sufficiently from prior situations to produce recordable physiological changes in the organism. By the term "thought" I will refer to the active uncertainty produced when an ordered set of memories mismatches the current novelties of the situation. And "choice" I will use to designate processes of resolution of uncertainty that lead to action. How I have arrived at these meanings will be the substance of this paper. The story begins in the histochemical laboratories of Holger Hydén.

Something Old

THE NEURON AS RNA PRODUCER

Rats are subjected to rotary stimulation. Rotation is through 120 degrees horizontally and 30 degrees vertically for 25 minutes per day up to 6 days. Microchemical analysis of the nerve cells in Deiters' vestibular nucleus shows a definite and marked increase in the production of respiratory enzymes (cytochrome and succinic oxydases) and in ribonucleic acids (RNA) and proteins.[19] Hydén and his collaborators had, in earlier research, already demonstrated the striking capacity of neurons to increase their production of RNA when artificially excited.[5] In fact, nerve cells have a vastly greater capacity to contain and to produce nucleic acids and proteins than do other cells in the body, so that this characteristic of nerve tissue is as conspicuous as is their ability to generate and transmit electrical potential changes.[17] The well-known role of the RNA molecule, together with its more stable sister substance, DNA, in the mechanisms of genetic "memory," stimulated the suggestion that RNA is somehow involved in the mechanisms of neural memory. But before the question "How?" can be properly posed, other observations and experiments must be detailed.

THE CONSOLIDATION HYPOTHESIS

Remembering is not always intensive activity; periods of rest may greatly enhance the effect of the waking effort. Consider also the retrograde amnesias commonly observed in conjunction with severe head injuries. Memory traces appear to require time to fix in the brain. This fixing process has been called consolidation and subjected to a good deal of recent experimental analysis.

The common method for producing retrograde amnesia in the laboratory is to administer electroconvulsive shock to rats. There is considerable evidence that the sooner after an experience the convulsion occurs, the greater is the interference with later performance relative to that experience. For instance, Duncan[9] found a maximum effect when convulsions followed an avoidance trial within 15 minutes; the effect is practically gone when an hour intervenes between the conditioning trial and the convulsion. There are some results, however, which do not neatly fit a straightforwardly simple consolidation notion.

Poschel[35] gave rats a two-day series of electroconvulsive shocks at the rate of five per day. The rats were trained to run an alley maze to a goal box that contained food. During the convulsive series, however, the rats experienced shocks to their feet in the goal box. Half of the subjects received the convulsions *prior* to the foot-shock experience; for the other half it *followed* the experience in approximately 24 hours. No differences were found between these groups, though both avoided the goal box significantly less than did their controls. The effect of the convulsion was, therefore, as much proactive as retroactive. An experiment by Brady[3] made use of the "conditioned emotional response." With this technique, a subject is taught to press a lever for a food-reward presented at intervals varying about some average period of time. A signal is turned on somewhere during the performance and this signal is invariably followed after a given time by a foot-shock. As a rule, the subject's response radically diminishes, or response ceases entirely while the signal is on. A normal rate of response is resumed once the shock has been experienced and the signal is off. In Brady's experiment, a series of 21 convulsions at the rate of three per day was begun 48 hours after the last conditioned emotional response trial. Testing was resumed four days after the completion of the convulsive series—all convulsed subjects failed to react to the signal at this time. Without further experience with the task, however, retests at 30 days after completion of the convulsive series showed recrudescence of the conditioned emotional response— and this performance was maintained on retests at 60 and 90 days. These experimenters, as did others, exceeded the crucial hour during which the consolidation process can be maximally affected—their results indicate, however, that some mechanism necessary to the retrieval of the memory trace is still fragile for as long as a day or two after an experience.*

McGaugh felt that if the consolidation hypothesis is to be taken seriously one ought to be able to find techniques to *improve* learning and not rest solely on demonstrations that remembering has been interfered with. He discovered an early work of Lashley's[23] where small doses of strychnine sulphate were found to facilitate learning in rats. Together with Petrinovich, McGaugh repeated the study.[28] Seventy-six rats were trained in a Lashley III maze. Each day 33 experimental subjects were injected with 1/3 to 1 mg./kg. of strychnine sulphate ten minutes prior to receiving five maze trials. Controls were injected with the normal saline. All subjects were tested to a criterion of five correct out of six consecutive trials. The controls averaged 46.9 errors in attaining criterion while the strychnine-injected animals averaged only 29.2 errors, a highly significant result.

---

* The suggestion has been repeatedly made that the retrograde amnesic effects of convulsions can be totally ascribed to the production of "fear" in the subjects.[7, 13, 23, 42] Madsen and McGaugh[26] have replied to these assertions with a simple experiment. They placed rats in a box on a raised platform. Both box and platform were covered with copper sheeting. The platform was then slowly lowered and when the rat stepped off, it completed the circuit and received a foot-shock. Half the rats were then given a convulsion within 5 sec. of the time they stepped off the platform. After 24 hours all rats were again placed on the platform and the platform lowered. Almost all of the convulsed rats stepped off, whereas only about half of the controls did so. Another direct test of the fear hypothesis has been made by Pearlman et al.[34] They taught rats to press a lever, then electrified it. Now lever-pressing resulted in foot-shock and the rats avoided the lever. If the rats were convulsed (with Metrazol) they returned to lever-pressing 100 per cent provided the convulsion occurred within 10 sec. after the foot-shock. In addition, there was significant impairment of retention when the convulsion occurred for as long as four days after the foot-shock trial. In this case the subjects went back to lever-pressing at 70 per cent of their prefoot-shock level, compared to 1 per cent for the nonconvulsed controls.

In a subsequent study, McGaugh[29] injected the strychnine sulphate solution 30 sec. after each trial—again highly significant results were obtained in favor of the strychnine-injected rats. Petrinovich extended these findings to discrimination learning; McGaugh and his students to other types of mazes, and so on. In addition, McGaugh and his co-workers[30] replicated and extended the experiments using picrotoxin and a new strychninelike-acting drug, diazadamantan, obtained from Daniele Bovet of the Istituto di Sanità in Rome.

These investigations uncovered one other interesting result that may have some practical applications. Some of the research was performed with two genetically different strains of rats—the one fairly "bright" in learning mazes, the other rather "dull." In some of McGaugh's experiments intertrial interval was simply varied, and in others drug injections and convulsions were juxtaposed to both massed and spaced trials. The results demonstrated that the maze-dull rats were dull because they took longer to consolidate the effects of each trial experience—e.g., spacing trials improved the performance of the "dulls" but not of the "brights"; convulsions administered 45 sec. after a trial affected both the "brights" and the "dulls" while such convulsions given 30 minutes after a trial affected only the performance of the "maze-dulls."

These experiments form an impressive body of evidence that some consolidation process must occur in laying down the memory trace. The brain must be involved in consolidation—but how?

In our own laboratories[14, 22, 36, 44-47] different areas of the brain cortex of monkeys have been treated with aluminum hydroxide cream to produce local irritations manifested by altered electrical activity (abnormal slow waves and spike discharges). Such irritative lesions, while they do not interfere with monkeys' capacity to remember the solution to problems repeatedly solved prior to the irritation, do slow their original learning of these problems some fivefold. Moreover, problem-solving in general is not affected; the defect is specific for those solutions to tasks which cannot even be remembered when that particular part of the brain has been removed. These results can be interpreted to suggest that such irritative lesions delay the consolidation process. A test of the suggestion would come from a comparison of learning by irritative-lesioned monkeys under spaced and massed trial conditions. Tentatively though, for the present purpose, the indication can be accepted that irritation with aluminum hydroxide cream interferes with memory consolidation.

Could the irritative lesion in some way alter the neural tissue's production of RNA and thus affect the memory mechanism? Chemical analysis of the tissue implanted with aluminum hydroxide cream would be messy, to say the least. Nonetheless, an ingenious answer to this question has been achieved by Morrell.[31, 32] He based his experiments on earlier reports that an irritative lesion made in one cerebral hemisphere produces, after some months, a "mirror focus" of altered electrical activity in the contralateral cortex by way of the interhemispheric connections through the corpus callosum. This "mirror focus" has not been directly damaged chemically, yet it possesses all of the epileptogenic properties of the irritative lesion. Morrell ascertained that the RNA in this mirror focus was considerably altered when compared to that found in normal brain tissue. The notion that RNA production by nerve cells is in some way involved in memory consolidation becomes somewhat more persuasive. However, the question of mechanism remains.

THE NEW NEUROLOGIA

To return to Hydén's laboratories: brain tissue is composed of two sorts of cells, neurons and glia. Glia were hitherto believed to serve only as support and nutrient for the all-important neurons. But recent evidence suggests that at least one type of glia, the oligodendroglia, which completely envelops neurons, functions with them as a glia-neural couplet both in the generation and modulation of electrical potential change and in the production and utilization of RNA.

Hydén[18] gently teased apart the neurons and the glia of the vestibular nucleus. He found that the increased production of RNA in nerve cells concomitant with their excitation was coupled with a simultaneous decrease in RNA concentration in oligodendroglia. During this period of excitation glia could provide the nerve cell with energy-rich compounds since the glia apparently resort, at least in part, to anaerobic metabolic routes such as glycolysis and lipid breakdown. In addition, however, Hydén finds that after excitation ceases, the glia in turn increase their RNA production while that of the adjacent neurons diminishes. On the basis of other experiments, Hydén suggests that the aerobic-anerobic balance is maintained through competition for inorganic phosphates (the Pasteur effect), with the respiratory phase of the process dominant over the fermentative glucose degradation, and the phases in the neuron dominant over those in the glia. This phase lock-in mechanism is assumed

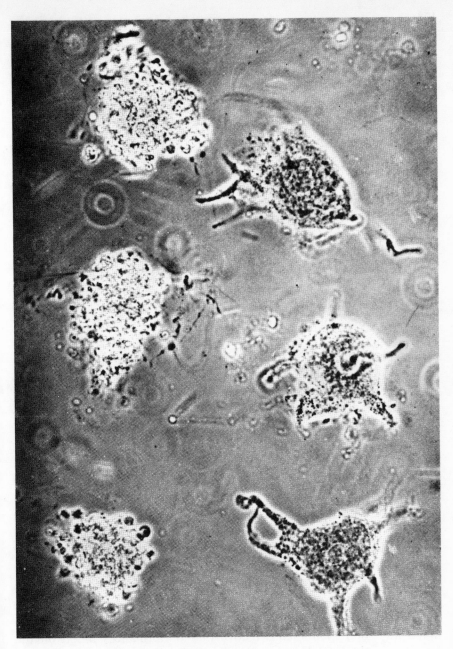

Fig. VI—1. *Neuron and glia teased apart.*

to operate through pinocytosis. There is ample evidence of possible pinocytosis from high resolution analyses of the structural arrangements of the glial-neural border. In addition, pinocytosis has been observed in glia and nerve cell tissue cultures where it can be induced by electrical stimulation.

Why this fuss about a glial-neural couplet? There are several reasons. For one, glial cells reproduce, while neurons do not. Should the memory storage mechanism turn out to be related to protein synthesis guided by RNA production, such stored protein could be replicated by glial cell division.

Second, nerve cells must remain constantly ready for new excitation. The time course of the effects of excitation is short, even when nerve nets rather than neurons per se are considered. In simulated nets, the difficulty has been to adjust the time an element "remembers" in such a fashion that "learning" can take place. Either the net remembers everything too much and so very quickly ceases to be sensitive to new inputs, or else in the process of retaining sensitivity, so little is remembered that learning can hardly have been said to occur. This difficulty can be overcome in simulated "memistors" by adding a longer time-course storage device which sets a bias on the reception of new inputs and is in turn itself altered by those inputs.[51] The glia could function in this fashion. Even their electrical responsivity is some thousandfold longer in duration than that recorded as impulsive activity from neurons. There is every reason to suppose that such graded electrical activity would influence the transmitted excitations of the adjacent neural net, which in turn, through the phase lock-in biochemical mechanism, could alter the state of the glia.

In any event, these processes take time: the time demanded by the consolidation hypothesis. But, as already indicated, the evidence on consolidation is not uniform. There appears to be one process that takes no more than an hour and reaches a maximum some seconds after an experience. When this process is interfered with, recall is obliterated. There is another process, taking hours and even days, which, when interfered with, produces only temporary amnesias with practically total spontaneous recovery of performances based on the experience obtained prior to the interference. This second type of evidence cannot be easily fitted to the electrobiochemical explanation of the memory mechanism so far proposed. Some process must be sought that has a longer duration and is more resistant to permanent interference yet in some ways is temporarily more fragile.

RETRIEVAL THROUGH NETWORK GROWTH

Though the brain's nerve cells do not divide, they can grow new branches. This has been dramatically demonstrated[39] in a study of the effects on brain of high-energy radiations produced by a cyclotron. Minute, sharply demarcated laminar destructions (often limited to a single cell layer, and this not necessarily the most superficial one) were produced in rabbit cerebral cortex when high-energy beams were stopped short by the soft tissue. The course of destruction and restitution was studied histologically. Intact nerve cells were seen to send branches into the injured area; these branches became progressively more organized until, from all that could be observed through a microscope or measured electrically, the tissue had been repaired (Figure VI–2).

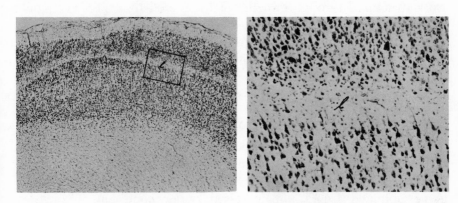

Fig. VI–2. *Laminar destruction in rabbit cerebral cortex produced by high energy radiation.*

The organization of the branches of nerve cells could well be guided by the glia that pervasively surround these branches. Such directive influences are known to be essential in the regeneration of peripheral nerves. Schwann's cells, close relatives of glia, form a column into which the budding fibers must grow if they are not to get tangled in a matted mess of their own making.

The assumption is that glial cell division is somehow spurred by those same activities recounted above as important to memory storage. The resulting pattern of the glial bed would form the matrix into which nerve cell fiber growth occurs. Thus guided, fiber growth is directed by its own excitation—the whole mechanism based, however, on the long-lasting intervention of glia. The mechanism would account for the later interfering effects obtained in the consolidation experiments and in the spontaneous "restitution" as well: the growing nerve cell fiber is ameboid and can temporarily retract its tip which is made up of a helical winding of small globular protein molecules. After the convulsive insult is over, first tentative, then more vigorous probings can again be resumed in some "random-walk" fashion by the nerve fiber tip as has been suggested for normal growth by von Foerster.[49] The glial substrate, assumed undamaged, will perform its guiding function to effect the apparent restitution.

The glially guided neural growth hypothesis, in addition to accounting for these late interference effect data, has another attractive feature. The electrochemical memory storage process per se has built in no satisfactory mechanism for information retrieval. A neural network structured through growth, glially guided by experience, could serve retrieval much as do the "feelers" on the magnetic memory core of a computer. The patterns of electrical signals that activate particular network configurations would correspond to lists or programs fed to a computer and to the schemata proposed by Bartlett[2] to account for the results of his studies on memory in man.

TISSUE EFFECTS OF EARLY SENSORY DEPRIVATION

Is there any evidence to support directly these notions about the memory storage and retrieval process? Most persuasive are the as yet meager results of histological and histochemical analyses of neural tissue obtained from animals raised under conditions of sensory deprivation. In the normal subject a considerable growth in the number of cellular and fiber elements takes place during the first months after birth[6] (Figure VI–3). This is associated, as would be expected, by production of substantial amounts of RNA.

Weiskrantz[50] has shown that in the retinas of dark-reared kittens, Mueller fibers are scarce—and Mueller fibers are glia. Brattgård,[4] Liberman,[24] and Rasch et al.[38] have all shown deficiencies in RNA production of the retinal ganglion cells in such dark-reared subjects. These are initial forays—they do indicate that even for mammals the techniques are available for a direct attack on the memory problem.

REGENERATE WORM-RUNNERS

Meanwhile, experiments by a group of "worm-runners" have added fuel to the RNA fire. Flatworms (Planaria) were trained by McConnell

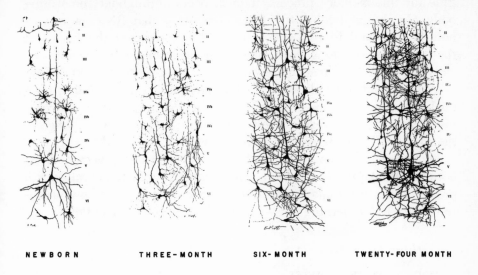

NEWBORN   THREE-MONTH   SIX-MONTH   TWENTY-FOUR MONTH

AREA   STRIATA, OC
HUMAN INFANT CORTEX

Fig. VI—3. *Stages in the developing human brain (Drawing from Golgi-Cox; after Conel.)*

et al.[27] in a water-filled trough illuminated from above. The animals were placed in a trough until they showed no reaction to the turning on and off of the light. Then each illumination of 3 sec. duration was accompanied for the last second by an electric shock passed through the water. Initially the worms contracted and turned only when the shock was on; gradually, the frequency of such responses increased during the first 2 sec. when only illumination was presented. Once a worm had reached criterion it was immediately cut in half transversely, the halves isolated and allowed to regenerate. About a month later when regeneration was complete, all subjects were retrained to the original criterion; whereas original training averaged 134 trials, subsequent to transverse sectioning, the original head ends averaged 40 and the original tail ends, 43.2 trials. (A trained but uncut group showed about the same amount of savings; a group trained after the cut took more trials than did the original group's initial training; thus a sensitization effect was ruled out.)

On the basis of these and other similar results, McConnell and his collaborators suggest that whatever the physiological change responsible for this memory process, it must occur throughout the worm's body. Corning and John[8] tested the hypothesis that RNA may somehow be involved in this mechanism. They immersed the halves of the trained worms in a weak solution of ribonuclease in order to destroy the RNA. The heads regenerated in ribonuclease showed savings as great as control heads; on the other hand, tails regenerated in ribonuclease showed no such savings. The brain-stored memory mechanism was apparently resistant to this exposure to ribonuclease, whereas the somatically mediated "worm memory" was destroyed.

Thus, the evidence for a dual memory mechanism accumulates: both an RNA-protein synthesis and a glially guided neural-growth process have to be taken into account in descriptions of how organisms react to "something old"—situations that no longer obtain.

Something New

HABITUATION AND NOVELTY

An entirely different series of experiments serves to link this elementary memory-trace mechanism to thought. These experiments show that at any moment current sensory excitation is processed by the memory trace which forms a representative record of the minute details of prior experiences. It is the match or mismatch between current excitation and this representative record that guides attention and action.

Sokolov[43] performed the following simple demonstration. A person is exposed to the beep of a horn: he ordinarily turns toward it. The electrical activity of his brain displays a characteristic "alerting" pattern—activation of the record obtained from the lateral cortex, especially the region of the auditory projections, and hypersynchrony of the record obtained from medial and basal forebrain structures such as the hippocampal formation. Additional physiological characteristics of orientation can be identified. The flow of blood to the head increases at the expense of flow to the fingertips; changes occur in the electrical resistance of the skin. Should the horn beep be frequently repeated, all these reactions gradually diminish and finally practically die out. The subject is said to be *habituated* to the stimulus.

The lack of reaction to the continuing beep is deceptive, however. Actually a great deal is still taking place. For if the smallest change is produced in the stimulus, such as a softer beep, all of the initial alerting reactions recur. Sokolov interpreted this to mean that the person must be matching the current sound against a stored representation of prior horn beeps—else why would a diminution in intensity call forth the full-blown orienting response? He tested his interpretation by habituating the person to a tone of a certain length. Then, suddenly, a shortened tone was presented. Now orienting reactions occurred when the tone ceased, i.e., alerting responses were recorded with the onset of silence. The reactions continued for the "expected" length of the tone, then slowly disappeared. We have all experienced this surprising reaction to sudden silence.

Only a few of the neural events that partake in habituation are known; the course of build-up of a central representative process against which input is matched has only begun to be analyzed. There is considerable evidence of the specificity of the buildup.[12, 15, 41] The process appears to be more rapid in nonmodality-specific than in modality-specific structures.[21] Attention to a noise diminishes the neural response to a flickering background light for the duration of the attention.[16] This match-mismatch mechanism, so intimately a part of the attentive process, is mediated in part at least through efferent control, exercised by central structures over their own afferent input. The evidence for such central regulation of input has been repeatedly reviewed in recent years.[25, 37] One need point out here only the important fact that this mechanism provides a way for gradual self-regulated modification of central processes. Modification follows mismatch. If input matches the central representation completely, neural habituation is established with concomitant behavioral inattention and boredom. Inputs completely outside the experience of the organism may be equally excluded from influence on behavior through efferent gating. Most effective guides of behavior are inputs but slightly dissimilar to prior familiar inputs. Such novel inputs mismatch —and so produce all of the consequences of mismatch.

To put it in another way, were there no memory mechanism, no representative record, we could not recognize novelty or similarity. Thus we could not direct our actions in an orderly way. In a creature without a self-modifying match-mismatch mechanism, the enormously potent intensity of momentary occurrences would make haphazard demands on attention and action so that no course could be charted between the Charybdis of disruptive differences and the Scylla of stultifying sameness.

It is this capacity to sense sameness and difference between recurring events that is also the basis for the detection of errors made in solving problems. Again, the laboratory has given us a beautiful demonstration—this time the laboratory of Adey.[1] The subjects were cats. Fine wires were inserted into the depth of the brain and tied to the skull so that they could do no harm. The cats were placed facing a Y-shaped raised drawbridge. At the ends of the arms of the "Y" were two boxes about a yard apart, one of which contained food. As a flashing light was turned on above the box with the food, the drawbridge was lowered to form a path to each box.

During the first exposure to this situation, electrical recordings made from the brain of the cat disclosed the characteristic pattern of alerting. With repeated exposure the recordings showed increasing habituation. Since the cat began to expect food when she reached a box, the alerting pattern occurred only when she had chosen the empty box. The cat's performance can be judged as reliably from the recordings as from her observed behavior.

This alerting and error-sensing are manifested by changes in the patterns of electrical activity made in the brain. These changes are dependent on the presence in the brain of a detailed record representing the effects of prior stimulation—a record conceived as composed of RNA-induced protein molecular change and, additionally, the progressive growth of nerve fibers guided by glial cell division. This record is matched against the effects of current excitation—a match results in habituation, the sensing of similarity; a mismatch in alerting, therefore in novelty and error-sensing.

Sometimes Thoughtful

UNCERTAINTY

Still more interesting, during the latter part of the drawbridge experiment when the cat's performance had become excellent, the electrical activity that accompanied error often occurred *before* the cat had had an opportunity to search the empty box. Actually, the "error patterns" began the moment the cat headed down the wrong path and, occasionally, some instants before. Her behavior reflects her uncertainty. If the cat could talk, she would probably say, as humans so often do after making an error, "All along I thought that something was wrong."

Since people can report on their thoughts, patterns of electrical activity of the brain can be related to thinking. For instance, when one ponders a mathematical problem, the entire brain wave record becomes choppy. Should one think merely of solving a manual puzzle, the choppy pattern is restricted to the part of the brain that directly controls the hand's actions. Different areas of the brain can be involved when different solutions are entertained.

PROBLEMS AND PROBLEM-SOLVING

How are match-mismatch mechanisms of our brains used? How are problems faced—how are problems made—how is uncertainty actively engaged? Experiments with monkeys[37] have given additional leads as to the nature of the matching process in use. A simple situation was devised to produce uncertainty. It resembles the popular shell game. A peanut was hidden according to some rules under one of several objects placed on a board. The monkey was allowed to choose among objects—he was allowed only one choice at a time. To all appearances, the monkeys seemed to be thinking when faced with the alternatives. They often reached tentatively toward an object only to withdraw, scratch their heads, and pause before the response was finally completed. One monkey, incredibly, sat before the confusing objects, elbow on knee, chin cupped in his paws, a furry, charmingly alive miniature of Rodin's famous statue, "The Thinker."

Groups of these monkeys had had brain operations which influenced the way they played the game. One operation—removing the inferotemporal cortex—changed the way the monkeys proceeded to search for the peanut. Another operation—removing the anterior frontal cortex—had no effect on the strategies of search but prevented the monkeys from following an obvious lead, that is, sticking to the object under which they first found the peanut. Almost anything distracted this group of monkeys. At times they seemed to make their own distractions, reminding one of a bored high school student doing homework; like the student, the monkey reacted swiftly to any change, any novelty introduced into the situation.

How a given problem is solved depends therefore on how it is searched and how a particular viewpoint is maintained in the face of alternatives. Should the memory traces be held too rigidly inviolate, nuances would never be remembered and the problem would become insoluble. The inflexible memory traces resist influence from the new situation; a match is never achieved. Inflexible sameness of thought results. On the other hand, habituation can be too evanescent, the memory traces can be held too lightly and changed by incidents which, though temporarily remembered, are displaced too soon by others. Then thinking is fleeting and disorganized. Each of these conditions has its counterpart in daily experience; each can be produced by a specific brain operation limited to one of the so-called "association

Fig. VI—4. *Rhesus monkey playing the multiple choice game.*

areas," but as yet there is no clue as to how these brain operations wreak their havoc. Anatomical and electrophysiological experiments are sorely needed to trace the connections from these "association areas" by which they exert control over the activities in the projection areas.

Meanwhile, much can be learned from a more direct approach to "thought" by both an in vivo and an in vitro analysis. For this purpose, monkeys will not do. People are needed when any but the most rudimentary of thought processes are to be studied; and when these processes must be manipulated, the behavioral science counterpart to the test tube, the computer, becomes indispensable.

People have an advantage over monkeys; people are able to express their thoughts. Through language their thoughts become inputs to others, and even to themselves, inputs which have the power to influence memory through the match-mismatch process, and so to alter further thinking. Indeed, the processes that govern the development of language in the infant are roughly the same as those involved in the development of thinking. The power of language is achieved slowly, in stages. Once an infant has passed the babbling stage, he notes the effect of the sounds he makes in the game he continually plays with his parents or some other child. Gradually he comes to remember and to bring to the game certain strategies, such as make raucous sounds for immediate attention; for prolonged play, a more gentle tone. These initial strategies quickly lead him to appreciate subtleties. "Mama," for example, will evoke a parent different from "Papa." Then the child is ready for a stage monkeys never achieve. He identifies his thoughts and expresses the identification. He does this by acknowledging the difference between the excitation in his brain produced by the current situation and the memory-trace record. He distinguishes objects from their previously acquired meaning and use to him. He knows "Mama" (object) is for feeding (meaning); the dog for petting; a hole for digging.

The child is now ready to meet the rules for speaking—the forms and usages that allow effective interchange with others. He is alert to the subtleties of language, and so language becomes his primary tactical tool for communication with himself—that is, for thinking.

PROGRAMS, PLANS, AND ORDERED COMPLEXITY

The utility of language as a tool of thought is perhaps most clearly demonstrated by that very special tongue, mathematics, and when logical mathematical processes are in question, those modern "thinking machines" (the electronic computers) come into their own. The algebra or logic they use in solving problems is built into programs by procedures similar to those that characterize all thinking. First, some rules are set down to establish the outline of the problem—for instance, the rules of chess or of compounding interest on savings. The computer "learns" these rules, that is, stores them in its "memory." Next, specific information—moves in chess, the number of dollars deposited— are fed into the computer. But the description of this information must be couched in terms the computer can understand—terms that match the appropriate rules so they can be summoned from storage. Only then can the information be processed and a solution achieved. Usually, the solution is relatively crude: a checkmate ends the chess game after only a few strategically simple moves; interest is compounded on the amounts on deposit as of 1 January each year. For greater sophistication new rules are added, programming the input of information within the context of the already established rules. The order of moves in the chess game is now based on instructions from a chess master; interest is computed first on a monthly—later on a daily—basis. These secondary tactical rules, or subroutines, have the same relation to the initial rules that subheadings have to the major items in an outline. The writing of utilizable outlines by computer programmers is much the same sort of task as making an outline for a theme in an English course, except that, since the computer's theme will never actually be written except in outline form, the program has to embody seemingly infinite, meticulously constructed detail.

The striking similarity between the way people think and a computer computes suggests that our brain organizes, "plans," our behavior much as a computer goes about solving problems.

Thus far, the discussion has ranged over several kinds of thinking, from the repetitive, rigidly fixed to the fleeting, poorly organized, to which everyone is at one time or another prone. Both kinds can result from damage to certain parts of the brain. In between is the more usual, productive kind of thinking, the thoughts being flexibly coordinated with the task to be performed within a structure outlined by experience. But what about creative thinking? As yet, no computer has achieved it. Are the characteristics of creative thought so mysterious as to defy understanding? Perhaps not.

Perhaps we harbor many misconceptions about creative thinking. According to the most prevalent conception, discoveries and inventions arise out of the blue; but the contrary is the case. In reality, discoverers make their discoveries through what they already know: they match the unfamiliar against a thoroughly incorporated body of fact. Columbus, for example, knew a great deal about navigation. He knew the assumed boundaries of a flat world and what could be expected if, as some people suspected, the world was really round. But other explorers had to repeat Columbus' feat before the discovery of America was admitted (should we say as a subroutine?) to the thinking of all sailors.

The inventor achieves novelty within the bounds of certainty. He comes upon, finds, only when properly prepared for the finding. The term "inventor" derives from the same root as "inventory." Edison expended his "ninety-nine per cent perspiration" by taking stock of the boundaries of known electrical science. Only then, at those boundaries, did new procedures strike him as plausible. The inventor innovates, as when, like Edison, he substitutes tungsten for iron to make an electric light bulb from an electric heating element.

The construction of a great symphony follows familiar lines: the rules of theme and subthemes, beat and counterpoint, form and movement, must all be thoroughly mastered before creative composition can begin. Beethoven created music by taking discipline even further than its already complex structured limits. He sensed nuances where none had been sensed before. He prepared musical programs more complicated than seemed possible.

And what of the poet, supposedly the freest of free souls? Perhaps more than any creator he is constrained by the known rules within which novelty can be expressed. Shall he choose iambic pentameter, rhyme or alliteration, couplet or sonnet? He must carefully tend the meaning of a word so that where several meanings are possible each is enhanced by the context in which the word appears. In such a wealth of rules and orderliness lies the creativity of the poet as well as his freedom. For freedom is not anarchy. Real freedom is intelligent, knowledgeable choice and rises out of order when order achieves sufficient complexity.

But What To Do?

THE TEMPORARY DOMINANT FOCUS

And so we are left with the problem of how choices among alternatives are possible; how thought, active uncertainty, ceases and action is engaged. Again we turn to the nervous system. One of its properties appears to be that, under the proper circumstances, a more or less temporary dominant focus can be established. John[20] reviews the literature relevant to this property. Experiments of the following sort have given rise to the concept. Early workers had established a conditioned avoidance response by pairing a metronome beat with a shock to the left rear paw of a dog. They then placed a small piece of filter paper soaked in strychnine on the part of the motor cortex that primarily controls action of the right forepaw. Following strychninization, presentation of the metronome beat elicited vigorous flexion of the right forepaw rather than the left rear. The chemically induced excitable focus dominates so that the afferent input which had previously been processed on the basis of experience in the situation now initiates a response consonant with the chemical manipulation.

Ukhtomski[48] is responsible for the concept and term "dominant focus." He characterized it as a (1) relatively heightened excitability of a group of nerve cells leading to summation of the excitations arriving from a variety of sources, and (2) a retention of this excitation once it has been established, thus leading to a capacity to continue a stable discharge when the original excitations have disappeared. In the presence of a dominant focus, therefore, the normally random distribution of excitation with a population of nerve cells would be altered to a massive response synchronized to the discharge of cells of the focus. Recently, the turn of investigation has centered around the production of such dominant foci by D.C. polarization of neural tissues applied during learning.[32, 40]

PATTERN FOR DECISION

John,[20] in his review, goes on to show how this process if repeated often could lead to the establishment, in the nervous system, of the representative records of repeated inputs. The discussion has come to full turn. But, of equal interest is the fact that the dominant-focus experiments provide a mechanism that accounts for choice among representations already established. Such a mechanism would be composed of a temporary *pattern* of dominant foci. These would mobilize and give precedence to a particular order of activation of the neural network configuration (plan or program) among the several that partake of the same stored structures.

The process involved is perhaps made most readily understandable by recounting one of Warren McCulloch's favorite analogies. Military organizations have employed two essentially different types of organization. One common type is characterized by a pyramidal system of communication and control. Communication goes up; decisions are made at the apex and handed back down for execution. The second type is of interest here. Navies have used it to a considerable extent since the Battle of Jutland. Organization is pyramidal much as in the first type. In this case, the pyramid is made of a system of rules rather than decisions, initiated at the top and communicated down. In addition, communication is allowed to take place horizontally. Any input to the organization is therefore transmitted in all directions. Wherever the input intersects a rule, a decision node is formed and this node takes command of the organization. For example: a rule, known to all members of the organization, states that when 100 or more enemy planes are sighted, the fleet is to withdraw; that 99 or fewer planes are to be attacked. The seaman who spots, counts, and immediately communicates (e.g., to the ship's radio operator) information about the strength of an enemy squadron has to all intents and purposes temporary command of the fleet until that squadron is engaged or disengaged. A node of decision—a dominant focus—has temporarily been embodied in that seaman and his immediate communicants.

According to this scheme, *choice* is determined by the interaction of sets of learned (and inherited) constraints on the randomness of neural activity with current inputs from the environment. These inputs must be sufficiently similar to the constraints to engage them, yet be dissimilar enough so as to be distinguishable as uniquely current, i.e., *novel*. Where these novel inputs and the systems of constraints, e.g., the memory structure, intersect, they form temporary *patterns of dominant foci*. These patterns, in turn, determine which of the systems of constraints is activated. While a pattern of such dominant foci is being formed, *active uncertainty exists*—in man this active uncertainty is expressed as *thought*. Once such a pattern of dominant foci has activated the system of constraints, the *record of experience* is augmented both by *biochemical change* and by *glially directed fiber growth*. Storage and accessibility, thus both assured, ready the organism for new novelties, further thoughtful uncertainties and the experienced wit to choose.

The brain, as more and more experimenters find, is truly made to accomplish what it must, behavior being what it is.

Acknowledgments

My thanks to James Schoonard and Allan Jacobsen whose unpublished reviews on electroshock and worm-running were of great help in preparing the manuscript; to the discussants of the academic lecture—especially Theodore Lidz, whose incisive comments sharpened the presentation considerably; to Mrs. Marilyn Johnson for typing and Mrs. Phyllis Ellis for supervision of the preparation of the paper. Dr. Jack H. Mendelsohn kindly supplied Figure VI–3.

References

1. ADEY, W. R., "Studies of Hippocampal Mechanisms in Learning," in UNESCO Symposium, *Brain Mechanisms and Learning*, Blackwell Scientific Publications, Oxford, 1961.

2. BARTLETT, F. C., *Remembering*, Cambridge University Press, Cambridge, Eng., 1932.

3. BRADY, J. V., "The Effect of Electroconvulsive Shock on a Conditioned Emotional Response: The Permanence of the Effect," *J. comp. physiol. Psychol.*, 41:507–511, 1951.

4. BRATTGÅRD, S., "The Importance of Adequate Stimulation for the Chemical Composition of Retinal Ganglion Cells During Early Post-Natal Development," *Acta Radiol.*, Suppl. 96, 1952.

5. BRATTGÅRD, S. and HYDÉN, H., "The Composition of the Nerve Cell Studied With New Methods," *Int. Rev. Cytol.* 3:455, 1954.

6. CONEL, J. LEROY, *The Postnatal Development of the Human Cerebral Cortex*, vols. I–IV, Harvard University Press, Cambridge, 1939–1959.

7. COONS, E. C. and MILLER, N. E., "Conflict vs. Consolidation of Memory Traces to Explain 'Retrograde Amnesia' Produced by ECS," *J. comp. physiol. Psychol.*, 53:524–531, 1960.

8. CORNING, W. C. and JOHN, E. R., "The Effects of Ribonuclease on Retention of Conditioned Response in Regenerated Planarian," *Science, 134*: 1363–1365, 1961.

9. DUNCAN, C. P., "The Retroactive Effect of Electro-Shock on Learning," *J. comp. physiol. Psychol.*, 42:32–44, 1949.

10. FREUD, S., "Project for a Scientific Psychology," Appendix in *The Origins of Psycho-Analysis. Letters to Wilhelm Fliess, Drafts and Notes—1887–1902.* Basic Books, New York, 1954, pp. 390–391.

11. *Ibid.*, pp. 359–360.

12. GALAMBOS, R., SHEATZ, G., and VERNIER, V. G., "Electrophysiological Correlates of a Conditioned Response in Cats," *Science, 123*:376–377, 1956.

13. HAYS, K. J., "Cognitive and Emotional Effect of Electroconvulsive Shock in Rats," *J. comp. physiol. Psychol.*, 41:40–61, 1948.

14. HENRY, C. and PRIBRAM, K. H., "Effect of Aluminum Hydroxide Cream Implantation in Cortex of Monkey on EEG and Behavior Performance," *Electroenceph. clin. Neurophysiol.*, 6:693, 1954.

15. HERNÁNDEZ-PEÓN, R., SCHERRER, H., and JOUVET, M., "Modification of Electric Activity in Cochlear Nucleus During 'Attention' in Unanesthetized Cats," *Science, 123*:331–332, 1956.

16. HORN, GABRIEL, "Electrical Activity of the Cerebral Cortex of Unanesthetized Cat During Attentive Behavior," *Brain*, 83:57–76, 1960.

17. HYDÉN, H., "Biochemical Aspects of Brain Activity," in FARBER, S. M. and WILSON, R. H., *Symposium, Man and Civilization: Control of the Mind*, McGraw-Hill, New York, 1961.

18. HYDÉN, H., "The Neuron," in BRACHET, J. and MIRSKY, A. E. (eds.), *The Cell*, Academic Press, vol. IV, Chap. 5:215–323, New York and London, 1961.

19. HYDÉN, H. and PIGON, A., "A Cytophysiological Study of the Functional Relationship Between Oligodendroglial Cells and Nerve Cells of Deiters' Nucleus," *J. Neurochem.*, 6:57–72, August 1960.

20. JOHN, E. R., "High Nervous Functions: Brain Function and Learning," *Ann. Rev. Physiol.*, 12:451–484, 1961.

21. JOHN, E. R. and KILLAM, K. F., "Electrophysiological Correlates of Differential Approach-Avoidance Conditioning in Cats," *J. nerv. ment. Dis.*, 131:183–201, 1960.

22. KRAFT, MARCIA S., OBRIST, W. D., and PRIBRAM, K. H., "The Effect of Irritative Lesions of the Striate Cortex on Learning of Visual Discriminations in Monkeys," *J. comp. physiol. Psychol.*, 53:17–22, 1960.

23. LASHLEY, K., "The Effect of Strychnine and Caffeine Upon Rate of Learning," *Psychobiol.*, 1:141–170, 1917.

24. LIBERMAN, R., "Retinal Cholinesterase and Glycolysis in Rats Raised in Darkness," *Science*, 135:372–373, 1962.

25. LIVINGSTON, R. B., "Central Control of Afferent Activity," in JASPER, H. H. *et al.* (eds.), *Reticular Formation of the Brain*, Chap. 7:177–186, Little, Brown & Co., Boston, 1958.

26. MADSEN, M. C. and McGAUGH, J. L., "The Effect of ECS on One-Trial Avoidance Learning," *J. comp. physiol. Psychol.*, 54:522–523, 1961.

27. McCONNELL, J. O., JACOBSON, A. L., and KIMBLE, D. P., "The Effects of Regeneration Upon Retention of a Conditioned Response in the Planarian, *J. comp. physiol. Psychol.*, 52:1–5, 1959.

28. McGAUGH, J. L. and PETRINOVICH, L., "The Effect of Strychnine Sulphate on Maze-Learning," *Amer. J. Psychol.*, 72:99–102, 1959.

29. McGAUGH, J. L., "Facilitative and Disruptive Effects of Strychnine Sulphate on Maze-Learning," *Psychol. Rep.*, 8:99–104, 1961.

30. McGAUGH, J. L., WESTBROOK, W., and BURT, G., "Strain Differences in the Facilitative Effects of 5–7–Diphenyl–1–3 Diazadamantan–6–1 (1757 I.S.) on Maze Learning," *J. comp. physiol. Psychol.* In Press.

31. MORRELL, F., "Lasting Changes in Synaptic Organization Produced by Continuous Neural Bombardment," in UNESCO Symposium, *Brain Mechanisms and Learning, Montevideo, 1959*, Blackwell Scientific Publications, Oxford, 1961, pp. 375–392.

32. MORRELL, F., "Effect of Anodal Polarization on the Firing Pattern of Single Cortical Cells," in FURNESS, F. N. (ed.), *Pavlovian Conference on Higher Nervous Activity, Ann. N.Y. Acad. Sci.*, 813–1198, 1961.

33. PAGE, J., "Studies in Electrically Induced Convulsions in Animals," *J. comp. physiol. Psychol., 31*:181–191, 1941.

34. PEARLMAN, C. A., JR., SHARPLESS, S. K., and JARVIK, M. E., "Retrograde Amnesia Produced by Anesthetic and Convulsant Agents," *J. comp. physiol. Psychol., 54*:109–112, 1961.

35. POSCHEL, B. P. H., "Proactive and Retroactive Effects of Electroconvulsive Shock on Approach-Avoidance Conflict," *J. comp. physiol. Psychol., 50*:392–396, 1957.

36. PRIBRAM, K. H., "Some Aspects of Experimental Psychosurgery: The Effect of Scarring Frontal Cortex on Complex Behavior," *Surg. Forum Neurosurg., 36*:315–318, 1951.

37. PRIBRAM, K. H., "The Intrinsic Systems of the Forebrain: An Alternative to the Concept of Cortical Association Areas," in FIELD, J. (ed.), *Handbook of Physiology: Section of Neurophysiology*, vol. II, American Physiological Society, Washington, D.C., 1960, Chap. LIV, pp. 1323–1344.

38. RASCH, E., SWIFT, H., RIESEN, A. H., and CHOW, K. L., "Altered Structure and Composition of Retinal Cells in Dark-Reared Mammals," *Exp. Cell Res., 25*:348–363, 1961.

39. ROSE, J. E., MALIS, L. I., and BAKER, C. P., "Neural Growth in the Cerebral Cortex After Lesions Produced by Mono-Energetic Deuterons," in ROSENBLITH, W. A. (ed.), *Sensory Communication*, Cambridge, Mass., The M.I.T. Press, 1961, Chap. 16, pp. 279–301.

40. RUSINOV, V. S., "Electrophysiological Research in the Dominant Area in the Higher Parts of the Central Nervous System," *Abstracts, XX int. physiol. Congr. Brussels*, 1956, pp. 785–786.

41. SHARPLESS, S. and JASPER, H., "Habituation of the Arousal Reaction," *Brain, 79*:655–680, 1956.

42. SIEGEL, P. S., "The Effect of Electroshock Convulsions in the Acquisition of a Simple Running Response in the Rat," *J. comp. physiol. Psychol., 36*:61–65, 1943.

43. SOKOLOV, E. N., "Neuronal Models and the Orienting Reflex," in BRAZIER, M. A. B. (ed.), *The Central Nervous System and Behavior*, Trans. Third Conference, Josiah Macy, Jr. Foundation, New York, 1960, pp. 187–276.

44. STAMM, J. S., "Electrical Stimulation of Frontal Cortex in Monkeys During Learning of an Alternation Task," *J. Neurophysiol., 24*:414–426, 1961.

45. STAMM, J. S. and PRIBRAM, K. H., "Effects of Epileptogenic Lesions in Frontal Cortex on Learning and Retention in Monkeys," *J. Neurophysiol., 23*:552–563, 1960.

46. STAMM, J. S. and PRIBRAM, K. H., "Effects of Epileptogenic Lesions in Inferotemporal Cortex on Learning and Retention in Monkeys," *J. comp. physiol. Psychol.*, 54:614–618, 1961.

47. STAMM, J. S. and WARREN, ANN, "Learning and Retention by Monkeys with Epileptogenic Implants in Posterior Parietal Cortex," *Epilepsia*, 2:229–242, 1961.

48. UKHTOMSKI, A. A., "Novoe y Refleksologie i Fiziologii Nervnoisystemy," [Concerning the Condition of Excitation in Dominance], *Psychol. Abstr.*, 2:3–15, 1926.

49. VON FOERSTER, H., *Das Gedächtnis*, Franz Deuticke, Wien, 1948.

50. WEISKRANTZ, L., "Sensory Deprivation and the Cat's Optic Nervous System," *Nature, Lond.*, 181:1047–1050, 1958.

51. WIDROW, B. and HOFF, M. E., *Adaptive Switching Circuits*, Stanford Electronics Laboratories, Stanford University, 1960.

Part *Two*

NEUROPHARMA-
COLOGICAL ASPECTS

VII

Quantitative EEG in Human Psychopharmacology: Drug Patterns

Max Fink

Recent interest in psychopharmacological agents has produced various classifications based on behavioral, biochemical, neurophysiological, and animal behavioral criteria. Symptom criteria as hallucinogenic, antianxiety, and antidepressant; energetic models as psychoinhibitors and psychoactivators; biochemical criteria as MAO-inhibition, noradrenalin releasing, and antiserotonin; and animal neurophysiological models, as arousal inhibition and arousal facilitation, provide poor definitions and lack clear relationships to the human behavioral effects of compounds. These models neither provide a theoretic framework for understanding or predicting drug action nor facilitate communication and classification.

On theoretical bases discussed earlier, it seems probable that the newer psychotropic agents are clinically potent to the extent that they directly alter human brain function.[3, 5, 7] Indeed, one characteristic of these agents is their ready access to the central nervous system, as reflected by prominent sensorial, motor, and mood-modifying effects, early and extensive changes in language behavior, and electrographic effects. These central nervous system effects provide the basis for a classification and study of psychotropic compounds.

In electrographic studies of mescaline and morphine in drug addiction, Wikler earlier had proposed a general theory of the relation of

Aided by grants M–927, MY–2092 and MY–2715 of National Institute of Mental Health, United States Public Health Service. This study was done at the Department of Experimental Psychiatry, Hillside Hospital, New York.

EEG changes to behavioral changes in man.[31] He suggested that "regardless of the nature of the drug administered, shifts in the pattern of the electroencephalogram in the direction of desynchronization occurred in association with anxiety, hallucinations, fantasies, illusions, or tremors, and in the direction of synchronization with euphoria, relaxation, and drowsiness." Other reports have reviewed various studies relating EEG changes and drug effects in relation to this and other hypotheses[10] and the application of frequency analyzer methods to the problem.[9] The present report summarizes our studies, which amplify the hypothesis presented by Wikler and suggest a number of applications for quantitative electroencephalography including an electrographic basis for the classification of psychotropic compounds.[4, 6, 7, 8, 10, 16]

Methods

The subjects were consecutive referrals for convulsive or drug therapy in a 200-bed voluntary, in-patient psychiatric facility. Patients varied in age between 17 and 65 years, with a mean age of 25 years. The syndromes of schizophrenia, severe psychoneuroses, manic-depressive and involutional depressive illnesses were most common.[19, 20] Posttraumatic states, organic psychoses, and problems of childhood, alcoholism, and drug addiction were specifically excluded. Drug therapy and electroshock therapy were available on referral to the experimental psychiatric unit only.

On referral, after the baseline electroencephalogram had been obtained, various compounds were injected in varying concentrations and at fixed rates per minute until clinical behavioral or electrographic changes were observed; and EEG samples taken until the EEG and behavioral patterns returned to preinjection levels. Occasionally, compounds were given orally in a single dose in the same setting. EEG recording techniques followed those of Strauss et al.[28]

Within a few days, each patient began a clinical regimen of drugs or convulsive therapy. Over the years, the choice of drugs and dosages varied according to the studies then in progress. At set intervals during and after cessation of treatment, EEG records were repeated. The various drugs used in intravenous and chronic oral studies are listed in Table VII–1.

The technical problems of defining and quantifying the electrographic and the behavioral changes were significant obstacles in these studies. The EEG was found to be easily recordable and a sensitive and quantifiable index of brain function in studies of the human convulsive therapy process.[11] With psychotropic drugs, the resting scalp-recorded EEG was again found to be a sensitive index and easily recorded, but the electrographic changes were small, and the descriptive and visual-hand measurements were awkward, permitting quantification only with difficulty. Electronic frequency analysis was examined as a quantification technique and was found suitable. The descriptions to follow reflect, therefore, three techniques of EEG

Table VII-1   *Drugs and Dosages*

GENERIC NAME	REGISTERED NAME	DAILY ORAL DOSE	SINGLE IV DOSE
		(milligrams)	(milligrams)
1. amobarbital	Amytal	250–1000	250–700
2. amphetamine	Dexedrine	5.0–15.0	2.5–5.0
3. atropine	—	—	0.5–4.0
4. azacyclonal	Frenquel	—	50–100
5. benactyzine	Suavitil	2–4	2.0–5.0
6. chlorpromazine	Thorazine	300–3600	5–25
7. deanol	Deaner	—	10–50
8. diethazine	Diparcol	—	175–250
9. imipramine	Tofranil	100–300	30–100
10. iproniazid	Marsilid	20–50	10–20
11. JB–318	*	—	1.0–4.0
12. JB–329	Ditran	—	1.0–2.5
13. JB–336	**	—	1.0–4.0
14. LSD–25	Delysid	0.02–0.10	0.01–0.05
15. methyl, ethyl glutarimide	Megimide	—	10–50 cc.
16. mepazine	Pacatal	100–300	—
17. meprobamate	Miltown	400–2000	—
18. methamphetamine	Methedrine	—	5–20
19. perphenazine	Trilafon	8–48	—
20. phenyltoloxamine	Bristamin	—	25–200
21. pipradrol	Meritran	4–8	—
22. procyclidine	Kemadrin	5–15	2.5–10
23. promazine	Sparine	300–1200	50
24. reserpine	Serpasil	2–10	5–10
25. thiopental	Pentothal	—	250–500
26. triflupromazine	Vesprin	20–60	10–20
27. WIN–2299	***	—	2.0–5.0

* n-ethyl–3-piperidylbenzilate
** n-methyl–3-piperidylbenzilate
*** 2–diethylaminoethyl cyclopentyl (2–thienyl) glycolate

analysis: visual description, visual-hand measurement, and electronic frequency analyses.

Visual descriptions include estimates of predominant rhythms, frequencies, symmetry, and special wave forms (as spike-wave, delta or theta paroxysms); and the effect of eye-opening and closure, and of

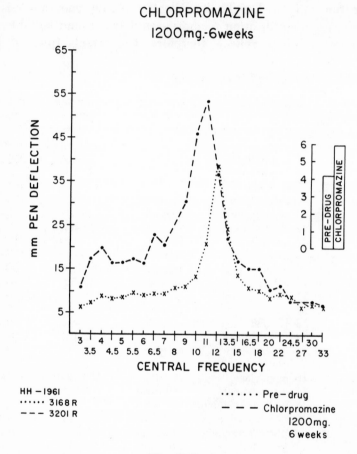

Fig. VII—1.

hyperventilation (180 sec.). Visual-hand measurements include the percentage time and central frequency of various bands and the average voltage for the record.[11]

The electronic frequency analysis consists of the measurement of the mean millimeters of pen deflection for each of 24 frequencies from 3 to 33 c./sec. for each of six 10-sec. epochs, by means of a

Ulett-Loeffel modification[29] of the Grey Walter instrument. The figures are then represented graphically as a spectrum (Figure VII–1) or combined to give numerical values to the abundance of various frequencies.*

Behavioral measurements in psychiatric research are even more awkward and difficult to quantify. During these studies, various techniques of behavioral assessment have been tried. In acute intravenous studies, changes in symptoms, mood, ideation, and language behavior[4, 21, 36] were recorded by the staff psychiatrist. In chronic studies, behavioral evaluations were recorded as changes in interview, ward, and self-rating behavior and in improvement estimates based on interviews with the patient, staff psychiatrists, and nurses. Ratings were based on psychiatric interview notes and various rating scales including the Malamud-Sands, Lorr and Clyde Mood Scales. Behavioral changes were also evaluated as changes in psychological task performance by using various perceptual, cognitive, and motor tests. Ratings were usually made at the height of the drug effect (short-term evaluation) and again at hospital discharge. Diagnoses were also based on hospital discharge classification. In our investigations, ratings of "behavioral change" are nonevaluative statements that measurable alterations have occurred, while "improvement" ratings are value judgments that these changes were "better" or "worse" in the context of the patient's adaptive behavior.[12]

Observations

EEG PATTERN CHANGES

The changes in the resting EEG induced by psychotropic drugs can be classified as the changes in frequency pattern, in abundance, and in the appearance of new wave forms and rhythms. These electrographic changes occur singly or in combination, giving variety to the observed electrographic patterns. The patterns are also dependent on electrode placement, population characteristics, dosage and route of drug administration, and the initial electrographic patterns. For example, the observed EEG changes vary depending upon whether the initial record is one of high abundance with high percentage time

---

* For this report, the recommended terminology of the International Federation for Electroencephalography will be followed.[1] In this terminology, "abundance" is the term recommended for total activity; and increase or attenuation in abundance are similar to the earlier terms of "synchronization" and "desynchronization."

alpha; or attenuated of low voltage and with considerable theta activity; or a record with high-voltage slow-wave activity as seen in postconvulsive states. These pretreatment variations make the range of manifest changes even broader. *The following descriptions are generalized summations of the drug-associated electrographic phenomena in which both the individual variability among subjects and the differences in pattern induced by dosage and route of administration have been minimized to provide a reasonable overview of the data.*

Shift in Dominant Frequency. An alteration in dominant frequencies is the principal measurable electrographic change. The appearance or increase in percentage time slow-wave activity and a slowing by 1 c./sec. or more of central alpha frequencies are prominent with phenothiazines. These patterns are seen with chlorpromazine, both on chronic oral and acute intravenous administration; and with per-

EFFECT OF CHRONIC ORAL ADMINISTRATION OF CHLORPROMAZINE
(22 YR. OLD FEMALE)
(1200 mg. CHLORPROMAZINE , 15 mg. PROCYCLIDINE DAILY)

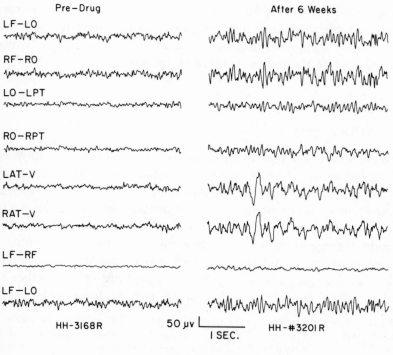

Fig. VII—2.

phenazine, triflupromazine, fluphenazine, promazine, and reserpine. With these compounds there is also a diminution in the percentage time of beta activity (Figure VII–2). The graphic analyzer spectrum for these records is seen in Figure VII–1.

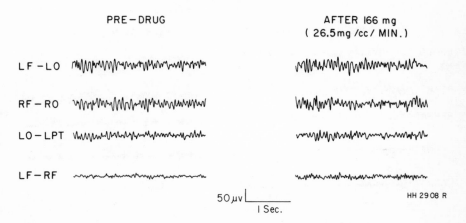

EFFECT OF INTRAVENOUS AMOBARBITAL
(59 YRS., FEMALE, F.L.)

PRE – DRUG   AFTER 166 mg
                              (26.5mg /cc/ MIN.)

LF – LO

RF – RO

LO – LPT

LF – RF

50 μv
1 Sec.

HH 29 08 R

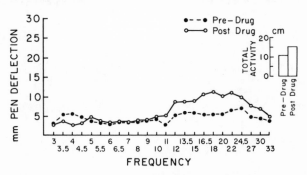

FREQUENCY – SPECTRUM – LEFT FRONTAL – RIGHT FRONTAL

Fig. VII—3.

An increase in percentage time beta activity is seen in a heterogeneous group of compounds—amphetamine, methamphetamine, epinephrine, meprobamate, barbiturates, various anesthetic agents, and imipramine (Figure VII–3). (The electrographic differences between these compounds appear in variations in abundance.)

In patients with postconvulsive slowing, an increase in the amount of slowing is seen after phenothiazines, barbiturates, and meprobamate; and a decrease with experimental hallucinogenic drugs including central anticholinergic agents, LSD, and mescaline; diphenhydramine, amphetamine, and imipramine (Figures VII—4 and VII—5).

EFFECT OF INTRAVENOUS AMOBARBITAL ON EEG SLOWING
PRE-TREATMENT AND POST-CONVULSIVE
(25 YRS., FEMALE, P.C.)

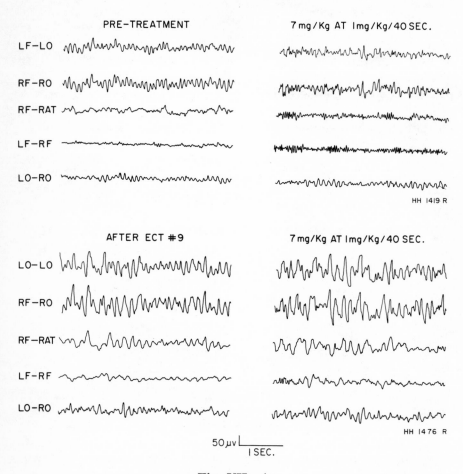

Fig. VII—4.

Change in Abundance. The principal agent that induces increased electrographic abundance (synchronization) is repeated convulsions (ECT).[11] Phenothiazines, iproniazid, meprobamate, and barbiturates in clinical dosage ranges are associated with increased amounts of electrographic activity (Figure VII—6). In higher dosage ranges, and in subjects with high percentage time alpha activity, phenothiazines and barbiturates are associated with a decrease in abundance in conjunction with their characteristic changes in frequency patterns.

A decrease in abundance is also prominent with LSD, mescaline, psilocybin, diphenhydramine, and a group of anticholinergic compounds including benactyzine, diethazine, and experimental compounds WIN–2299, JB–329 (Ditran), JB–318 and JB–336. The

EFFECT OF IV LSD ON EEG DELTA
(FEMALE, AGE 44 - 24 HOUR POST CONVULSION #9)

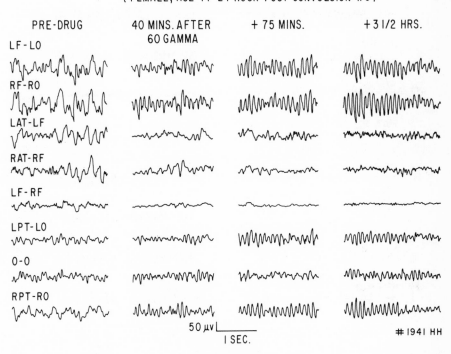

Fig. VII—5.

desynchronization process is prominent in records prior to convulsive therapy (Figure VII—7) but is more readily seen in subjects with post-convulsive slow-wave rhythms and paroxysms (Figure VII—5).

New Wave Forms. High-voltage slow-wave activity in paroxysmal patterns follows induced convulsions, phenothiazines, especially promazine, sernyl, and such seizure-inducing agents as Metrazol, megimide,[16] and NP–274. With the latter compounds, spike and slow waves are also prominent (Figure VII—8). Beta rhythms and spindling are seen with barbiturates and less prominently with meprobamate.

Not all suggested psychotropic compounds, however, have demonstrable electrographic effects by these techniques. Of presumed psychotropic compounds the following demonstrated no effects in clinical

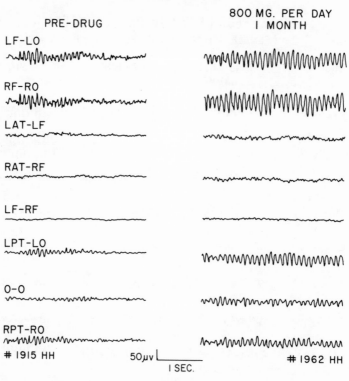

EFFECT OF ORAL CHLORPROMAZINE
(FEMALE, AGE 34)

PRE-DRUG   800 MG. PER DAY
                                        I MONTH

LF-LO

RF-RO

LAT-LF

RAT-RF

LF-RF

LPT-LO

O-O

RPT-RO

1915 HH   50 μv   # 1962 HH
                              I SEC.

Fig. VII—6.

dosage ranges: deanol and congeners (Deaner), pipradrol (Meratran), mepazine (Pacatal), azacyclonal (Frenquel) and phenyltoloxamine (Bristamin).

SIGNIFICANCE OF EEG PATTERN CHANGE

These descriptions are of changes in the visual and electronic frequency records, and one must inquire as to their retest reliability and the extent to which the changes may be fortuitous. In these descriptions, the changes are those seen when subjects receiving drugs are compared to control groups receiving either placebo or a known active compound under similar conditions.

For example, in a recent study the six-week administration of imipramine, of a chlorpromazine-procyclidine mixture, and of placebo were compared. Utilizing frequency analyzer methods, we noted a high degree of stability for each frequency band except theta in the placebo group in our initial analyses.[9, 10] The final covariant analysis

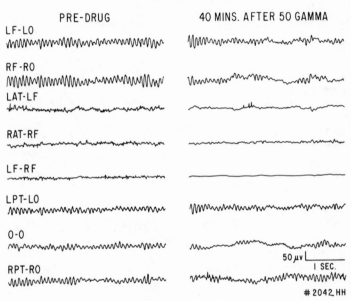

Fig. VII—7.

for our total population indicated significant increases in the abundance of delta and theta activity with chlorpromazine and an increase in beta and a decrease in alpha activity with imipramine. Then changes were reflected in significant F ratios for the means for all bands except 13.5–20 c./sec., significant t-tests for delta and theta for chlorpromazine, and alpha and higher fast frequencies for imipramine.[10]

BEHAVIORAL PATTERNS

In the earlier studies of convulsive therapy, we noted that behavioral change was dependent upon the development of high-voltage slow-wave activity. The principal behavioral effects associated with EEG slowing were sedation, tranquillization, and euphoria in agitated, depressed subjects; and a decrease in somatization, paranoid ideation, hallucinations, and delusions in schizophrenic and excited subjects. Increasing agitation, paranoid ideation, and panic were observed in less than 10 per cent of the subjects.[12]

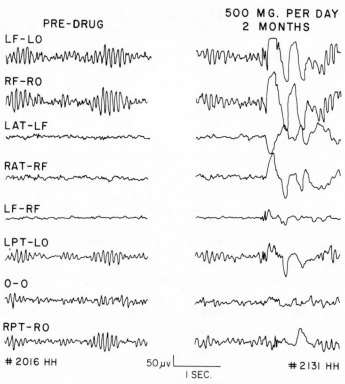

Fig. VII—8.

Administration of chlorpromazine, promazine, and triflupromazine in acute experiments to patients with a variety of psychopathological states was generally associated with sedation, increased drowsiness, denial, and euphoria, decreased agitation, panic, excitement, and delusional activity, and the minimization and displacement of symptoms. Sedation, euphoria, denial, and minimization were similarly associated with amobarbital.

The acute administration of imipramine was associated with an increase in agitation, tension, and nausea, followed by relaxation and drowsiness. On chronic imipramine administration in depressed, sleepless, and retarded subjects, there was a decrease in depression and an increase in well-being, sleeping, ward participation, and activity. In young schizophrenic subjects, however, there was an increase in excitement, ideational distortion, and behavioral disorganization.

On administration of amphetamine and methamphetamine, there was an increase in excitement, tension, verbalization, and motor activity. In addition to these patterns, illusory sensations, hallucinations, and delusional and paranoid ideation were observed with LSD–25 and experimental anticholinergic compounds benactyzine, diethazine, WIN–2299, JB–318, and JB–336.

LINGUISTIC PATTERNS

While these behavioral patterns are descriptive of the type of changes seen on drug administration, we sought more quantifiable measures in language behavior. One method is syntactic content analyses.[21, 30] In convulsive therapy, we analyzed the verbal responses of subjects to a structured questionnaire after the administration of intravenous amobarbital by this method. Consistent changes in tense, person, use of clichés, and cryptic remarks, and expressions of denial, displacement, evasion, and minimization[21] were observed. A second type of analysis is that of verbal diversification. In this measure, the ratio of the number of different words to the total number of words in pooled samples of the speech of patient and therapist in unstructured interviews is the index of diversity of speech. With this measure, the dyadic speech manifested a significant reduction in diversification with increased stereotypy and repetitiveness during convulsive therapy.[18]

Following acute administration, amobarbital and chlorpromazine were associated with a decreased variability of words (more repetitive speech) and with an increase in the variability of consecutive scores. These changes are similar to those seen after induced convulsions. Diethazine, benactyzine, and LSD, however, induced a greater variability in words (less repetitive speech) with a decreased variability in consecutive scores.[14]

Syntactic language pattern analyses demonstrated concurrent changes. Chlorpromazine exhibited an increase in such syntactic changes as the use of displacement and clichés, alteration in tense, and evasive responses; while benactyzine, LSD, and diethazine exhibited a decrease in these symptoms.

The language indices thus provided quantification of the behavioral changes with the drugs, and were seen as reflective of neurophysiological change.[14]

Discussion

At the recent international conference on EEG and Human Psychopharmacology two questions were asked of the participants[9a]:

1. Are there any consistent electrographic patterns following acute and chronic administration of psychopharmacological agents in man?
2. What is the significance of the EEG patterns for the behavioral changes induced by these agents in psychiatric patients?

It was concluded by the participants, and it seems clear from these data, that there are, indeed, recordable electrographic changes with psychotropic drugs in man. This alone is of interest, for these investigators agreed that not only do changes occur, but also that the techniques for measurement are available. The descriptive, hand measurement and electronic frequency analytic techniques described here are a beginning. These techniques have been applied in resting records primarily, but by simple "activating" techniques it is possible to broaden the range of measurable electrographic patterns. The electrographic responses to such simple procedures as eye-opening, hyperventilation, sleep, and visual flicker are significantly enhanced or inhibited by drugs. For example, a decreased abundance of frequencies in initial trials of eye-opening is commonly observed during routine EEG recording. Prior administration of phenothiazines will inhibit this change, while diethazine will enhance it. The slowing in frequency, increase in abundance and in paroxysmal activity seen with hyperventilation, can be augmented by induced convulsions[11] and barbiturates[25] and inhibited by amphetamine, LSD, and diethazine.[8]

The detailed study of the electrographic response to intravenous test agents provides another activation measure. The pentothal index studies of Goldman[15] and of Itil[17] and the sedation threshold described by Shagass[26] are examples. Each worker has shown that prior administration of psychotropic compounds alters the EEG effects of the injected test agent. Other indices of electrographic change may lie in applications of averaging cortical evoked potentials to visual flicker or ulnar nerve stimulation[27] or auto- and cross-correlation measures by means of recently developed computer techniques. Studies of each of these activation techniques with psychotropic drugs have just begun, however, and more data are needed.

BEHAVIORAL RELATIONS

The second question—that of the behavioral significance of these observations—is unanswered. In part, this reflects a paucity of adequate human studies. Many clinical reports indicate that electroencephalograms were recorded during drug therapy and occasionally even with pretreatment baseline recordings. While the behavioral observations in these studies are usually well defined, the EEG data are sparse or described ambiguously as "within normal limits" or with changes "due to drowsiness" and "of little significance." In contrast, studies with the special techniques of implanted electrodes in freely moving animals, intracerebral microinjections, intraventricular drug administrations, and *cerveau isolé* preparations are elaborate in electrographic detail but present limited meaningful behavioral data. Also, the authors' alacrity to generalize beyond the species under study, to make undue assumptions of equivalent physiological responses in animals and man, and to use anthropomorphic behavioral scales have confused rather than clarified the issues involved.

The studies reported here provide the basis for a more sanguine view. The data indicate that Wikler's hypothesis is tenable. Administration of active psychotropic drugs has elicited measurable electrographic effects, while behaviorally inactive compounds have not elicited measurable effects. Compounds that develop increased EEG slowing with or without increased abundance are clinically associated with tranquillization, sedation, and decreased psychotic ideation; while a decrease in abundance and an increase in irregular beta activities is associated with increased excitement, motor restlessness, and psychotic ideation. In these studies, when electrographic changes are definable, the behavioral changes are measurable.

Is one to expect a univariate relationship between electrographic change and behavioral change as implied in this discussion? Within the limitations of the group data reported here, such relationships are observable and provide a basis for drug classification. However, in this exposition, we have minimized the differences in psychiatric populations and the individual differences among subjects. The behavioral manifestations on drug administration are indeed dependent on the central neurophysiological effects reflected in the EEG, but they are also dependent on pretreatment behavioral and personality repertoires of subjects, the environmental setting, and observer and subject expectations.[3] This aspect of the neurophysiological-behavioral interrelationships is commonly disregarded in univariate studies.

We attempted to correlate these behavioral and neurophysiological factors in our studies of convulsive therapy. The variables of brain change, psychological factors, and environmental tolerance were equally complex and were encompassed in a neurophysiologic-adaptive formulation.[3] A "single" central neurophysiological change, varying in intensity and duration, was reflected in the similarity of the electrographic patterns among a wide range of subjects. A variety of behavioral patterns were described, however, and these were clearly related to pretreatment personality and adaptive patterns.[12, 13] The more common behavioral manifestations of euphoria, denial, minimization of symptoms and "clinical improvement" were seen in patients with pretreatment depressive affect, agitation, insomnia, withdrawal, a minimal education, and a high degree of denial and stereotypy. In patients with clinical anger, aggressivity, and agitation, the behavioral pattern of increasing panic, excitement, withdrawal, and complaining was seen. These patients exhibited test characteristics of minimal denial, a low degree of stereotypy, and a high degree of imaginativeness.[13] Thus, in a framework of similar electrographic change, the behavioral changes were as much a reflection of the personality and behavioral repertoire of the subject as of the induced neurophysiological change. A similar interrelationship of neurophysiological, personality, and environmental aspects defines the electrographic-behavioral correlations sought in drug therapy, and is also applicable to an understanding of the behavioral changes in spontaneous convulsions[24] and cerebral dysfunction due to mass lesions, trauma, and vascular disease.[30]

BEHAVIORAL TYPOLOGY

Indeed, one may look upon this interrelationship of brain change and behavior not as the basis of a neurophysiological classification, but as a basis for the classification of subjects and populations. By the administration of compounds affecting behavior, it is possible to describe populations having a common electrographic or a common behavioral response or both. The electrographic classifications of Goldman[15] and

Shagass[26] are an example of the former; the behavioral typologies from this laboratory are examples of the second.[12, 22, 23] Further studies with various psychotropic drugs are now in progress, and may amplify the behavioral electrographic relationships implied here.

In the present era when the quantitative tools of biochemistry, cellular biology, and neurophysiology are being applied with increasing frequency to studies of the etiology of schizophrenia and depressive psychoses, there is a need for the identification of homogeneous subpopulations. Phenotypic typologies based on behavioral or electrographic criteria may provide the operational foundations for these basic science studies.[23]

EARLY DRUG SCREENING

These observations lend themselves to two specific applications— that of the screening and classification of new psychotropic compounds and that of human neurohumoral assay. Compounds without electrographic effects in man (regardless of their effects in vitro or in lower species) are ineffective psychopharmaceuticals. Comparison of the human electrographic patterns of a novel agent with the electrographic patterns of known psychotropic compounds provides a basis for specifying the types of behavioral effects and applicable populations expected for these compounds.

Within the limitations of the neurophysiologic-adaptive hypothesis described earlier,[3] it is possible to generalize the findings in these studies. For homogeneous populations selected according to such conventional criteria as diagnosis, age, years of illness, and principal symptoms, compounds may be classified according to their electrographic patterns and compared to one another and to the patterns of induced behaviors. For example, the development of electrographic slowing and increased abundance of slow and alpha frequencies (as with phenothiazines) provides an electrographic standard for compounds which may decrease behavioral excitement and ideational distortion and induce sedation and tremulousness in agitated schizophrenic subjects, or which may decrease depression and apathy and increase ward participation of agitated depressed subjects. It is also possible to show that compounds having novel electrographic patterns or exhibiting electrographic changes in populations not otherwise responsive to drug effects will have novel clinical behavioral effects.

NEUROHUMORAL ASSAY

These electrographic changes are reflective of the altered biochemical equilibrium in the human central nervous system. While animal studies allow the direct mapping of neurohumoral and enzymatic concentrations as well as drug-induced changes at various brain sites, the human data must be conjectural. Since numerous recent hypotheses of psychotropic drug activity have implicated the neurohumors epinephrine, norepinephrine, serotonin, and dopamine, electrographic measures may also be applicable as indices of neurohumoral activity.

In studies of induced convulsions, we indicated that there was a direct relation among the number and frequency of induced convulsions, spinal fluid acetylcholine activity, and the degree and duration of EEG paroxysmal activity. Concomitantly, drugs with potent in vitro anticholinergic activity, like WIN–2299, benactyzine, diethazine, JB–336, JB–318, induced EEG attenuation of abundance (desynchronization); and this electrographic change was associated with behavioral alerting and irritability. On the basis of these data, we suggested that human EEG changes may be viewed as an index of central cholinergic activity.[8]

In present-day paradigms, epinephrine and norepinephrine are seen as competitively oppositional to acetylcholine at central receptor sites. In subjects with postconvulsive paroxysmal activity, these compounds or their precursors have actions on EEG similar to anticholinergic agents. The antihistamine agent, diphenhydramine, and the sympathomimetics, LSD, mescaline, and psylocybin, also have similar electrographic activity. In contrast, cholinesterase inhibitors such as DFP (diisopropyl fluorophosphate) and TEPP (tetraethyl pyrophosphate) induce electrographic spiking and paroxysmal activity in conjunction with increased central acetylcholine activity. Also, the varying dose-related effects of atropine in man as described by Danielopolu[2] and myself are consistent with this view.[8] Thus, the exploration of human electrographic activity as veridical indices of central neurohumoral activity is warranted, as it may provide a useful adjunct to the elaborate biochemical studies in progress.

These studies suggest that quantitative, activated electroencephalography is a potent research tool for human psychopharmacology. As behavioral criteria and indices become more refined, we can anticipate meaningful neurophysiologic-behavioral relationships and theories to develop which should significantly complement the extensive subhuman studies of the past decade.

SUMMARY

This report summarizes data of scalp-recorded resting EEG on acute and chronic administration of various compounds in voluntary psychiatric subjects. The electroencephalograms were measured by visual means, visual-hand measurement, and frequency analysis. Behavioral changes were evaluated in clinical descriptions, rating scales, language measures, and psychological task performance.

The EEG measures demonstrated changes in frequency, abundance, and new wave forms, which varied for drugs and classes of drugs. A range of behavioral changes, varying with the measures employed, were observed. In general such attributes as tranquilization and somnolence were clearly defined with some agents, and excitement, illusory sensations, and anxiety with others.

Compounds with human behavioral effects evinced consistent electrographic changes, while those without consistent behavioral effects evinced no recordable electrographic changes. These relationships were compatible with the hypothesis of Wikler[31] and the neurophysiologic-adaptive view of drug therapies.[3]

Amplification of electrographic measurements by various activation techniques is recommended, as is the application of these observations to problems of screening psychotropic compounds, the delineation and characterization of more homogeneous psychiatric populations, and the biological assay of active neurohumors.

References*

1. BRAZIER, M. A. B. *et al.*, "Preliminary Proposal for an EEG Terminology by the Terminology Committee of the International Federation for Electroencephalography and Clinical Neurophysiology," *Electroenceph. clin. Neurophysiol.*, 13:646–650, 1961.

2. DANIELOPOLU, D., GIURGEA, C., and DROCON, G., "Electroencephalographic Study of the Non-Specific Pharmacodynamics of the Stimulatory Effects of Atropine on the Cerebral Cortex," *Fiziol. Ž., Mosk.*, 41:601–611, 1955.

3. FINK, M., "A Unified Theory of the Action of Physiodynamic Therapies," *J. Hillside Hosp.*, 6:197–206, 1957.

* More extensive bibliographical references may be found in the articles cited in 8, 10, and 11.

4. FINK, M., "Effect of Anticholinergic Agent, Diethazine, on EEG and Behavior: Significance for Theory of Convulsive Therapy," *Arch. Neurol. Psychiat., Chicago, 80*:380–387, 1958.

5. FINK, M., "Alteration of Brain Function in Therapy," in *Psychopharmacology Frontiers,* KLINE, N. (ed.), Little, Brown & Co., Boston, 1959, pp. 325–332.

6. FINK, M., "Electroencephalographic and Behavioral Effects of Tofranil," *Canad. psychiat. Ass. J., 4*:166S–171S, 1959.

7. FINK, M., "EEG and Behavioral Effects of Psychopharmacologic Agents," in *Neuro-Psychopharmacology,* BRADLEY, P. (ed.), Elsevier, Amsterdam, 1960, pp. 441–446.

8. FINK, M., "Effect of Anticholinergic Compounds on Post-Convulsive EEG and Behavior of Psychiatric Patients," *Electroenceph. clin. Neurophysiol., 12*:359–369, 1960.

9. FINK, M., "Quantitative Electroencephalography and Human Psychopharmacology, I: Frequency Spectra and Drug Action," *Medicina Experimentalis, 5*:364–369, 1961.

9a. FINK, M., "EEG and Human Psychopharmacology," *Electroenceph. clin. Neurophysiol., 15*:133–137, 1963.

10. FINK, M. and KAHN, R. L., "Quantitative EEG and Human Psychopharmacology, III: Changes on Acute and Chronic Administration of Chlorpromazine, Imipramine and Placebo (Saline)," in WILSON, W. P. and ULETT, G. A. (eds.), *Applications of EEG to Psychiatry,* Amer. Psychiat. Ass. Regional Research Conference, Durham, 1962 (In press).

11. FINK, M. and KAHN, R. L., "Relation of EEG Delta Activity to Behavioral Response in Electroshock: Quantitative Serial Studies," *Arch. Neurol. Psychiat., Chicago, 78*:516–525, 1957.

12. FINK, M. and KAHN, R. L., "Behavioral Patterns in Convulsive Therapy," *Arch. gen. Psychiat., 5*:30–36, 1961.

13. FINK, M., KAHN, R. L., and POLLACK, M., "Psychological Factors Affecting Individual Differences in Behavioral Response to Convulsive Therapy," *J. nerv. ment. Dis., 128*:243–248, 1959.

14. FINK, M., JAFFE, J., and KAHN, R. L., "Drug Induced Changes in Interview Patterns," in SARWER-FONER, J. (ed.), *The Dynamics of Psychiatric Drug Therapy,* Charles C Thomas, Springfield, Ill., 1960.

15. GOLDMAN, D., "Specific Electroencephalographic Changes With Pentothal Activation in Psychotic States," *Electroenceph. clin. Neurophysiol., 11*:657–667, 1959.

16. GREEN, M. and FINK, M., "Clinical and Electroencephalographic Effects of Megimide in Patients without Cerebral Disease," *Neurology, 8*:682–685, 1958.

17. ITIL, T., "Die Veränderungen der Pentothal-Reaktion im Elektroencephalogramm bei Psychosen unter der Behandlung mit psychotropen Drogen," *Electroenceph. clin. Neurophysiol., 15,* 1963 (in press).

18. JAFFE, J., FINK, M., and KAHN, R. L., "Changes in Verbal Transactions with Induced Altered Brain Function," *J. nerv. ment. Dis., 130*:235–239, 1960.

19. KAHN, R. L., POLLACK, M., and FINK, M., "Social Factors in Selection of Therapy in a Voluntary Mental Hospital," *J. Hillside Hosp., 6*:216–228, 1957.

20. KAHN, R. L., POLLACK, M., and FINK, M., "Sociopsychologic Aspects of Psychiatric Treatment in a Voluntary Mental Hospital: Duration of Hospitalization, Discharge Ratings and Diagnosis," *Arch. gen. Psychiat., 1*:565–574, 1959.

21. KAHN, R. L. and FINK, M., "Changes in Language During Electroshock Therapy," in HOCH, P. and ZUBIN, J. (eds.), *Psychopathology of Communication,* Grune & Stratton, New York, 1958, pp. 126–139.

22. KLEIN, D. F. and FINK, M., "Psychiatric Reaction Patterns to Imipramine (Tofranil)," *Amer. J. Psychiat., 119*:432–438, 1962.

23. KLEIN, D. F. and FINK, M., "Behavioral Reaction Patterns with Phenothiazines," *Arch. gen. Psychiat., 7*:449–459, 1962.

24. LANDOLT, H., "Serial EEG Investigations During Psychotic Episodes in Epileptic Patients and During Schizophrenic Attacks," in DEHAAS, A. M. L. (ed.), *Lectures in Epilepsy,* Elsevier, Amsterdam, 1958, Chap. 3.

25. ROTH, M., "Changes in the EEG Under Barbiturate Anesthesia Produced by Electro-Convulsive Treatment and their Significance for the Theory of ECT Action," *Electroenceph. clin. Neurophysiol., 3*:261–280, 1951.

26. SHAGASS, C. and JONES, A. L., "A Neurophysiological Test for Psychiatric Diagnoses: Results in 750 Patients," *Amer. J. Psychiat., 114*:1002–1009, 1958.

27. SHAGASS, C. and SCHWARTZ, M., "Evoked Cortical Potentials and Sensation in Man." *J. Neuropsychiat., 2*:262–270, 1961.

28. STRAUSS, H., OSTOW, M., and GREENSTEIN, L., *Diagnostic Electroencephalography,* Grune & Stratton, New York, 1952.

29. ULETT, G. A. and LOEFFEL, R. G., "A New Resonator-Integrator Unit for the Automatic Brain Wave Analyzer," *Electroenceph. clin. Neurophysiol., 5*:113–115, 1953.

30. WEINSTEIN, E. A. and KAHN, R. L., *Denial of Illness: Symbolic and Physiological Aspects,* Charles C Thomas, Springfield, Ill., 1955.

31. WIKLER, A., "Clinical and Electroencephalographic Studies on the Effects of Mescaline, n-Allylnor-morphine and Morphine in Man," *J. nerv. ment. Dis., 120*:157–175, 1954.

VIII

Brain Amines, Electrical Activity, and Behavior

Daniel X. Freedman
Nicholas J. Giarman

Introduction

Current interest in the relationship of amines to neural function and behavior stems from a confluence of a number of approaches—pharmaceutical, clinical, basic research, theoretical—all grouped under the somewhat awkward rubric of "neuropsychopharmacology." The intent of this paper is not to present an exhaustive review of the existing literature but rather to bring into at least dim focus the basis for some of the ongoing research and to orient the nonspecialist to some of the conceptual pitfalls, methodologic problems, and substantive gaps which can be encountered in these areas. Major emphasis will be placed upon serotonin (5–hydroxytryptamine, or 5–HT) since among the amines of current interest (catechol amines, histamine, acetylcholine, γ-aminobutyric acid, and related compounds) this indolealkylamine has been extensively studied in our laboratories.

Questions concerning the role and function of amines have been generated from three different but related standpoints. The broadest of these seeks to delineate the relationship of neurochemical states to the organization of patterns and sequences of physiological and behavioral functions. Pathophysiology constitutes a second basis; i.e., the causal or contributory relationship of altered brain chemistry to the clinically encountered states (e.g., the epilepsies, mental retardations, and psychoses). From basic and clinical pharmacology come questions concerning the way in which drugs may induce alterations

Supported in part by grants MY–3363 and MH–18,566 from the National Institute of Mental Health, United States Public Health Service.

198

in amine metabolism and thus alter a prior behavioral or physiological state.

Currently, we are in a phase of "mapping out" critical parameters and mechanisms in order to discern the nature of amine systems in brain. The business of modelmaking, of establishing a systematic neuropsychopharmacology, has only just begun.[33, 35] In terms of general theory, we still lack sufficiently *specified* models detailing how it is that biochemical change *could* become behaviorally manifest. Even for a single drug-induced psychosis, we lack *empirically* based postulates which could establish criteria for correlating biochemical states with *particular* organizations of psychological functions. We do not appreciate the extent to which a particular behavioral sequence is invariably or contingently induced or sustained by biochemical change, nor have we identified those general *classes* of behavioral processes which could be relevant to neural, physiological, and chemical states. In the dimensions of time, mass, and kinetics, we must assess the orders of magnitude which could be relevant. Are we to deal with molar or molecular levels, with milliseconds and millimicrograms, or with hours and milligrams; with local brain changes or general metabolic changes, or, if with both, at what phases of a biochemical or behavioral sequence do we intervene and measure?

Given these gaps, there is no paucity of theory or explanatory schemata. Indeed, the relatively rapid development of empirical findings has not kept pace with kaleidoscopically shifting theory, and, while experts are bewildered and neophytes enlightened, operationally derived data are easily lost from view. Pharmacologists are accustomed to sifting out operationally derived data from the web of conceptual schemata linking such data so that confusion beyond normally tolerable limits results from the misapplication of theory in this field where there is a recognized urgency to pioneer breakthroughs. There is, in fact, a "metapharmacology" which is useful in launching research and bridging gaps in knowledge but which sometimes becomes too entrancing to yield to available data. The arbitrary selection of data for theory construction is quite a different matter from the use of theory to arbitrate the validity of empirical findings.

ROLE OF AMINES

It is possible to understand developments in amine research in terms of empirically established data and to locate where in current thinking and writing assumptions have to be made for convenience. A few facts have emerged with clarity. Amines are remarkably potent biological materials, synthesized within the organism, and in millimicrogram amounts capable of influencing the operation of different physiological, chemical, and behavioral systems. Research has not yet yielded definitive answers as to the neurohumoral role of these substances. Psychoactive drugs have been shown to influence amine metabolism, but the ultimate relationship of such facts to neural and behavioral function is not known. Detailed and sufficiently dovetailed systematic knowledge of the mode of action of amines and drugs at a number of levels relevant to neural function or behavior is simply lacking.

PROBLEMS IN EVALUATION

The task of evaluating the role of amines is formidable partly because of the technical problems in measuring and identifying them in micro quantities. Progress has been so rapid that many laboratories will currently be found to be using a variety of different methods. Essentially there are two different methods for measuring amines once they have been specifically extracted and separated: fluorescence spectrometry[160] and the bioassay[2, 36, 57, 62, 159, 163] which utilizes a number of different responses in vivo or test organs in vitro. Some confusion in the literature may be attributed to the fact that in different laboratories the detailed steps of either procedure are differently executed. Another technical source of difficulty may arise from the hard fact of laboratory life, i.e., a procedure generally has to be run a number of times by the same hands in any one laboratory for reliable results. Variations in sensitivity of the instruments in the case of fluorescence spectrometry or in sensitivity of the biological organ with the bioassay also present a problem. Biological sources of variability with either procedure account for the fact that values for normal levels of amines vary; they vary with species and with strains within species, perhaps with age, sex, and diurnal and seasonal cycle.[1, 96] Recent evidence indicates that some of this variability may be referable to the rat's state of activation and adaptation in response to stress and extremes of temperature.[37, 44, 45, 61, 103]

A number of considerations are necessary to interpret natural or drug-induced variations in amine levels. Species differences are practically important when amine response to neuroactive drugs is studied; dose-response data in man, however, should not be used as an arbitrary criterion for assessing the relevance of inferences from animal data concerning the mechanism of action of the amines. Whatever dose of a drug elicits the desired neural or amine response in a particular species is the relevant dose for study. Man is generally more sensitive than other species to drugs which shift levels of amines, but the basis for this sensitivity is not at all clear. The explanation for dose differences or differences in level of amines among species is rarely sought, but in some instances the lack or presence of specific enzymes seems clearly accountable; other factors may be the ease of access or rate of transport of a substance to critical sites. Where there is a similarity in amine metabolism across species, the relationship of a similar biochemical mechanism to particular physiological or behavioral effects will depend upon the intra- and intercellular, as well as the psychosocial, milieu in which that mechanism operates.

Without dose-effect curves for any one particular response, the relevance of data may be hard to assess. It could almost be said that one is dealing with a different drug after critical dosage increments; not only the range of responses but the accountable mechanisms may be greatly changed with dose changes. The route of administration of a drug, the vehicle in which it is suspended, the rate of administration (and hence the rate of change of activity at receptor sites), the sequence of administrations, and the prior state of the receptor system are all pharmacological parameters which profoundly influence drug action.[38] Finally, interpretations of experiments based on operations in vitro depend upon appreciation of physiological levels of the amine as well as pharmacological and toxicological levels. Because of the newly recognized importance of the compartmentalization of cell machinery, it is essential to bear in mind that the role of amines in structure-integrated function may have quite different characteristics than if deductions are derived solely from preparations of isolated elements in vitro.

Brain Amines

In mammals, the amines are derived from dietary amino acids and are formed by synthesis in several steps at various sites in the body. The biological activity that can be described for any one amine is extensive. The catecholamines, for example, play some role in nerve transmission at peripheral synapses, at specific neuromuscular junctions in smooth and cardiac muscle, in the intrinsic neural plexuses of smooth muscle, as well as in baro- and chemoreceptors. They also have activity in the metabolism which influences cellular membranes and intracellular structures. Serotonin was chemically identified in 1948.[132] While it has been less extensively studied than the catechol amines, a number of smooth muscle actions, a role in biosynthesis,[8] and a metabolic effect[108, 109] have already been demonstrated.

Less than 5 per cent of dietary tryptophan is hydroxylated to 5–hydroxytryptophan (5–HTP), which is then decarboxylated in various organs including brain to 5-hydroxytryptamine or serotinin. The same decarboxylase is also involved in the synthesis of norepinephrine (NE).

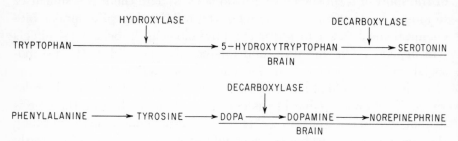

Platelets "take up" serotonin by an active transport and store it; no specific physiological function is known for serotonin in platelets, which seem to be carriers for the stored amine in blood. Isolated slices of brain do not appear to have a system for the active transport of serotonin.[142, 143] This is manifest in the whole animal by the poor ability of serotonin to cross the blood-brain barrier. The precursor of serotonin (5–HTP) has been shown to be actively transported into slices of rat brain; similarly, in the whole animal, 5–HTP is easily transported across the blood-brain barrier. Within discrete areas of brain, serotonin is rapidly synthesized from the precursor and stored. This cerebral serotonin represents less than 1 per cent of the total amine within the body. The amine is "handled" rapidly by brain as demonstrated by the calculated half life of 10–30 minutes. This "handling" has been assumed to involve the liberation or release of serotonin from its intracellular storage sites upon "physiological need"; the amine is believed then to become available to specific receptor sites and also available to destruction by the enzyme, monoamine oxidase (MAO). The oxidative deamination of serotonin (through an unstable aldehyde) to 5-hydroxy indole acetic acid (5–HIAA) is the major but not the sole degradative pathway.

Unlike the amine and the synthesizing enzyme, MAO is ubiquitously distributed in brain. This pattern of general distribution and the rather nonspecific substrate requirement of MAO (senotonin, dopamine, norepinephrine, epinephrine are all destroyed by it) leads to the speculation that its function is one of keeping amine levels within an optimum physiological range and that it therefore has a general protective function. While this function is considered by some to be similar to that proposed for cholinesterase with respect to acetylcholine levels, the mechanism for maintaining levels of acetycholine within physiological limits seems to be more efficient. This can be observed when MAO is inhibited by a number of drugs; a three- to fivefold increase in norepinephrine and serotonin ensues, whereas when cholinesterase in the brain is completely inactivated it is uncommon to find more than a twofold increase in levels of acetylcholine.

Serotonin in the brain is presumably associated with neural elements. Dorman and Giarman[31] failed to find serotonin or associated enzymes in freshly excised human astrocytoma or in glioma cells maintained in tissue culture; nor were Freedman and Picard-Ami[52] able to find measurable amounts of serotonin in human spinal fluid following the chronic administration of MAO inhibitors or the ingestion for five days of 1–3 g. daily of tryptophan.[139] Table VIII—1 shows the regional distribution of serotonin in the brain of man, monkey, and dog.[34, 53, 70, 120] The amine is low in neocortical regions, whereas the nuclei and cortex of limbic structures and the brain stem are areas with high amine

Table VIII-1 *Serotonin in Brain Regions (Mean Values, mμg./g., and Rank Order)*

	HUMAN PSYCHOTIC (N = 11)		MONKEY (N = 17)		DOG (N = 6)	
	Mean HT*	Rank	Mean HT	Rank	Mean HT	Rank
Amygdala	145	6	147	4	384	4
Septal Region	54	9	77	8	126	9
Hippocampus	56	8	27	9	165	8
Caudate	152	5	152	5	222	7
Thalamus	61	7	107	7	231	6
Hypothalamus	273	4	197	3	660	2
Midbrain (Central Gray)	482	2	289	2	544	3
Medulla (Reticulum)	425	3	132	6	294	5
Pineal Body	3,140	1	3,280	1	—	—

*HT = Serotonin. Data compiled from studies by Freedman, Picard-Ami, and Giarman[53, 70, 120] and Fisher.[34]

levels. High levels are found in the spinal cord.[2a, 12] The pineal body stands out as the neural region containing the highest levels in man and monkey; these levels approach those found in peripheral tissues such as the intestinal tract.[70] Axelrod and Weissbach[8] have shown that the pineal body contains the enzymes necessary for the conversion of serotonin to melatonin, a skin-lightening hormone for which we found no pyschoactive effects;[51] synthetic derivatives of melatonin, however, were shown to be psychoactive[114] and the 6-hydroxymetabolite of melatonin might be expected to be psychotomimetic. Two other richly vascular areas of the brain—the area postrema and the intercolumnar tubercle—are relatively high in serotonin; part of all of the amine in these regions could conceivably be delivered by way of the blood, although the pineal does have the decarboxylase for synthesizing serotonin *in situ.*[69] This pattern of distribution for serotonin is quite similar to that described for catechol amines in brain[9, 20] with the notable exception of the corpus striatum, which lacks both serotonin and norepinephrine but shows very high levels of the norepinephrine precursor, dopamine (3-hydroxytyramine); studies of this amine in Parkinsonism (where urinary levels are changed) and in extrapyramidal drug action will be of great interest.[89] The distribution of these amines and acetylcholine is not as closely correlated. While MAO is generally distributed throughout the brain,[20] the distribution of the synthesizing enzyme roughly correlates with the distribution of the amines; exceptions are the area postrema where the decarboxylase is lacking, and sympathetic ganglia where it is present but the amine is not stored.[55]

The storage form of all of the amines in brain as well as other structures is now generally accepted to be one in which the amine is bound to elements within subcellular granules; this is true for histamine, acetylcholine, the catechol amines, and serotonin. The amine-containing granules in brain have not as yet been elegantly described by electron microscopy, but they are believed to be smaller and less dense than mitochondrial particles. Whittaker[172] found both serotonin and acetylcholine present in granular fractions which contain, in addition, pinched-off nerve endings. The localization of noradrenalin in similar subcellular fractions has been reported.[117] The extent of this binding with respect to serotonin in brain may be seen from the studies of Giarman and Schanberg[72] who found 70 per cent of the serotonin in homogenates of rat brain to be associated with the particulate fraction. The subcellular localization of amines in such fractions suggests an integral role for particulate entities in the uptake, storage, and release of amines.

Given this newly emerging picture—that the biologically active substances are differentially distributed among subcellular elements—it is likely that drug effects as well as physiological effects may be reflected in select areas of brain by changes in distribution among the subcellular pools not only of one but of the related amines. This is indeed a new universe for study, in which the techniques of electron microscopy, differential centrifugation, density gradient distribution, microanalytical assays of amines and studies of energy characteristics of these particulates will be emerging.

Methods for Manipulating Amine Mechanisms

TRANSPORT OF PRECURSOR

There are a number of pharmacological tools available for shifting levels of serotonin in the whole brain and various sites and mechanisms at which such agents act. The precursor of serotonin is actively transported into the brain, which means that there is an energy-yielding enzyme system involved. It is therefore likely that drugs or structural analogues may be found which could interfere with this enzyme system and thereby deprive the brain of the precursor for serotonin. Schanberg[141] has recently shown that a number of naturally occurring amino acids such as phenylalanine, tyrosine, leucine, and tryptophan have this ability to compete with 5–hydroxytryptophan for transport into brain slices. McKean *et al.*[115] in these laboratories concluded that the net effect of high circulating levels of these amino acids *in the animal* is a reduction in the amount of 5–hydroxytryptophan which arrives in brain and therefore a fall in the level of serotonin. A number of potent neuroactive drugs have been tested for their ability to interfere with this uptake system, but as yet none has been found. We do not know whether or not the synthesis and/or storage of 5–HTP can occur in brain.

SYNTHESIS OF AMINE

There has been interest in finding an agent which could inhibit the next step, i.e., the enzyme which synthesizes serotonin from the precursor. The only currently known drug potent in this respect is alpha methyl dopa (alpha-methyldihydroxyphenylalanine). After administration of this drug, brain levels of both serotonin and nor-epinephrine are reduced. It is now known that this effect is attributable not only to interference with synthesis but also to the ability of the compound to cause a release, which leads to the depletion of the amines. This is an instance, frequently encountered, of the multiple actions of a single drug. Insulin coma, among other effects, inhibits the enzyme and depletes norepinephrine in brain.[22] Thyroxin, perhaps through general metabolic or pyretogenic effects of the hormone, evokes an increase in levels of serotonin, while no effect is seen with thyroidectomy[130] (or hypophysectomy[45] or adrenalectomy[107]). Pyridoxal is believed to be a cofactor for the enzyme, and pyridoxal-deficient animals demonstrate a reduced 5–HTP decarboxylase activity.[169] There is no known agent which induces (or "desuppresses") the decarboxylase or, in effect, changes the kinetic characteristics of this enzyme.

One of the most frequently used tools in pharmacological, behavioral, and EEG studies is 5–HTP. Since in the synthesis of serotonin the supply of precursor is the rate-limiting factor, pretreatment with 5–HTP leads to increased levels of amine. While pretreatment with 5–HTP raises amine levels appreciably, the subcellular distribution of serotonin is not that found under normal circumstances. It cannot be assumed that such pretreatment unmasks the effects of normal levels of amine (by exaggerating them) nor that effects of such pretreatment depend solely upon an excess of "free" amine, since the consequences to cellular function of changed concentrations and intracellular distributions are conceivably important.

"RELEASE" OF AMINE

Reserpine is one of the most fascinating drugs related to the pharmacology of the amines. This agent is used as a "releaser" of amines which is reflected by a gradual fall in the total amine level in the brain and other cells following drug administration; dosage requirements for amine depletion in brain and periphery differ. Studies in platelets indicate that this action is a complex one. There is inability of platelets to take up the amine from the environment by active transport[87] as well as inability of platelets to hold the endogenous amine within their lipoid barriers. Release, then, refers to kinetic processes and reflects the balance between uptake and holding capacity; the reciprocal of release, in this sense, is storage. The mechanism of reserpine-induced release or impairment of storage capacity is not known.

Platelets are limited as a model system for events in the complete cell; they lack, e.g., enzymes for synthesis or destruction of amines. It is conceivable that, within the cell, at the granular surface, there is an active transport of the amine; thus, the precursor is actively transported across the cell membrane and the amine is synthesized in extragranular compartments and then may be actively transported into granules. This would be effected by energy-yielding enzyme systems, so-called amine pump mechanisms; it has been speculated that these, as well as intracellular binding sites, constitute the loci of reserpine action.

The substances to which the amine is complexed or held are, in pharmacological terms, receptors: i.e., components of the substructure which are the sites of chemical or physicochemical interaction of the drug or agent in question. Such sites may have direct physiological consequence ("active receptors"), or they may constitute a sequence prior to the physiological effect. The receptor substance to which the amine is held (by as yet unknown binding forces) is believed to be ATP in the platelet and heparin in the mast cell. It is unknown in brain and other cells; mucopolysaccharides in brain may serve as amine-binding substances.[75] The identification of such receptor substances and transport mechanisms is a crucial and unsolved problem in the pharmacology of brain amines.

The picture, in summary, would be of an energy-yielding system transporting the precursor into the nerve cell; an extragranular compartment in which the amine is synthesized, transport systems for the amine into compartments or receptors, and various binding forces holding the amine at these sites. Finally, some release process from storage sites to sites of activity or inactivation occurs as a part of this dynamic equilibrium. Inactivation which occurs largely by MAO must involve some factors governing the accessibility of the substrate to the enzyme which is believed to be largely held within the mitochondria.

An effect of reserpine in releasing serotonin is reflected in the fact that the particulate fraction of brain homogenates normally constituting 70 per cent of the amine shows the greatest relative decrease.[72] The action of reserpine is fairly nonspecific since levels of both serotonin and norepinephrine are lowered. More puzzling is the fact that the drug is not detectable by sensitive assay with fluorescence spectrometry 24 hours following administration, but a single dose shows effects which, in the human, are detectable for four to five weeks, and several doses may show effects on amine levels for months.[46] Even if minute amounts of drug remained within the body, the dose necessary to induce depletion and the quantity necessary to maintain it are remarkably discrepant. This long-lasting effect of a single dose has been described as a "hit and run" effect; i.e., there is a persistent change in the status of receptor substances. Rates of repletion of amines in brain following reserpine vary according to species and dose,[82] perhaps in the human according to body size and weight;[27] while depletion is fairly uniform throughout brain regions, rates of repletion of serotonin or norepinephrine may be found to differ.[147] Factors governing repletion rates have not been investigated, but a single dose of LSD–25 shows an effect upon the level of repleted brain amines which is measurable only four days later, at a time when rates of endogenous repletion may be more rapid than depletion.[36, 37] Various periods or phases of drug-induced neurochemical change may, therefore, have to be described in order to correlate behavioral and EEG effects following pharmacological manipulation of amine mechanisms.[37, 39]

SELECTIVE RELEASE

A more discrete and rapidly dissipated effect upon amine levels is obtained with alpha methylmetatyrosine (MMT) which (through its decarboxylation product) releases norepinephrine specifically and not serotonin.[85] Agents which reduce serotonin levels but not norepinephrine are unknown. Syrosingopine reportedly depletes NE peripherally, but not centrally. Tetrabenazine, a synthetic benzquinolizine derivative which has reserpinelike effects on behavior, leads to a release of serotonin and, to a somewhat greater degree, of norepinephrine, these levels returning to normal in 24 hours.[83, 131] A closely related agent, benzquinamide, has similar behavioral effects at doses which do not induce measurable changes in total amine level.[3, 127] Morphine depletes levels of brain norepinephrine (until tolerance appears),[113] but not serotonin, and this, presumably, is a releasing effect.[147] A change in level could be arrived at by various means. One must be prepared to study other mechanisms—transport, synthesis, and destruction—and especially their kinetics in order to differentiate drugs on the basis of mechanisms rather than simply on the extent and direction of change of total levels.

These agents can be employed (if diligent caution is used to ground one's assumptions in pharmacological fact) to test various hypotheses concerning the relationship of amines, and mechanisms governing them, to a particular effect. It is popular to guess: what do the amines mean? Agents such as these listed are often used to divine the discrete role of serotonin in brain physiology as distinct from norepinephrine. This exercise requires rather adroit metapharmacological footwork. It does seem to be established that lowered levels of amines are accompanied by a crudely defined sedation; among Rauwolfia derivatives only those which markedly lower serotonin lead to this "sedated" picture; with the exception of benzquinamide, the fact that brain levels of acetylcholine rise after reserpine[124] may, among other considerations, force a more refined psychobiological definition of sedation induced by amine-depletion and that induced by other means. Similarly, patterns of excited behavior can be associated with drug-induced increases in NE levels, but these are not without exception.[22]

BLOCKING RELEASE

It is theoretically possible to find agents which would "reverse" the effects of releasing drugs; reserpine could be used to uncover such actions. Some inhibitors of MAO, such as iproniazid, were shown to resist the releasing action of reserpine in a number of systems, e.g., platelets, guinea pig atria,[125] and the particulate fraction of whole brain homogenates.[72] This inhibition of the releasing action of reserpine by MAO inhibitors and antidepressants[159] indicates that such agents have more than one action and more than one site of action. It also reinforces the conception of an equilibrium sustained by a number of mechanisms and processes which can be manipulated at various sites by various means. Obviously the critically important manipulation is nature's, and here we are in utter ignorance as to what normally regulates this balance. Because we know little about physiological occasions (*vide infra*) or means for release (or blockade of release) we cannot assert that deductions based on pharmacological manipulations apply in the context of the physiological organization of the amines and their neurobehavioral interactions.

INHIBITION OF DESTRUCTION

Inhibitors of MAO, frequently employed to raise levels of amines, differ in potency and ease of reversibility. The effects of the "irreversible" agents on amines are long-lasting and seem to be the most efficacious in clinical practice. In the dog and cat, brain serotonin is elevated, but norepinephrine is not; the animals are not excited in response to these inhibitors. In the rat and rabbit, on the other hand, both norepinephrine and serotonin are elevated, and the rabbit is "excited" following MAO inhibition. The dog and cat have an alternate pathway for the metabolism of norepinephrine, catechol-O-methyltransferase (COMT), described by Axelrod et al.[7] Norepinephrine can therefore be degraded in cat and dog and this may account for the failure to observe elevation of the amine in these animals, whereas the enzyme is not active in the brain of the rabbit. It is believed that in man COMT is important in the peripheral but not central metabolism of norepinephrine.[6] Some MAO inhibitors are structurally similar to sympathomimetic amines, and they exert both an aminelike action as well as inhibition of MAO (e.g., "Parnate," tranylcypromine).[176] Thus direct actions of the drug, the long-lasting inhibition of MAO after the drug is discontinued, species-differential enzymatic activity, and differential rates of amine response may provide tools for study of effects on EEG and behavior. Reserpine-sedation reportedly can be promptly reversed with tranylcypromine, which also induces a prompt (four hours postdrug) rise in the previously depleted level of amines and also has aminelike actions.[76] This picture is not obtained with iproniazid, perhaps because of the prolonged time course for onset of effects on amine levels with this drug and perhaps because it lacks amine mimetic effects. Species differences are apparent in the rate of change of amine levels following MAO inhibitors, and differential rates of change of such levels in various regions of brain are described.[22, 25]

The estimate of the extent of MAO inhibition in vivo presents both methodological and interpretative problems. It cannot be assumed that MAO-inhibited preparations sharply reveal the normal action of amines, since among other considerations the enzyme does not seem to be the sole mechanism for terminating the action of amines. In fact, the consequence of MAO inhibition is not an imitation of amine effects. Frequently behavioral or EEG effects appear only when the precursor or other amine is administered,[138] and when this is the case the extent of in vivo inhibition in brain must be determined rather than assumed.

RECEPTOR SITES: BLOCKING AGENTS AND AMINE LEVELS

Blocking agents are known largely from analysis of peripheral systems. A peripheral organ which shows a specific response to the application or endogenous release of an amine is said to have "active receptors" for that amine. These receptors are "blocked" by drugs when the smooth muscle is still reactive to the range of effective stimuli other than the amine. LSD–25 and a number of ergot derivatives block the effects of serotonin on the clam heart, uterus, and other smooth muscles;[2, 57, 171] depending upon dosage, the drugs may imitate effects of HT.[23] The extent to which central effects of antihistamines and adrenergic and cholinergic blocking drugs[123] are comparable to effects of peripheral blocking are not at all clear. Similarities to peripheral mechanisms in terms of direction of effects are evident (*cf.* Gault, this volume), but the whole area of the central mode of action of peripherally characterized autonomic agents stands in need of critical review. There is no a priori reason to assume that an agent which blocks the action of serotonin would change amine levels, yet we consistently find a 30–40 mμg./m. rise in brain serotonin following chlorpromazine (which can block the amine in the periphery[23] and a 80–100 mμg./g. increase in brain levels following LSD–25.[36] Drug-receptor events *in brain* are reflected, in part, by changes in the level and distribution of amines as well as by "end-organ" response.[37]

RECEPTOR SITES: BINDING AND PERMEABILITY

Investigation of LSD–25[36, 37, 39, 40, 49, 144, 151] has led to the description of agents which increase levels by enhancing the binding of serotonin in the particulate fraction of whole brain. Psychotomimetic agents related to LSD–25 (mescaline, ALD, MLD) have a similar effect;[36, 37, 39] the mechanism by which binding is induced is not known. Another mechanism by which pharmacological agents may shift brain levels is through affecting the permeability of cellular and intracellular membrane barriers. Chlorpromazine has been shown to decrease permeability in several test systems,[65, 66] and this may be accountable for the slight rise in whole brain levels. Such membrane changes should be manifest in studies with the electron microscope as well as with pharmacological studies. The mechanism for the small increase seen after sedating agents such as barbiturates[13, 144] and some of the antiepileptic agents[14] is not known; rates of change of binding and release too small and rapid for measurement by current methods may be critical factors. Such changed levels may only partially reflect alterations in underlying mechanisms.[49]

BRAIN AMINES IN MAN

A crucial problem is how to deduce what is occurring in the brain of man following such agents. The problem of drawing inferences across species was discussed above. Peripheral measures of blood, spinal fluid,[139] or urine levels cannot be relied upon to indicate events in brain. For practical reasons, measurements of autopsied and biopsied brain are scarce. Recently, iproniazid, 75–125 mg. daily for three weeks (in patients with terminal carcinoma), was found to double levels of serotonin, norepinephrine, and dopamine and to reduce markedly MAO activity of these brains.[63] Inferences concerning brain events become possible as correlations between changes in level of brain amines, and measurable EEG and autonomic and physiological response become more precise. For example, the miosis following reserpine was shown to be centrally mediated; this has been used to infer the change of brain levels in individual animals and man.[46]

Neurohumoral Role of Serotonin

The pharmacologist's interest in these amines derives from the fact of their high biological activity. His attempts to link structure with function, microevents at the receptor level with observable behavioral response, creates some uncomfortable theoretical problems. He is, as it were, dealing with a pharmacological version of the mind-body problem. The natural recourse in an attempt to link physicochemical actions to bodily response is to search for a neurohumoral action at critical transducer sites, and in the case of neuroactive compounds one such compelling site would be the synapse. A neurohumor may be defined as a diffusable metabolite, presumably of neurons, which may act in one of two ways. One is as a synaptic transmitter substance, and the other is as a substance which modifies the environment in which the transmitter acts. In this latter sense one could refer to a neuroregulatory substance, or to a neuromodulator, and neuromodulator (rather than neurotransmitter) action implies different temporal, physicochemical, and structural sequences.

The evolution of interest in the neurohumoral role of serotonin in brain has been recent and rapid. Between 1954 and 1956 a number of observations and generative hypotheses were advanced concerning the relevance of endogenous amines of brain to behavior. Page *et al.*[157] and Gaddum and Hameed[56] had remarked upon a possible central role of serotonin. Woolley and Shaw[148, 174] noted that the psychotomimetic LSD–25 and congeners were "structurally analogous" to serotonin and that they blocked, imitated, or facilitated the effect of serotonin on various isolated peripheral tissues. They proposed that an "excess or deficiency" of serotonin in brain would account for both drug-induced and clinically encountered mental dysfunction. In effect, an altered (but, in fact, probably unmeasurable) *balance* of the amine *at* the neuroactive receptor was to be etiologically involved. In a short time, some nonpsychotogenic but psychoactive compounds such as reserpine[149] or inhibitors of monoamine oxidase were found to increase or decrease measurable *levels* of amines in *whole* brain. The large decrease in levels induced by reserpine was correlated with a crudely defined sedation; the increases due to the serotonin precursor or MAO inhibitors were correlated with various patterns and levels of excitement. These rather large excesses and deficiencies were measurable in whole brain or regions, not at a synaptic receptor, but changes in whole brain levels became an index for knowledge of microevents at the active synaptic receptor. A canon came to be established whereby the significance of changes in levels could be evaluated prior to data. In terms of measurable processes, we actually know very little even about acetylcholine even at peripheral receptors, but the quanta of acetylcholine required for transmission are minute and are not currently measurable by fluorescence spectrometry. Whether the "excesses or deficiencies" which are critical for *synaptic* response are reflected in measures of excess and deficiency in *whole* organs is not known.

If the relevance of macromeasures to receptor events cannot be known a priori, it is nevertheless convenient to assume that—whatever the tissue level—when an organ responds to an amine, a requisite quantum of amine is available to act upon an available receptor site. That amine is then said to be "free" or available and not "bound." This concept of free and bound amine helps us to bridge the gap between structure and function. There is ample reason in the pharmacology of peripheral organs to make these assumptions, but the terms are not as yet operationally descriptive and do not refer to the physicochemical status of amines nor to the sequence of relevant receptor events. Some of these receptor events may be "silent" with respect to a recordable response (e.g., a muscle contraction). Neuropharmacological study of the brain is undergoing a conceptual wrench similar to that which occurred in neurophysiology when the "on-off" description of the nerve impulse was complemented by the discovery of the graded response.

The question, then, is whether serotonin is a neuromodulator or neurotransmitter agent. Criteria[67] for *implicating* a substance as a neurotransmitter have been advanced. (1) The substance must be discretely distributed in the central nervous system. (2) Enzymatic or other mechanisms for synthesis and destruction and dissipation of the action of a neurotransmitter must be shown, and these mechanisms should be characterized by a high velocity to correlate with the rapidity of synaptic events. Synthesis need not keep pace with demand if storage mechanisms are present. (3) Clearly demonstrable effects should result from a deliberate increase or decrease of effective local concentrations. (4) Physiologically, such changes in local levels and attendant effects should be demonstrated by strategic nerve stimulation. (5) Known blocking agents should produce effects, e.g., blockade of a destructive enzyme should produce amine mimetic effects (and this is not the case with inhibition of MAO). Within the central nervous system acetylcholine fulfills these criteria, including the finding that upon nerve stimulation (or afferent input) it has been recovered from an effluent from certain brain regions.[54a] In terms of rigorous, critical experiments, the synaptic action of acetylcholine is shown only in a peripheral neuromuscular junction.

Serotonin in peripheral systems seems to have a buffer or modulator function with the possible exception of the clam heart, where transmitter function is suggested.[170] In the peristaltic reflex of the gut, the amine facilitates the response of sensory endings in the mucosa to pressure, inhibits the mediating "ganglion," and facilitates the response of serosal muscle.[19] The effect on the gut of different levels of serotonin depends upon the sensory input and balance of effects throughout the intrinsic neural plexus. Similar effects of serotonin in modifying the threshold for stimulation of cardiopulmonary and carotid sinus receptors have been demonstrated. [73, 146] Effects in the superior cervical ganglion have been described as facilitatory, depending upon amount. Small quantities facilitated and large amounts inhibited electrical or acetylcholine-induced transmission. Quantities of the amine in the "physiological range" tend purely to enhance transmission at this cholinergic site.[71] In the case of blood pressure, the effect of serotonin depends upon the prior state and tone.[121, 122] In general, the prior state, the milieu of neurohumors, as well as the quantity and form of serotonin, determine its peripheral effects.

A similar problem of balances, multiple sites, and parameters of input may be involved in central function. There are no data in mammals which show that serotonin in the central nervous system can be recovered in an effluent following physiological stimulation. The appearance of serotonin in the perfusate of the functioning superior cervical ganglion of the intact cat is the first demonstration of the production of serotonin by a functioning neural structure *in situ*, but its appearance was not regulated by preganglionic nerve stimulation.[64] The response of brain serotonin to stimulation of specific neural systems is not known. Small rises in brain serotonin have been reported following electrically induced convulsive seizure,[60] and a lower level of endogenous serotonin has recently been described following lesions in the septum and medial forebrain bundle systems.[84] Serotonin levels increase following severe cold or heat[45, 59, 61, 103] exposure. In response to stress which involves a concentrated period of severe muscular exertion, serotonin levels increase 17–20 per cent and NE levels decrease 20 per cent. As rats show physiological and behavioral recovery from the stress, amine levels return to normal.[37, 45] These latter represent the first evidence of response of these amines to nonpharmacological procedures and indicate that the amines constitute some component of certain conditions of stress.

If there are few concrete data to establish serotonin as a neurotransmitter, the data for neuromodulatory function do seem convincing. When we come to the question of how the amine may lead to physiological effects, we must note the paucity of studies at the basic level at various transducer sites within the neuron and the synapse. An effect of serotonin on the passage of sodium and potassium across membranes has been noted.[126] It is conceivable that the receptors leading to effect, the active receptors, may be located in the postsynaptic neural elements. It is equally possible that they are located within the cell and that shifts in levels and distribution of the amine lead to altered conditions for response of a neuron to stimulation.[36] Such neuromodulator action could be at the postsynaptic membrane, on the soma membrane, or on intracellular membranes ultimately to influence the reactivity of a neuron, its thresholds for firing, recovery cycles, or transmission characteristics. Within the cell, the amine could interact with mechanisms for regulating other amines, acetylcholine systems, and conceivably metabolic systems influencing membranes and ultrastructures within the soma and neurofibrils. Finally, since neurons differ in their biophysical or chemical requirements, it is obvious that considerable work to establish either the transmitter or the modulatory theory remains to be done.

When we actually measure changes in levels of amines, we are measuring effects in a number of complicated processes prior to events at the active synaptic receptor. Many of these can be named but are only beginning to be defined operationally. In speaking of

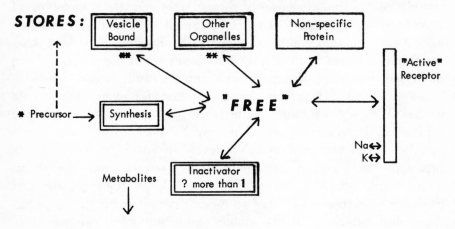

* Precursor is actively transported into cell
** Transport may or may not be a factor

Fig. VIII—1. *Mechanisms governing brain amine levels.*

the significance of changes in levels we have proposed that it may be best to refer to changes in mechanisms regulating the various pools of amines within subcellular compartments of neurons.[49, 68] Total levels, then, will reflect the net result of those processes; and in inferring the mode of action of a drug on endogenous chemicals located in cellular substructures, one should probably anticipate the general rule in pharmacology: that a drug has more than one action and more than one site of action (Figure VIII—1). A drug, then, may influence intra- or intercellular transport of the amine or its precursors; influence accessibility to sites of synthesis, storage, and inactivation; block or induce enzymes, alter physicochemical properties of membranes, ion flux, metabolic processes, or rates of binding and release. Whatever the drug may do, we have little knowledge as yet as to the intrinsic regulators of this traffic, and we certainly lack knowledge of physiological releasers.

EEG and Behavioral Effects

The distribution of the amines and their subcortical sites of action indicate a role in limbic, hypothalamic, and midbrain systems and hence in those physiological adjustments which must be integrated in the service of survival, appetitive needs, and environmental demands. These neural systems bring us physiologically into contact with both the internal and external milieu and appear to mobilize the central and peripheral implements of consciousness (e.g., perception and attention or motor and glandular response[28, 41, 48]). The speculative grouping into functional systems of those central and peripheral activities which conserve (trophotropic) or expend (ergotropic) bodily energies has served to provoke major experiments and generate research problems by Brodie.[18] He has viewed serotonin as a central transmitter for the parasympathetic component of the trophotropic system of Hess and norepinephrine as the transmitter for the sympathetic component of the ergotropic system. The neural organization of a number of commonly encountered states of hyper- or hypoactivation is in fact not known, but it is conceivable that central substructures selectively respond to amines acting as neuromodulators rather than transmitters. Whether the integration of central autonomic and somatic functions can operationally be so neatly divided is not clear. The selectivity of a small area to implanted drugs was shown by Grossman,[77] who found that cholinergic and adrenergic agents in the lateral hypothalamus differentially influenced eating and drinking behavior; there is some question whether these larger generalizations will hold as we come to deal with local components of the sequences which underlie complex behaviors such as eating or drinking, both of which are necessary for survival.

In view of the neural activity of amines, relatively little experimental work on their bioelectrical effects has been compiled. There is no body of work which quite matches the systematic effort of Bradley and Elkes[15, 16] and Key[97] to correlate the regional chemistry of acetylcholine with EEG effects and behavior and to distinguish conditions with psychotropic drugs where EEG and behavioral effects are dissociated. With some exceptions reviewed below (*cf.* Sutin *et al.* and Gault) amines and drugs influencing them have not been imaginatively employed for the study of the electrophysiology of discrete interneural systems and areas. They have not as yet been studied systematically on the axodendritic and axosomatic differentia employed by Grundfest[78, 79] nor applied in more fundamental studies of nerve activity. The combinations of techniques available to neuropharmacologists for the study of neurochemistry and behavior (e.g., EEG and local implantation and specific neurobehavioral systems such as hypothalamic areas for eating and drinking; self-stimulation systems; single cell recording and specific psychophysical systems; the use of computer averaging techniques for evoked potentials) have yet to be extensively explored with respect to the amines. As basic pharmacology compiles more detailed data concerning amine mechanisms, the drugs which influence them, and the temporal characteristics of amine mechanisms, progress can be expected. A number of well-known psychotropic drugs can now be included among those influencing amines so that correlations of neurobehavioral studies with them are possible. Finally, we would anticipate that the impetus for EEG and behavioral studies may be derived not only from some special interest (illumination of a pet meta-pharmacological theory or conceptual nervous system) but also from the sober task of discovering the details of the intrinsic and necessary relatedness of the amine systems, their physiological and behavioral effects.

The effects of serotonin, per se, upon behavior cannot readily be deduced by the exogenous administration of the substance. Effects on peripheral receptors and smooth muscle partially determine the neurophysiological response of brain to exogenously administered serotonin. Whether administration of serotonin is intraventricular, intravenous, or intra-arterial, the effects are generally described to be of a sedative nature. There are too few experiments with intracerebral injection of serotonin to permit critical analysis; excitement has been described in mice.[80] In patients with carcinoid tumor in whom the peripheral production of serotonin is excessive, no particular behavioral effects can be described.[152] When the gamut of manipulations of *endogenous* serotonin is surveyed, correlations with behavior and EEG are, without question, established. At this juncture, the one perhaps insipid generalization which can be safely made is that the amines are related to a number of discrete autonomic effects and to some aspect of behavior along the dimension of sedation and excitement.

EFFECTS ON EVOKED POTENTIALS

Early in the development of this area Marrazzi[110, 111] proposed that an adrenergic transmission mechanism was capable of operating in cat brain. This was based on studies with a transcallosal pathway connecting similar points in the right and left optical cortex. Following intracarotid injections of minute amounts of serotonin (less than 1 μg.) or hallucinogens (LSD–25, mescaline), inhibitions of the evoked potential, ipsilateral to the side of the injection, was observed following electrical stimulation of the opposite cortex. Similar results were obtained by stimulating the visual pathway and recording at the contralateral cortex. Because serotonin was the most potent amine studied, Marrazzi and Hart were led to ascribe an inhibitory transmitter role to it.[112] The interpretation of changes in surface-negative evoked potential with respect to specific synaptic activity remains to be determined.

Koella and co-workers[101, 102] have analyzed extraneural and intracerebral sites at which exogenous serotonin can affect evoked cortical potentials. Presso- and chemoreceptors of carotid sinus constitute one important site; a second set of receptors was inferred to be in the brain stem reticulum (whether in inhibitory or facilitatory systems is yet to be determined). A third site is thought either to be in the synapses in the transcallosal pathway or in special vascular chemoreceptors influencing synaptic function. Intracerebral homeostatic mechanisms, i.e., interneural feedback among neural systems responsive to serotonin, were suggested on the basis of those studies.

Intravenous serotonin was found markedly to reduce hippocampal potentials evoked by electrical stimulation of the amygdala;[133] peripheral receptors were again important in central response since the effect did not occur in bilaterally vagotomized cats. Similarly, when endogenous brain levels of serotonin are increased by administration of the precursor, potentials evoked in the hippocampus of cat[26] or peripherally evoked cortical potentials[105] were reduced, an effect potentiated by iproniazid (increasing serotonin levels) and antagonized by reserpine (which decreases levels). Thus an inhibitory effect of serotonin on these systems seems to prevail; similarly, inhibitory effects are described in the cord.[32]

Thresholds for electrical stimulation of limbic pathways were reduced after precursor-induced elevations of serotonin.[26, 98] The Killams reported that reserpine induced seizures in the amygdala.[99] In the reticular formation an alert pattern is seen after reserpine.[58, 135] Killam has referred to a long-lasting reduction (many months) in thresholds for electrically evoked hippocampal seizures following reserpine depletion of serotonin levels. Electrically evoked seizurelike waves in the amygdala were facilitated and prolonged by reserpine.[150] Studies of thresholds to peripherally or centrally evoked response in a number of structures following manipulation of amine levels and mechanisms would be of interest in view of a finding by Bonnycastle et al.[14] that a number of antiepileptic medications (barbiturates, hydantoins, and oxazolidinediones) increase the level of serotonin in rat brain. In all probability antiepileptic action is not related simply to increased levels[129] since increase produced by other means did not have an anticonvulsant effect. Wada[165] studied effects of altered amine mechanisms in animals in which experimental epilepsy had been induced; procedures which increased serotonin levels in these animals activated EEG abnormalities. This may be an instance of the prior receptor-state changing the expected pharmacological effect. The relevance of amines to threshold changes and seizure activity could be clarified with dose effect studies. There are interactions[158] among amine receptors related to convulsive discharge but the accountable mechanisms are obscure. At this juncture, what is clear is that changes in the level of serotonin in either direction influence the reactivity of limbic and subcortical systems.

EEG AND BEHAVIORAL EFFECTS OF 5-HTP

One of the most interesting methods for inducing an elevation in endogenous brain serotonin is through administering the precursor which should lead to increased levels at all sites where transport for 5–HTP is available and where the synthesizing enzyme is present. Udenfriend and co-workers pioneered this approach [161, 162] and found that brain levels of serotonin were elevated with the precursor. Animals exhibited symptoms similar to those produced by the hallucinogenic drug, LSD-25. In an extensive pharmacological study[11] they described a biphasic effect following 5–HTP. Low doses induced a generally sedated picture. Higher doses lead to a disoriented kind of excitement, accompanied by depressant effects on certain reflexes, motor control, and sensory functions. With high doses they observed fear in dogs, sham rage in cats, excitement and increased spontaneous activity in rodents, later followed by depression. Costa and Himwich[22, 25] found that 5–10 mg. 5–HTP/kg. caused sedation and a tendency to sleep in dogs; 20 mg./kg. led to sedation, panting and extensor rigidity; after 40 mg./kg. a steppage gait and "obstinate aimless progression" was noted, the animals showing indifference to the environment and unresponsiveness to sound and light, exhausting themselves in uncoordinated efforts and manifesting either an expiratory dyspnea or occasional spontaneous orgasms. Increasing the dose of precursor decreases the time during which the initial sedative effects are seen and determines the occurrence of excitatory effects. It is interesting that following injection of any dose of 5–HTP, a period of sedative effects precedes any excitatory effects, both in behavioral and EEG studies. The physiological effects of 5–HTP injections (many of which are central in origin) were mydriasis, piloerection, tachycardia, salivation, lacrimation, retching, vomiting, and increased intestinal motility.

A similar biphasic effect of 5–HTP on EEG has been demonstrated by Costa *et al.*[25] in animals with section of the vagi and denervation of the carotid sinus. With low dosage or in the initial sedative phase following high dosage, hippocampal theta rhythm could not be elicited by peripheral stimulation, and the neocortical EEG pattern showed high-voltage slow waves. When the increase of brain serotonin is maximal following a high dose of 5–HTP, a low-voltage fast activity is seen in cortical leads, and hippocampal activity is characterized by theta rhythms. These effects can be abolished by atropine, but the synchronizing effect of atropine may be an independent effect. Only those animals which had three times the normal brain concentration of serotonin exhibited the desynchronization; dose effects as determined by change of local concentrations in brain were correlated with EEG effects and varied with different routes of administration. The excitability of the reticular formation was found to be depressed after low doses of 5–HTP, while that of the thalamic intralaminar system was enhanced; high doses led to persistent activation in the isolated brain.[118] Much work still remains to be done to clarify the mechanisms of these various effects, but the correlated brain levels and biphasic EEG and behavioral effects are impressive, and the presence of central neural elements which are electrically or physiologically responsive to endogenous serotonin has been demonstrated.

MAO INHIBITORS, EEG, AND BEHAVIOR

The effects of MAO inhibitors on EEG depend on the particular inhibitor as well as species. Drugs such as tranylcypromine produce a marked and prompt rise in brain amines and an associated persistent activation of EEG; in continued dosage, both serotonin and NE are elevated and the EEG is activated. Chronic or acute administration of iproniazid, while leading to increases of amines, does not lead to EEG activation. Pretreatment with iproniazid, however, will enhance the EEG or behavioral effects of injected precursor. With alpha-methyltryptamine (an MAO inhibitor) in the rabbit, EEG alerting and sleep patterns correlated with the rise and fall of brain serotonin.[86] There were two phases of action: an immediate "amphetamine-like alerting" and a delayed activation. Immediate activation was seen with carotid injections following midpontine transection or occlusion of the basilar artery; vertebral injections in these conditions produced the delayed arousal. Thus, depending on the MAO inhibitor, different brain stem sites (rostral and caudal to the midpontine section) and pharmacological mechanisms of effect on EEG can be shown. In general, the behavioral effects following MAO inhibition are unimpressive unless the agent has amine-mimetic properties or a precursor is given, or unless one is testing for the reactivity as well as the spontaneous behavioral activity of an animal.

LSD-25, EEG, AND BEHAVIOR

In the rat, LSD–25 induces effects on brain amines, behavior, and EEG. Five to ten minutes after 130 μg/.kg. of drug, brain serotonin is elevated about 100 mμg./g. (norepinephrine levels begin to drop[37]), and the onset of a 20–40 minute period of no responding is seen in rope-climbing rats[42] or rats pressing a bar for food.[43] The rat assumes a characteristic posture, dragging the hindlimbs in abduction in an "LSD crouch."[81] While Freedman et al.[50] found that no alteration in hippocampal activity could be detected with bipolar recordings, the cortex shows an absence of spindling and spiking and an alert period. The onset of the alert period is similar to the onset of both the crouch and the serotonin effect and persists for a few minutes beyond duration of the crouch. With daily doses, tolerance to the behavioral effects (including the crouch) of LSD–25 is seen. The EEG effects similarly develop tolerance although the time course is somewhat longer than that for the crouch. Tolerance to EEG effects of drugs, to our knowledge, has not hitherto been demonstrated. Here we see a correlation between behavioral and EEG effects. The evidence concerning tolerance to the effect on serotonin levels is not as yet clear; NE levels do tend to show tolerance. With tolerance (decrement of effect contingent upon dosage schedule) a method is provided for the study of the association or dissociation of amine, behavioral, and EEG systems (Figures VIII–2 and VIII–3.)

RESERPINE, EEG, AND BEHAVIOR

Effects of reserpine on EEG behavior are of interest because of the amine-depleting effect of the drug. There is marked variability between species as to the dose-inducing depletion; the dose required for peripheral and central depletion differs, and within any one species there is variability with any given dosage schedule. There are different rates of repletion for central and peripheral structures which have yet to be systematically correlated with shifts in physiological and behavioral effects. By the fourth or fifth day after an effective depleting dose, brain levels in rat begin to show a substantial return toward normal (endogenous mechanisms presumably have begun to regenerate a capacity to bind); by the eighth day levels are often said to be normal although, with the sensitive bioassay, we find that many weeks may actually be required for levels to be fully restored. Many workers have been discouraged from using the drug because of the variability encountered (a generally unpublicized reason) and because the persisting effects of the drug make replication in individuals and crossover designs difficult. On the other hand, the drug permits study of amine-behavior rather than drug-behavior interactions, and analysis of the variability may lead to a clue as to what intrinsic factors regulate the amine pump which reserpine presumably impairs. Correlation of amine-EEG rather than drug-EEG effects may be anticipated, since the periods of interest (those following reserpine-induced change of amines) are becoming better understood.

A convincing demonstration that amine levels in brain are correlated with EEG effects was found by MacLean *et al.*[106] prior to discovery of the depleting effect of reserpine and of the subsequent time course for repletion of brain amines. They showed distinctive EEG changes in the hippocampus and less pronounced changes in the posterior hypothalamus which were restored to normal over a twenty-day

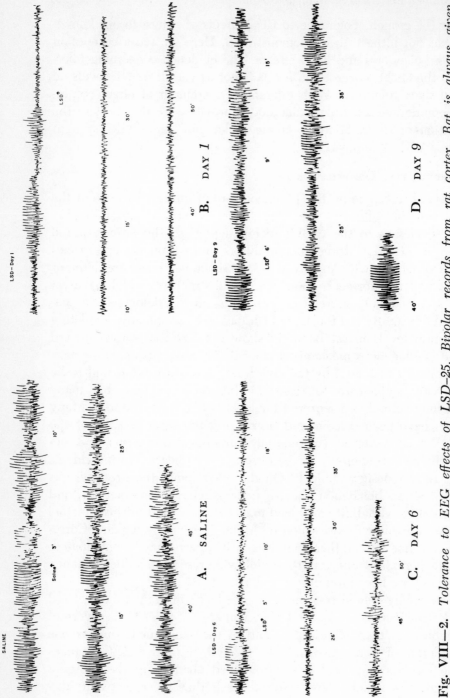

Fig. VIII—2. *Tolerance to EEG effects of LSD-25. Bipolar records from rat cortex. Rat is always given 10 minutes accommodation period in the box and then injected with saline or 130 μg./kg. LSD-25 and recorded at intervals during the hour following injection.*

period, a period which follows the expected repletion rate of serotonin. Similar time-locked changes in excitability of the amygdala and concomitant sedation have been recently observed.[134]

The first phase of reserpine effects has been detailed by Brodie's group,[10] which showed that the miosis, salivation, and lacrimation following reserpine are induced by central stimulation of parasympathetic outflow rather than by diminution of sympathetic activity. Such changes in parasympathetic outflow, however, should not be incontro-

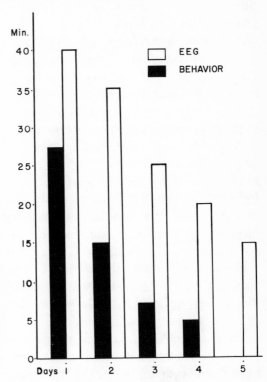

Fig. VIII—3. *Tolerance to behavioral and EEG effects of LSD–25. Duration in minutes of EEG effect and "LSD–25 crouch" are shown. Tolerance occurred in this rat to behavioral effects after four daily doses of 130 μg./kg. and to EEG effects after seven doses. From Freedman, Hartman, and Flynn (unpublished).*

vertibly ascribed to a primary drug effect, since they may well represent a secondary, compensatory response to a primary central effect of reserpine. Two mechanisms are thought to be involved in pupillary response: a direct stimulation of pupilloconstrictor centers causing miosis in the dark and a facilitation of the light reflex which accounts for the prolonged miosis and active ptosis in the light. A central depression of sympathetic outflow apparently is not a consequence of reserpine pretreatment; e.g., electrical activity of preganglionic fibers of the splanchnic[30] or cervical sympathetic nerves[88] is not diminished.

On the other hand, reserpine induces what in effect is a "peripheral sympathectomy"[164] by depleting stores of amines in the adrenal and at many neuroeffector junctions. The adaptation to the effects on gut seen in humans[46] could be both a local and central readjustment of autonomic balance; miosis shows no tolerance,[46] but it is not clear whether other parasympathetic effects do. The parasympathetic syndrome shows an onset which correlates with a fall in brain serotonin; in the human, miosis may be measured for some time after discontinuation of the drug, but miosis does not correlate precisely with repletion rates in blood.[46]

The reserpine-induced psychophysiological state called "sedation" is based on gross observations (the active ptosis and comportment of the animal)[10, 24] of this characteristic parasympathetic syndrome. Effects of the drug have also been studied with various objective measures, including operant conditioning situations.[17, 29] In general, these objective measures show depression of response rate on all schedules tested and, usually, diminished avoidance-behavior in pole jumping and shuttle box studies.[21, 74, 90, 93, 94, 100, 136, 153, 154, 167, 173] When a signal announces a period of unavoidable shock to an animal performing for food, he usually shows physiological signs of fear and ceases to bar-press, and this conditioned emotional response (CER), or conditioned suppression, is diminished with reserpine.[17] The drug does not impair acquisition of the CER in rats,[155] but it may in monkeys.[168] John and Killam describe an effect of reserpine which would make it appear that the brain treats a previously conditioned stimulus as if it were new or novel.[91, 92] There are relatively few studies of the effect of brain amines on habituation to stimuli.[97]

From objective behavioral measures there is evidence of various phases of reserpine-induced effects. Appel et al.[3] in this laboratory have been studying onset, duration, and recovery from the effects of reserpine in a number of operant situations. Ptosis and signs of parasympathetic stimulation were frequently observed prior to any change in objective measures. With the onset of measurable behavioral effects, the ptosis syndrome was almost invariably present but disappeared before recovery from objective behavioral effects. In contrast to drugs such as chlorpromazine and LSD–25, recovery was gradual, usually from three to five days after onset. Thus immediate and subsequent effects following a change in amines are evident, and various "periods" of physiological and behavioral change must be taken into account.

EFFECTS OF ALTERED AMINE MECHANISMS

Environmental contingencies may have different consequences depending upon the particular phase of amine depletion. Levison *et al.*[104] in this laboratory found that, in classical avoidance situations, the rat placed in the box from six to 30 hours following reserpine failed to recover normal avoidance behavior over the following 12 weeks of testing; this was in marked contrast to rats treated with another "tranquillizer," chlorpromazine. If the rat is "rested" and does *not* return to the box for 48–72 hours following the dose of reserpine there is no such prolonged effect on avoidance behavior. Yet at 48–72 hours the actual levels of amines do not significantly differ from those at 30 hours. Apparently there are critical periods during which drug-behavior interactions are crucial for subsequent effects, and neither physiological signs nor level of amines can predict this order of correlation between amines and behavior. The critical period of amine depletion does not cause rats to "forget" to bar-press on other schedules of reinforcement, so that specific factors in the avoidance situation must interact with the central state in order to induce such long-lasting behavioral effects.

Alteration of normal rates of binding and release of the amines by MAO inhibitors and by releasers such as reserpine and tetrabenazine change the chemical, autonomic, and behavioral response to LSD–25.[3, 39] During periods of neurochemical change which are behaviorally "silent" the effect on behavior of a number of agents may be changed. For example, in pigeons, injections of the precursor, 5–HTP, diminished the rate of pecking while iproniazid did not. When MAO was blocked by pretreatment with iproniazid, the effects of 5–HTP were enhanced over weeks, returning to normal roughly with the recovery of brain MAO activity.[5] The correlation here is with the inhibition and recovery of a mechanism governing the amines. The milieu of amine mechanisms in which 5–HTP acts is one determinant of subsequent effects. With MAO inhibition, the administration of methionine or tryptophan leads to behavioral disturbances in schizophrenic patients.[138]

Ninety-six hours after reserpine or iproniazid and in the absence of measurable effects, the effect of threshold doses of LSD–25 on bar-pressing in rat is enhanced; similar effects were seen after tetrabenazine but not after the closely related benzquinamide (which does not release amines), so that alteration of the milieu of brain amines was consequential for the enhanced LSD effect. Similarly, the altered amine state was consequential in humans when the LSD–25 was given 48–72 hours after a single dose of reserpine; prolongation of clouded consciousness, numerous extrapyramidal symptoms, and altered autonomic effects of LSD were observed.[39]

SUMMARY REMARKS

In view of the effects and correlations reviewed, some desiderata for future studies and some general considerations seem warranted. Time factors for EEG recordings should be locked with temporal parameters for shifts in amine mechanisms, physiological states, and behavioral sequences. The site of injection of agents such as 5–HTP is related to the regional locus and rate of brain amine changes, and every drug, whatever its ascription of convenience (e.g., MAO inhibitor) has its specific characteristics, so that actual rather than presumptive measures of amines are required. This is especially so if the milieu of brain amines has been altered. These considerations and species differences are sufficient to limit (not prohibit) generalization on the role of a specific amine. The presence of a prior shift in amine mechanisms, of a drug per se at a receptor, and of the various "periods" of change in endogenous mechanisms are shown to be partial determinants of drug response.[39]

Another problem which emerges from this area involves an appreciation that such ascriptions of convenience as "sedated," "excited," "inhibited," "arousal," are not mechanisms or descriptions applicable to every level of operational analysis. When we describe tranylcypromine as "reversing" the effects of reserpine we are not describing the operative mechanisms. Similarly, LSD has an effect on reserpine-treated rats; the level of serotonin is increased and the ptosis "reversed," but with both "reversing" agents profound effects are still seen in operant conditioning situations.[3] In humans, the effect of this reserpine-LSD interaction is different, not "turned about." The effect of LSD on bar-pressing for food is to "depress" bar-pressing at a time when the EEG shows a period of "activation." Such apparently alerted, excited, and depressed behaviors can be quite differently organized at both neural and neurochemical levels; the details of these actions— and interactions—are, after all, one task for research in neuropharmacology.

CONCLUSIONS

The data show that the endogenous level of amines, the intrinsic status of mechanisms governing them, can constitute a "state" which becomes consequential for both physiological adjustments and behavioral sequences only with appropriate stimuli and conditions. MAO inhibition, e.g., was seen to become "behaviorally manifest" and a consequential determinant of measured events when 5–HTP was administered. In general, drugs induce "periods" of neurochemical and neurophysiological change—states for which certain sets of observations are highly probable and others evident only upon special test. By "state" is meant an organization of functions which endures for a period during which one must specify the range and category of determinants which _can_ become operative with respect to manifest chemical, neural, or behavioral response. There apparently are limits beyond which, and conditions with which, shifts in neurochemical states become operative and consequential for psychophysiological function.

In general, pharmacological studies can make only an "initial statement" about the effects of a drug on behavior, e.g., reserpine-induced "sedation" or 5–HTP "excitement." Such statements are descriptive and important, and they should not be extended beyond the usual laboratory conditions for examining drug effects, i.e., they describe the change of psychophysiological state which is consequent upon proximal environmental and changing neurochemical events. The reserpine sedation correlates with a change in amines and a heightened parasympathetic outflow, but on extended examination there are various periods of biochemical change and various periods in which specific sets of behavioral contingencies are significant. Thus shifts in the level or status of brain amines correlate with the _onset_ of a psychophysiological state; but the specific succession of autonomic and behavioral events—even when searched for—have yet to be linked with a specific program of central neurochemical events.

The altered status of amine mechanisms following reserpine was seen to provide a different milieu for the interaction of the structure of past and present behavioral contingencies (e.g., in avoidance behavior). This order of correlation can hardly be descriptively encompassed by terms such as sedation or excitement. It is preferable to recognize (1) a prebehavioral, psychophysiological state contingent upon the immediate period of neurochemical change, and (2) subsequent periods in which new sets of interacting neurochemical and behavioral contingencies are added and operative through time. In order to correlate chemical change and behavior we must not only employ multiple behavioral measures, as Miller and Barry[116] have emphasized, but we must link these cogently with periods of physiological and chemical change.

One of the important consequences of research in this field has been the attempt to correlate behavioral and physiological changes not only with the levels of amines but with changes in mechanisms governing synthesis or rates of binding and release within brain cells. While we may not yet be able to measure the kinetics of the relevant subcellular mechanisms, it is possible that genetic or chemical impairment of these endogenous mechanisms could be consequential in clinically encountered syndromes. The notion that some of the neurobehavioral disorders of childhood such as phenylketonuria involve faulty *brain* metabolism of the monoamines has been approached experimentally.[166, 175] Schanberg *et al.*[145] in this laboratory found phenylketogenic diets in animals lead to changed brain amines and behavior; tryptophan supplements increased brain levels of serotonin and improved performance in maze tests, and temporal discrimination in operant tests,[4] for rats on phenylketogenic or control diets. In clinical studies the blood of severely retarded children, and most strikingly the autistic subgroup, showed abnormally elevated levels of serotonin.[140] The relationship of the amines to neurobehavioral development is similarly under study.[119] Brodie's group[95] report that brain levels of amines and MAO activity are low in the newborn rat (whose functional development is poor), but in several weeks (when functional activity has developed) amine activity is that of adult rats. In contrast, the newborn guinea pig, whose functional activity is well developed at birth, shows normal adult levels of the monoamines and MAO. In this regard the finding of Pepeu and Giarman[124] that the neonatal goat brain has higher cerebral serotonin levels than the mother is of interest, since the newborn of this species is more advanced in competence than even the guinea pig at birth.

Interest in a toxic basis for the psychoses and, specifically, in indole metabolism, comprises a long and doleful story of unsustained research;[137] toxic substances from the excreta of schizophrenic patients have hung more rope-climbing rats and poisoned more submammalian creatures than one would care to count. The role of catechol amines in emotional states and the variable tolerance to amine-mediated stimulation of smooth muscle in psychosis[54] has a similar history of interest and neglect. Nevertheless, it should be appreciated that current research has a firmer basis both in methodology and basic knowledge through the experiences of the past ten years. We seem to be nearer to discovering intrinsic enzymatic mechanisms through which psychotoxic substances could be synthesized by the body, perhaps dimethyl serotonin (bufotenin) and 6–hydroxy-serotonin.[156]

Finally, through research on central amine mechanisms and behavior, it is becoming clear that psychotoxins are not the only means by which neurochemical states can affect behavior. It has been seen that periods of neurochemical change which are behaviorally silent can, in response to select behavioral contingencies *or* to chemical sequences, profoundly influence both behavior and its electrical correlates. Recent studies by Freedman *et al.*[37, 44, 45] show that endogenous monoamines are responsive to some parameter or parameters of intense stress and hence that the *physiological* response of the organism can produce altered central amine states. This would provide some link between the psychoactive drugs and their effects upon amine metabolism and conditions which give rise to the need for such drugs. Perhaps, if endogenous amine mechanisms are chemically or genetically impaired, this would be reflected in altered psychophysiological function in the face of excessive activation or demand.

At this stage of attempting correlations between amines, behavior, and electrical activity it is clear that the proposition of neurochemical correlates for behavioral and electrical changes cannot be prejudged, whatever our prejudices. The experimentally derived correlations are already impressive; but the relevant parameters could not have been logically predicted prior to experiment. We shall have to entertain both a neuromodulator and neurotransmitter theory until new methods and the pedestrian filling in of detail provide the basis for more firmly grounded knowledge and new conceptual leaps. A number of new substances may come to the fore; but this is not a conspiracy to confound the weary with an "amine of the month." Rather there is a cogent basis in fact for unraveling the means by which these bioactive substances play specific roles in the organization of various levels of behavior. If the amines had been invented solely to bring conceptual clarity to neurobehavioral theories they probably could not function (as experiment shows them to) in micro quantities to modulate and regulate aspects of various physiological systems and levels of neural integration.

References

1. ALBRECHT, P., VISSCHER, M. B., BITTNER, J. J., and HALBERG, F., "Daily Changes in 5–HT in the Mouse Brain," *Proc. Soc. exp. Biol., N.Y.,* 92:703, 1956.

2. AMIN, A. H., CRAWFORD, T. B. B., and GADDUM, J. H., "The Distribution of Substance P and 5–Hydroxytryptamine in the Central Nervous System of the Dog," *J. Physiol., 126*:596, 1954.

2a. ANDERSON, E. G. and CUDIA, J., "The Anatomical Localization of Norepephrine and 5–Hydroxytrytotamine in the Cat Spinal Cord," *Fed. Proc., 21*:341, 1962.

3. APPEL, J. B., LEVISON, P. K., and FREEDMAN, D. X. Unpublished data.

4. APPEL, J. B., McKEAN, C. M., SCHANBERG, S. M., and FREEDMAN, D. X., "Behavioral Effects of Tryptophan." Unpublished data.

5. APRISON, M. H. and FERSTER, C. B., "Neurochemical Correlates of Behavior. II. Correlation of Brain Monoamine Oxidase Activity with Behavioral Changes after Iproniazid and 5–Hydroxytryptophan Administration," *J. Neurochem., 6*:350, 1961.

6. AXELROD, J., "Metabolism of Epinephrine and Other Sympathomimetic Amines," *Physiol. Rev., 39*:751, 1959.

7. AXELROD, J., INSCOE, J. K., SENOH, S., and WITKOP, B., "O-Methylation, the Principal Pathway for the Metabolism of Epinephrine and Norepinephrine in the Rat," *Biochim. biophys. Acta, 27*:210, 1958.

8. AXELROD, J. and WEISSBACH, H., "Enzymatic O-Methylation of N-Acetylserotonin to Melatonin," *Science, 131*:1312, 1960.

9. BERTLER, Å. and ROSENGREN, E., "On the Distribution in Brain of Monoamines and Enzymes Responsible for their Formation," *Experientia,* XV/10:382, 1959.

10. BOGDANSKI, D. F., SULSER, F., and BRODIE, B. B., "Comparative Action of Reserpine, Tetrabenazine and Chlorpromazine on Central Parasympathetic Activity: Effects on Pupillary Size and Lacrimation in Rabbit and on Salivation in Dog," *J. Pharmacol. exp. Ther., 132*:176, 1961.

11. BOGDANSKI, D. F., WEISSBACH, H., and UDENFRIEND, S., "Pharmacological Studies with the Serotonin Precursor, 5–Hydroxytryptophan," *J. Pharmacol. exp. Ther., 122*:182, 1958.

12. BONNYCASTLE, D. D., Personal communication.

13. BONNYCASTLE, D. D., BONNYCASTLE, M. F., and ANDERSON, E. G., "The Effect of a Number of Central Depressant Drugs Upon Brain 5–Hydroxytryptamine Levels in the Rat," *J. Pharmacol. exp. Ther., 135*:11, 1962.

14. BONNYCASTLE, D. D., GIARMAN, N. J., and PAASONEN, M. K., "Anticonvulsant Compounds and 5–Hydroxytryptamine in Rat Brain," *J. Physiol.*, *12*:228, 1957.

15. BRADLEY, P. B., "The Central Action of Certain Drugs in Relation to the Reticular Formation of the Brain," in *Reticular Formation of the Brain, Henry Ford Hospital International Symposium*, Little, Brown & Co., Boston, 1958.

16. BRADLEY, P. B. and ELKES, J., "The Distribution of Cholinergic and Noncholinergic Receptors in the Brain: Electrophysiological Evidence," in RICHTER, D. (ed.), *Metabolism of the Nervous System*, Pergamon Press, New York, 1957.

17. BRADY, J. V., "A Review of Comparative Behavioral Pharmacology," *Ann. N.Y. Acad. Sci.*, *66*:719, 1957.

18. BRODIE, B. B., "Interaction of Psychotropic Drugs with Physiologic and Biochemical Mechanisms in Brain," *Mod. Med., Minneapolis, 60*, 1958.

19. BULBRING, E. and CREMA, A., "Observations Concerning the Action of 5–Hydroxytryptamine on the Peristaltic Reflex," *Brit. J. Pharmacol.*, *13*:444, 1958.

20. CARLSSON, A., "The Occurrence, Distribution and Physiological Role of Catecholamines in the Nervous System," *Pharmacol. Rev.*, *11*:490, 1959.

21. COOK, L. and WEIDLEY, E. F., "Behavioral Effects of Some Psychopharmacological Agents," *Ann. N.Y. Acad. Sci.*, *66*:740, 1957.

22. COSTA, E., "The Role of Serotonin in Neurobiology," *Int. Rev. Neurobiol.*, *2*:175, 1960.

23. COSTA, E., "Effects of Hallucinogenic and Tranquilizing Drugs on Serotonin Evoked Uterine Contraction," *Proc. Soc. exp. Biol., N.Y.*, *91*:39, 1956.

24. COSTA, E. and PSCHEIDT, G. R., "Correlations Between Active Eyelid Closure and Depletion of Brain Biogenic Amines by Reserpine," *Proc. Soc. exp. Biol., N.Y.*, *106*:693, 1961.

25. COSTA, E., PSCHEIDT, G. R., VAN METER, W. G., and HIMWICH, H. E., "Brain Concentrations of Biogenic Amines and EEG Patterns of Rabbits," *J. Pharmacol. exp. Ther.*, *130*:81, 1960.

26. COSTA, E. and REVZIN, A. M., in COSTA, E., "The Role of Serotonin in Neurobiology," *Int. Rev. Neurobiol.*, *2*:175, 1960.

27. DEJONG, J., PACHL, S. J., and FREEDMAN, D. X. Unpublished data.

28. DELL, P. C., "Humoral Effects on the Brain Stem Reticular Formation," in *Reticular Formation of the Brain, Henry Ford Hospital International Symposium*, Little, Brown & Co., Boston, 1958.

29. DEWS, P. B., "Modification by Drugs of Performance on Simple Schedules of Positive Reinforcement," *Ann. N.Y. Acad. Sci.*, 65:268, Art. 4, 1956.

30. DONTAS, H. S., "Effects of Reserpine and Hydralazine on Carotid and Splanchnic Nerve Activity and Blood Pressure," *J. Pharmacol. exp. Ther.*, 121:1, 1957.

31. DORMAN, J. and GIARMAN, N. J. Unpublished data.

32. EDISEN, C. B., "Methamphetamine, Serotonin, Reserpine and Effects on Cat Spinal Cord," *Arch. Neurol. Psychiat.*, Chicago, 79:323, 1958.

33. ELKES, J., "Psychopharmacology: 'The Need for Some Points of Reference,'" in *A Pharmacologic Approach to the Study of the Mind*, Charles C Thomas, Springfield, Ill., 1959.

34. FISHER, R. Unpublished data.

35. FREEDMAN, D. X., "Information Needs in Psychopharmacology," unpublished paper read at Psychopharmacology Serv. Cntr., November 1960.

36. FREEDMAN, D. X., "Effects of LSD–25 on Brain Serotonin," *J. Pharmacol. exp. Ther.*, 134:160, 1961.

37. FREEDMAN, D. X., "Psychotomimetic Drugs and Brain Biogenic Amines," *Amer. J. Psychiat.* In Press, 1963.

38. FREEDMAN, D. X., "Neural Factors in Drug Action," unpublished manuscript, 1954.

39. FREEDMAN, D. X., "Studies of LSD–25 and Serotonin in the Brain," *Proc. III World Congr. Psychiat.*, Montreal, 653–658, 1962.

40. FREEDMAN, D. X., "LSD–25 and Brain Serotonin in Reserpinized Rat," *Fed. Proc.*, 19, No. 1:266, 1960.

41. FREEDMAN, D. X., "Psychopharmacologic Drugs," *McGraw-Hill Encyclopedia of Science and Technology*, McGraw-Hill Book Co., 1960, pp. 76–77.

42. FREEDMAN, D. X., AGHAJANIAN, G. K., ORNITZ, E. M., and ROSNER, B. S., "Patterns of Tolerance to Lysergic Acid Diethylamide and Mescaline in Rats," *Science*, 127:1173, 1958.

43. FREEDMAN, D. X., APPEL, J. B., HARTMAN, F., and MOLLIVER, M. Unpublished data.

44. FREEDMAN, D. X., BARCHAS, J. D., and PACHL, S. J. Unpublished data.

45. FREEDMAN, D. X., BARCHAS, J. D., and SCHOENBRUN, R. L., "Response of Brain Amines to Exhaustion Stress or LSD–25," *Fed. Proc.*, 21, No. 2:337, 1962.

46. FREEDMAN, D. X. and BENTON, A. J., "Persisting Effects of Reserpine in Man," *New Engl. J. Med.*, 264:529, 1961.

47. FREEDMAN, D. X., FRAM, D. H., and GIARMAN, N. J., "The Effect of Morphine on the Regeneration of Brain Norepinephrine After Reserpine," *Fed. Proc., 20*:321, 1961.

48. FREEDMAN, D. X. and GIARMAN, N. J., "Apomorphine Test for Tranquilizing Drugs: Effect of Dibenamine," *Science, 124*:264, 1956.

49. FREEDMAN, D. X. and GIARMAN, N. J., "LSD–25 and the Status and Level of Brain Serotonin," *Ann. N.Y. Acad. Sci., 96*:98, Art. 1, 1962.

50. FREEDMAN, D. X., HARTMAN, F., and FLYNN, J. Unpublished data.

51. FREEDMAN, D. X., HARTMAN, F., and LERNER, A. Unpublished data.

52. FREEDMAN, D. X. and PICARD-AMI, L. Unpublished data.

53. FREEDMAN, D. X., PICARD-AMI, L., and GIARMAN, N. J. Unpublished data.

54. FREEDMAN, D. X., REDLICH, F. C., and IGERSHEIMER, W. W., "Psychosis and Allergy: Experimental Approach," *Amer. J. Psychiat., 112*:873, 1956.

54a. GADDUM, J. H., "Substances Released in Nervous Activity," *Proc. First int. Pharmacol. Meeting*, Stockholm, Sweden, 1961.

55. GADDUM, J. H. and GIARMAN, N. J., "Preliminary Studies on the Biosynthesis of 5–Hydroxytryptamine," *Brit. J. Pharmacol., 11*:88, 1956.

56. GADDUM, J. H. and HAMEED, K. A., "Drugs Which Antagonize 5–Hydroxytryptamine," *Brit. J. Pharmacol., 9*:240, 1954.

57. GADDUM, J. H. and PAASONEN, M. K., "The Use of Some Molluscan Hearts for the Estimation of 5–Hydroxytryptamine," *Brit. J. Pharmacol., 10*:474, 1955.

58. GANGLOFF, H. and MONNIER, M., "Tropic Action of Reserpine, Serotonin, and Chlorpromazine on the Unanesthetized Rabbit's Brain," *Helv. physiol. pharmacol. Acta, 15*:83, 1957.

59. GARATTINI, S., "Farmaci Psicotropi che Agiscono Attraverso Supposti Mediatori Centrali," *Schweiz. Arch. Neurol. Psychiat., 84*:271, 1959.

60. GARATTINI, S. KATO, R., and VALZELLI, L., "Biochemical and Pharmacological Effects Induced by Electroshock," *Psychiat. et Neurol., Basel, 140*:190, 1960.

61. GARATTINI, S. and VALZELLI, L., "Researches on the Mechanisms of Reserpine Sedative Action," *Science, 128*:1278, 1958.

62. GARVEN, J. D., "The Estimation of 5–Hydroxytryptamine in the Presence of Adrenalin," *Brit. J. Pharmacol., 11*:66, 1956.

63. GAUROT, P. O., ROSENGREN, E., and GOTTFRIES, C. G., "Effect of Iproniazid on Monoamines and Monoamine Oxidase in Human Brain," *Experientia, 18*:260, 1962.

64. GERTNER, S. B., PAASONEN, M. K., and GIARMAN, N. J., "Studies Concerning the Presence of 5–Hydroxytryptamine (Serotonin) in the Per-

fusate from the Superior Cervical Ganglion," *J. Pharmacol. exp. Ther.,* *127*:268, 1959.

65. GEY, K. F. and PLETSCHER, A., "Interference of Chlorpromazine with the Metabolism of Aromatic Amino Acids in Rat Brain," *Nature, Lond.,* *194*:387, 1962.

66. GEY, K. F. and PLETSCHER, A., "Influence of Chlorpromazine and Chlorprothixene on the Cerebral Metabolism of 5–Hydroxytryptamine, Norepinephrine and Dopamine," *J. Pharmacol. exp. Ther.,* *133*:18, 1961.

67. GIARMAN, N. J., "Neurohumors in the Brain," *Yale J. Biol. Med.,* *32*:73, 1959.

68. GIARMAN, N. J., "Discussion," *Fed. Proc., 20, No. 4*:897, 1961.

69. GIARMAN, N. J. and DAY, S. M., "Presence of Biogenic Amines in the Bovine Pineal Body," *Biochem. Pharmacol., 1*:235, 1958.

70. GIARMAN, N. J., FREEDMAN, D. X., and PICARD-AMI, L., "Serotonin Content of the Pineal Glands of Man and Monkey," *Nature, Lond.,* *186*:480, 1960.

71. GIARMAN, N. J. and REIT, E. Unpublished data.

72. GIARMAN, N. J. and SCHANBERG, S. M., "The Intracellular Distribution of 5–Hydroxytryptamine (HT, Serotonin) in the Rat's Brain," *Biochem. Pharmacol., 1*:301, 1958.

73. GINZEL, K. H. and KOTTEGODA, S. R., "The Action of 5–Hydroxytryptamine and Tryptamine on Aortic and Carotid Sinus Receptors in the Cat," *J. Physiol., 123*:277, 1954.

74. GLEIDMAN, L. H. and GANTT, W. H., "The Effects of Reserpine and Chlorpromazine on Orienting Behavior and Retention of Conditioned Reflexes," *Sth. med. J., Bgham., Ala., 49*:880, 1956.

75. GREEN, J. P., "Binding of Some Biogenic Amines in Tissues," *Advanc. Pharmacol., 1*:349, 1962.

76. GREEN, H. and SAWYER, J. L., "Intracellular Distribution of Norepinephrine in the Rat Brain: I. Effect of Reserpine and Monoamine Oxidase Inhibitors, Trans–2–Phenylcyclopropylamine and 1–Isonicotinyl –2–Isopropyl Hydrazine," *J. Pharmacol. exp. Ther., 129*:243, 1960.

77. GROSSMAN, P., "Eating or Drinking Elicited by Direct Adrenocortical or Cholenergic Stimulation of the Hypothalamus," *Science, 132*:301, 1960.

78. GRUNDFEST, H., "Functional Specifications for Membranes in Excitable Cells," in KETY, S. S. and ELKES, J. (eds.), *Regional Neurochemistry,* Pergamon Press, New York, 1961, p. 378.

79. GRUNDFEST, H., "General Problems of Drug Actions on Biolectric Phenomena," *Ann. N.Y. Acad. Sci., 66*:537, 1957.

80. HALEY, T. J., "5–Hydroxytryptamine Antagonism by Lysergic Acid Diethylamide after Intercerebral Injection in Conscious Mice," *J. Amer. pharm. Ass., sci. Ed.*, XLVI:428, 1957.

81. HARTMAN, F. Unpublished data.

82. HAVERBACK, B. J. *et al.*, "Serotonin Changes in Platelets and Brain Induced by Small Daily Doses of Reserpine: Lack of Depletion of Platelet Serotonin on Hemostatic Mechanisms," *New Engl. J. Med.*, 256:343, 1957.

83. HEISE, G. A. and BOFF, E., "Behavioral Determination of Time and Dose Parameters of Monoamine Oxidase Inhibitors," *J. Pharmacol. exp. Ther.*, 129:155, 1960.

84. HELLER, A., HARVEY, J. A., and MOORE, R. Y., "A Demonstration of a Fall in Brain Serotonin Following Central Nervous System Lesions in the Rat, *Biochem. Pharmacol.*, 11:859, 1962.

85. HESS, S. M., CONNAMACHER, R. H., and UDENFRIEND, S., "Effect of Alpha-methylamino Acids on Catecholamines and Serotonin," *Fed. Proc.* 20:344, 1961.

86. HIMWICH, H. E., "Experiments with Alpha-Methyltryptamine," *J. Neuropsychiat.*, Suppl. 1:136, 1961.

87. HUGHES, F. B., SHORE, P. A., and BRODIE, B. B., "Serotonin Storage Mechanism and Interaction with Reserpine," *Experientia*, 41:178, 1958.

88. IGGO, A. and VOGT, M., "Preganglionic Sympathetic Activity in Normal and in Reserpine-Treated Cats," *J. Physiol.*, 150:114, 1960.

89. International Symposium on Extrapyramidal System and Neuroleptics, Editions Psychiatriques, BORDELEAU, J. M. (ed.), Montreal, 1961.

90. JACOBSEN, E., "The Effect of Psychotropic Drugs Under Psychic Stress," in GARATTINI, S. and GHETTI, V. (eds.), *Psychotropic Drugs*, Elsevier, Amsterdam, Holland, p. 119, 1957.

91. JOHN, E. R. and KILLAM, K. F., "Electro-Physiological Correlates of Differential Approach-Avoidance Conditioning in Cats," *J. nerv. ment. Dis.*, 131:183, 1960.

92. JOHN, E. R. and KILLAM, K. F., "Studies of Electrical Activity of Brain During Differential Conditioning in Cats," *Rec. Advanc. biol. Psychiat.*, 2:138, 1960.

93. JOHN, E. R., WENZEL, B. M., and TSCHIRGI, R. D., "Differential Effects of Reserpine on Conditioned Responses in Cats," *Science*, 127:25, 1958.

94. JOHN, E. R., WENZEL, B. M., and TSCHIRGI, R. D., "Differential Effects on Various Conditioned Responses in Cats Caused by Intraventricular and Intramuscular Injections of Reserpine and Other Substances," *J. Pharmacol. exp. Ther.*, 123:193, 1958.

95. KARKI, N., KUNTZMAN, R., and BRODIE, B. B., "Storage, Synthesis and Metabolism of Monoamines in the Developing Brain," *J. Neurochem.*, 9:53, 1962.

96. KATO, R., "Serotonin Content of Rat Brain in Relation to Sex and Age," *J. Neurochem.*, 5:201, 1960.

97. KEY, B. J., "Effects of Chlorpromazine and Lysergic Acid Diethylamide on the Rate of Habituation of the Arousal Response," *Nature, Lond.*, 190:275, 1961.

98. KILLAM, E. V., GANGLOFF, H., KONIGSMARK, B., and KILLAM, K. F., "The Action of Pharmacologic Agents on Evoked Cortical Activity," *Rec. Advanc. biol. Psychiat.*, 1:53, 1959.

99. KILLAM, E. K. and KILLAM, K. F., *Brain Mechanisms and Drug Action*, Charles C Thomas, Springfield, Ill., 1957.

100. KLUPP, H. and KIESER, W., "Zur Testung von Tranquillizern an Bedingten Reflexen von Ratten," *Naunyn-Schmiedeberg's Arch. exp. Path. Pharmak.*, 236:97, 1959.

101. KOELLA, W. P., SMYTHIES, J. R., BULL, D. M., and LEVY, C. K., "Physiological Fractionation of the Effect of Serotonin on Evoked Potentials," *Amer. J. Physiol.*, 198:205, 1960.

102. KOELLA, W. P., SMYTHIES, J. R., LEVY, C. K., and CZICMAN, J. S., "Modulatory Influence on Cerebral Cortical Optic Response from the Carotid Sinus Area," *Amer. J. Physiol.*, 199:381, 1960.

103. LEVI, R. and MAYNERT, E. W., "Effects of Stress on Brain Norepinephrine," *Fed. Proc.*, 21, No. 2:337, 1962.

104. LEVISON, P. K., APPEL, J. B., and FREEDMAN, D. X. Unpublished data.

105. LEWIS, G. P., "5-Hydroxytryptamine," *J. Pharm., Lond.*, 10:529, 1958.

106. MACLEAN, P. D., FLANIGAN, S., FLYNN, J. P., KIM, C., and STEVENS, J. R., "Hippocampal Function: Tentative Correlations of Conditioning, EEG, Drug and Radioautographic Studies," *Yale J. Biol. Med.*, 28:380, 1955/6.

107. MAICKEL, R. P., WESTERMAN, E. O., and BRODIE, B. B., "Effects of Reserpine and Cold Exposure on Pituitary-Adreno-Cortical Function in Rats," *J. Pharmacol. exp. Ther.* 134:167, 1961.

108. MANSOUR, T. E., "The Effect of Serotonin and Related Compounds on the Carbohydrate Metabolism of the Liver Fluke, Fasciola Hepatica," *J. Pharmacol. exp. Ther.* 126:212, 1959.

109. MANSOUR, T. E., SUTHERLAND, E. W., RALL, T. W., and BUEDING, E., "The Effect of Serotonin (5-Hydroxytryptamine) on the Formation of Adenosine-3', 5'-Phosphate by Tissue Particles from the Liver Fluke, Fasciola Hepatica," *J. biol. Chem.*, 235:466, 1960.

110. MARRAZZI, A. S., "Some Indications of Cerebral Humoral Mechanisms," *Science, 118*:367, 1953.

111. MARRAZZI, A. S., "The Effects of Certain Drugs on Cerebral Synapses," *Ann. N.Y. Acad. Sci., 66*:496, 1957.

112. MARRAZZI, A. S., and HART, E. R., "The Possible Role of Inhibition at Adrenergic Synapses in the Mechanism of Hallucinogenic and Related Drug Actions," *J. nerv. ment. Dis., 122*:435, 1955.

113. MAYNERT, E. W. and KLINGMAN, G. I., "Tolerance to Morphine. I. Effects of Catecholamines in the Brain and Adrenal Glands," *J. Pharmacol. exp. Ther., 135*:285, 1962.

114. MCISAAC, W. M., KHAIRALLAH, P. A., and PAGE, I. H., "10–Methoxyharmalan, a Potent Serotonin Antagonist Which Affects Conditioned Behavior," *Science, 134*:674, 1961.

115. MCKEAN, C. M., SCHANBERG, S. M., and GIARMAN, N. J., "A Mechanism for the Indole Defect Found in Experimental Phenylketonuria," *Science, 137*:604, 1962.

116. MILLER, N. E., and BARRY, H., "Motivating Effects of Drugs: Methods Which Illustrate Some General Problems in Psychopharmacology," *Psychopharmacologia, 1*:169, 1960.

117. MIRKIN, B. L., GIARMAN, N. J., and FREEDMAN, D. X., "Uptake of Noradrenalin by Subcellular Particles in Homogenates of Rat Brain," *Biochem. Pharmacol.*, 1963. In Press.

118. MONNIER, M. and TISSOT, R., "Action de la Reserpine et de ses Mediateurs (5–Hydroxytraptophan-Serotonine et Dopa-Noradrenaline) sur le Comportement et le Cerveau du Lapin," *Helv. physiol. pharmacol. Acta, 16*:255, 1958.

119. NACHMIAS, V. T., "Amine Oxidase and 5–Hydroxytryptamine in Developing Rat Brain," *J. Neurochem., 6*:99, 1960.

120. PAASONEN, M. K., MACLEAN, P. D., and GIARMAN, N. J., "5–Hydroxytryptamine (Serotonin, Enteramine) Content of Structures of the Limbic System," *J. Neurochem., 1*:326, 1957.

121. PAGE, I. H., "Serotonin (5–Hydroxytryptamine) the Last Four Years," *Physiol. Rev., 38*:277, 1958.

122. PAGE, I. H. and MCCUBBIN, J. W., "The Variable Arterial Pressure Response to Serotonin in Laboratory Animals and Man," *Circulat. Res., 1*:354, 1953.

123. PEPEU, G. and GIARMAN, N. J., "The Effect of Certain Neuropharmacologic Agents on Brain Acetylcholine," *Fed. Proc., 19*:182, 1960. (See also GIARMAN, N. J. and PEPEU, G., "Drug-induced Changes in Brain Acetylcholine," *Brit. J. Pharmacol., 19*:226, 1962.)

124. PEPEU, G. and GIARMAN, N. J., "Serotonin in the Developing Mammal," *J. gen. Physiol., 45*:575, 1962.

125. PEPEU, G., ROBERTS, M., SCHANBERG, S. M., and GIARMAN, N. J., "Differential Action of Iproniazid ('Marsilid') and Betaphenylisoprolhydrazine ('Catron') on Isolated Atria," *J. Pharmacol. exp. Ther.*, *132*:131, 1961.

126. PICKLES, V. R., "The Effects of 5–Hydroxytryptamine on the Passage of Water, Sodium and Potassium Through the Isolated Amphibian Skin," *J. Physiol.*, *135*:59, 1957.

127. PLETSCHER, A., BESENDORF, H., and BÄCHTOLD, H. P., "Benzo [a] Chinolizine, eine Neue Körperklasse mit Wirkuna auf den 5–Hydroxytriptamin—und Noradrenalin—Stoff Wechsel des Gehirns," *Naunyn-Schmiedeberg's Arch. exp. Path. Pharmak.*, *232*:499, 1958.

128. POLLIN, W., CARDON, P. V., JR., and KETY, S. S., "Effects of Amino Acid Feedings in Schizophrenic Patients Treated with Iproniazid," *Science*, *133*:194, 1961.

129. PROCKOP, D. J., SHORE, P. A., and BRODIE, B. B., "An Anticonvulsant Effect of Monoamine Oxidase Inhibitors," *Experientia*, *15*:145, 1959.

130. PUT, T. R. and HOGENHUIS, L. A. H., "Brain Serotonin and Thyroid Function," *Acta physiol. pharmacol. neerl.*, *10*:343, 1962.

131. QUINN, G. P., SHORE, P. A., and BRODIE, B. B., "Biochemical and Pharmacological Studies of RO 1–9569 (Tetrabenazine), a Non-Indole Tranquilizing Agent with Reserpine-Like Effects," *J. Pharmacol. exp. Ther.*, *127*:103, 1959.

132. RAPPORT, M. M., GREEN, A. A., and PAGE, I. H., "Crystalline Serotonin," *Science*, *108*:329, 1948.

133. REVZIN, A. M. and COSTA, E., "Effects of Serotonin on Evoked Hippocampal Potentials," *Fed. Proc.*, *18*:436, 1959.

134. REVZIN, A. M., SPECTOR, S., and COSTA, E., "Relationship Between Reserpine-Induced Facilitation of Evoked Potentials in the Limbic System and Change in Brain Serotonin Level," *Biochem. Pharmacol.*, *8*:39, 1961.

135. RINALDI, F. and HIMWICH, H. B., "A Comparison of Effects of Reserpine and Some Barbiturates on the Electrical Activity of Cortical and Subcortical Structures of the Brain of Rabbits," *Science*, *61*:27, 1955.

136. RIOPELLE, A. J. and PFEIFFER, C. C., "Effects of Acute and Chronic Administration of Reserpine on Test Performance," *Arch. Neurol. Psychiat., Chicago*, *79*:352, 1958.

137. RODNIGHT, R., "Body Fluid Indoles in Mental Illness," *Int. Rev. Neurobiol.*, *3*:251, 1961.

138. SCHAIN, R. J., "Some Effects of a Monoamine Oxidase Inhibitor Upon Changes Produced by Centrally Administered Amines," *Brit. J. Pharmacol.*, *17*:261, 1961.

139. SCHAIN, R. J., "Neurohumors and Other Pharmacologically Active Substances in Cerebrospinal Fluid. A Review of the Literature," *Yale J. Biol. Med.*, 33:15, 1960.

140. SCHAIN, R. J. and FREEDMAN, D. X., "Studies on 5–Hydroxyindole Metabolism in Autistic and Other Mentally Retarded Children," *J. Pediat.*, 58:315, 1961.

141. SCHANBERG, S. M., "A Study of the Transport of 5–Hydroxytryptophan and 5–Hydroxytryptamine (Serotonin) into Brain," *J. Pharmacol. exp. Ther.* In Press.

142. SCHANBERG, S. M. and GIARMAN, N. J., "Uptake of Serotonin (5–HT) and 5–Hydroxytryptophan (5–HTP) by Brain Slices," *Pharmacologist*, 2, No. 2, 1960.

143. SCHANBERG, S. M. and GIARMAN, N. J., "Uptake of 5–Hydroxytryptophan by Rat's Brain," *Biochim. biophys. Acta*, 41:556, 1960.

144. SCHANBERG, S. M. and GIARMAN, N. J., "Drug Induced Alterations in the Sub-Cellular Distribution of 5–Hydroxytryptamine in Rat's Brain," *Biochem. Pharmacol.*, 11:187, 1962.

145. SCHANBERG, S. M., McKEAN, C. M., and GIARMAN, N. J., "A Mechanism of the Indole Defect in Experimental Phenylketonuria," *Fed. Proc.*, 21, No. 2:269, 1962.

146. SCHNEIDER, J. A. and YONKMAN, F. F., "Species Differences in the Respiratory and Cardiovascular Response to Serotonin (5–Hydroxytryptamine)," *J. Pharmacol. exp. Ther.*, 111:84, 1954.

147. SEIL, D. Unpublished data.

148. SHAW, E. and WOOLLEY, D. W., "Some Serotonin-like Activities of Lysergic Acid Diethylamide," *Science*, 124:121, 1956.

149. SHORE, P. A., SILVER, S. L., and BRODIE, B. B., "Interaction of Reserpine, Serotonin, and Lysergic Acid Diethylamide in Brain," *Science*, 122:284, 1955.

150. SIGG, E. B. and SCHNEIDER, J. A., "Mechanisms Involved in the Interaction of Central Stimulants and Reserpine," *Electroenceph. clin. Neurophysiol.*, 9:419, 1957.

151. SIVA SANKAR, D. V., SANKAR, D. B., PHIPPS, E., and GOLD, E., "Effect of Administration of Lysergic Acid Diethylamide on Serotonin Levels in the Body," *Nature, Lond.*, 191:499, 1961.

152. SJOERDSMA, A., KORNETSKY, C., and EVARTS, E. V., "Lysergic Acid Diethylamide in Patients with Excess Serotonin," *Arch. Neurol. Psychiat., Chicago*, 75:488, 1956.

153. SLATER, I. H. and JONES, G. T., "Pharmacologic Properties of Ethoxybutamoxane and Related Compounds," *J. Pharmacol., exp. Ther.*, 122:69A, 1958.

154. SMITH, R. P., WAGMAN, A. I., and RIOPELLE, A. J., "Effects of Reserpine on Conditioned Avoidance Behavior in Normal and Brain-operated Monkeys," *J. Pharmacol. exp. Ther.*, 117:136, 1956.

155. STEIN, L., "Reserpine and the Learning of Fear," *Science*, 124:1082, 1956.

156. SZARA, S. and AXELROD, J., "Hydroxylation and N-demethylation of N, N-dimethyltryptamine," *Experientia*, 15:216, 1959.

157. TAYLOR, R. D., PAGE, I. H., and CORCORAN, A. C., "A Hormonal Neurogenic Vasopressor Mechanism," *Arch. intern. Med.*, 88:1, 1951.

158. TEDESCHI, D. H., TEDESCHI, R. E., and FELLOWS, E. J., "The Effects of Tryptamine on the CNS; Including a Pharmacological Procedure for the Evaluation of Iproniazid-like Drugs," *J. Pharmacol. exp. Ther.*, 126:223, 1959.

159. TWAROG, B. M. and PAGE, I. H., "Serotonin Content of Some Mammalian Tissues and Urine and a Method for Its Determination," *Amer. J. Physiol.*, 175:157, 1953.

160. UDENFRIEND, S., *Fluorescence Assay in Biology and Medicine*, Academic Press, New York, N.Y., 1962.

161. UDENFRIEND, S., WEISSBACH, H., and BOGDANSKI, D. F., "Biochemical Findings Relating to the Action of Serotonin," *Ann. N.Y. Acad. Sci.*, 66:602, 1957.

162. UDENFRIEND, S., WEISSBACH, H., and BOGDANSKI, D. F., "Increase in Tissue Serotonin Following Administration of Its Precursor 5–Hydroxytryptophan," *J. biol. Chem.*, 224:802, 1957.

163. VANE, J. R., "A Sensitive Method for the Assay of 5–Hydroxytryptamine," *Brit. J. Pharmacol.*, 12:344, 1957.

164. VOGT, M., p. 574 in *Adrenergic Mechanisms*, Ciba Symposium, Ciba, Summit, New Jersey, 1961.

165. WADA, J. A., "Epileptogenic Cerebral Electrical Activity and Serotonin Levels," *Science*, 134:1688, 1961.

166. WANG, H. L. and WAISMAN, H. A., "Experimental Phenylketonuria in Rats," *Proc. Soc. exp. Biol., N.Y.*, 108:332, 1961.

167. WEISKRANTZ, L., "Reserpine and Behavioral Non-Reactivity," in GARATTINI, S. and GHETTI, V. (eds.), *Psychotropic Drugs*, Elsevier, Amsterdam, Holland, 1957.

168. WEISKRANTZ, L. and WILSON, W. A., JR., "Effect of Reserpine on Learning and Performance," *Science*, 123:1116, 1956.

169. WEISSBACH, H., BOGDANSKI, D. F., REDFIELD, B. G., and UDENFRIEND, S., "Studies on the Effect of Vitamin B_6 on 5–Hydroxytryptamine (Serotonin) Formation," *J. biol. Chem.*, 227:617, 1957.

170. WELSH, J. H., "Excitation of the Heart of Venus Mercenaria," *Naunyn-Schmiedeberg's Arch. exp. Path. Pharmak., 219*:23, 1953.

171. WELSH, J. H. and McCoy, A. C., "Actions of d-Lysergic Acid Diethylamide and Its 2-Bromo Derivative on Heart of Venus Mercenaria," *Science, 125*:348, 1957.

172. WHITTAKER, V. P., "The Subcellular Localization of Transmitter Substances in the Central Nervous System," *Biochem. Pharmacol., 5*:392, 1961.

173. WINTER, C. A. and FLATAKER, L., "Further Experiments on the Performance of Trained Rats Treated with Lysergic Acid Diethylamide," *J. Pharmacol. exp. Ther., 119*:194, 1957.

174. WOOLLEY, D. W. and SHAW, E., "A Biochemical and Pharmacological Suggestion about Certain Mental Disorders," *Proc. nat. Acad. Sci., Wash., D.C., 40*:228, 1954.

175. YUWILER, A. and LOUITTIT, R., "Effects of Phenylalanine Diet on Brain Serotonin in the Rat," *Science, 134*:831, 1961.

176. ZBINDEN, G., RANDALL, L. O., and MOE, R. A., "Clinical and Pharmacological Considerations on Mode of Action of Monoamine Oxidase Inhibitors," *Dis. nerv. Syst., 21*: Suppl. *89*, 1960.

IX

Effect of Catecholamines and Brain Stem Stimulation upon the Hypothalamic Ventromedial Nucleus

Jerome Sutin
Lucas Van Orden
Takashi Tsubokawa

The studies of Hetherington and Ranson[29] and of Brobeck *et al.*[11] clearly demonstrated that destruction of the ventromedial nuclei leads to hyperphagia and obesity. Subsequent work by several investigators has extended our understanding of this aspect of feeding behavior. Together with the existence of a lateral hypothalamic region in which lesions produce aphagia,[4] the observations that animals with ventromedial lesions will not perform a manual task or tolerate unpleasant stimuli in order to get food as well as do normal hungry animals,[42, 43] and may not eat excessively or as rapidly if the food offered is hard and dry,[28, 52] have led to the association of the ventromedial nucleus with "satiety" rather than with "hunger." The regulation of this satiety mechanism has been intensively studied. Factors related to body temperature[6, 10] glucose availability to C.N.S. glucoreceptors,[41] lipids,[26, 34] and visceral changes[32, 42] have been thought to play an important role in triggering or inhibiting the satiety mechanism, but definitive data concerning the primacy of any one of these are not yet available.

The ventromedial nuclei also play a role in certain aspects of aggressive behavior. Wheatly[56] found that bilateral lesions involving this nucleus resulted in a lowering of the rage threshold. This increased emotional display may or may not be associated with hyperphagia.

Supported by National Science Foundation grants G–4434 and G–13274 and by the Dysautonomia Association.

244

The rage reaction of these animals was well coordinated and directed. Unlike most changes in emotional behavior following brain lesions, rage following ventromedial nuclei lesions frequently persists for the life of the animal. Often the rage appears to be associated with behavior suggestive of fear.[31] Electrical stimulation of lateral portions of the anterior hypothalamus can evoke a behavioral response similar to that produced by ventromedial lesions.[27, 30] Small subtotal bilateral lesions of the ventromedial nuclei seem to produce a heightened sensitivity to tactile stimulation in the sacral and lumbar dermatomes about the base of the tail and genitalia, leading to attack directed at the source of stimulation.[23, 51]

A third important function requiring the integrity of this region relates to the release of reproductive hormones. Lesions of the tuberal portion of the hypothalamus, involving mainly the arcuate and ventromedial nuclei, interfere with gonadotropin release,[29, 46] and have been associated with an increased secretion of prolactin[24] from the adenohypophysis. Thus, stimulation and ablation experiments have shown that the region of the hypothalamus encompassing the ventromedial nucleus is involved in satiety, rage, and endocrine mechanisms.

Since there is evidence that modification of food intake and gonadotropin release may depend upon blood-borne substances reaching the C.N.S. regulatory elements, it is necessary to examine the ventromedial nucleus with respect to the blood-brain barrier. A number of structures associated with the ventricular system, such as the area postrema, pineal gland, intercolumnar tubercle and subfornical organ are readily accessible to circulating electrolytes, metabolites, or hormones. The remainder of the central nervous system permits these substances to enter it at variable rates. For example, glucose penetrates the nervous system readily, electrolytes enter more slowly than in nonnervous tissues, and proteins or protein-bound substances penetrate very little. This selective permeability, or blood-brain barrier, is also absent in the neurohypophysis and to some extent the tuberal region of the hypothalamus,[58] but there is no evidence that the ventromedial nucleus is selectively permeable in any way.

The apparent participation of all or part of the ventromedial nucleus in eating and emotional and sexual behavior has led us to study the effect of metabolic and hormonal substances and brain stem stimulation upon the activity of this structure. Initially, an electrophysiological investigation of the forebrain regions which can evoke responses in the hypothalamic ventromedial nucleus was undertaken. This study will be reported elsewhere. On the basis of data obtained from this study, the afferent pathways to the ventromedial nucleus from the amygdala and from the septum were chosen for more detailed analysis. The amygdala was selected because of its association with changes in aggressive behavior,[16, 36, 59] influences upon eating behavior,[36, 59] sexual behavior,[47] and endocrine activities.[35, 48, 60] The septal area has also been associated with changes in aggressive behavior in some species.[9, 50]

ANATOMICAL CONSIDERATIONS

The amygdaloid complex of nuclei may be divided, on comparative anatomical grounds, into a corticomedial and baso-lateral group.[33] A major efferent bundle, arising mainly from the corticomedial group and the medial and caudal parts of the baso-lateral group, is the stria terminalis.[19] This tract passes along the lateral wall of the lateral ventricle between the caudate nucleus and the thalamus to reach the region of the anterior commissure. At this point a portion of the stria terminalis, the preoptic component, passes caudal to the anterior commissure to terminate in the preoptic area and the paraventricular region of the anterior hypothalamus. A second portion of the stria terminalis, the supracommissural component, passes rostral to the anterior commissure and then bends caudally beneath the commissure to reach the ventromedial and dorsomedial hypothalamic nuclei.[2, 3, 8] Efferent fibers from the baso-lateral portion of the amygdala take a different route to the hypothalamus, entering the longitudinal association bundle which sends a projection component beneath the internal capsule to the preoptic and anterior hypothalamic regions.[18, 19] The remainder of the course of these fibers is uncertain, but many appear to enter the medial forebrain bundle and, after synapsing in the lateral hypothalamus, relay to the ventromedial nucleus.[21] Reflecting this pattern of efferent projections, stimulation of the medial portions of the amygdala evoke short-latency responses in the ventromedial nucleus, while lateral stimulation yields longer latency responses.[21]

A generally similar pattern of direct and indirect connections with the ventromedial nucleus arises from the septal nuclei and underlying preoptic region. Fibers from the dorsal septum run along with precommissural fornix fibers passing through this area and enter the medial forebrain bundle.[19] Electrophysiological evidence indicates that a portion of these fibers relay to the ventromedial nucleus after synapsing in the lateral hypothalamus. More ventrally in the septum, fibers of the supracommissural stria terminalis may be activated. Some of the features of the amygdaloid and septal efferents to the ventromedial nucleus are diagrammatically indicated in Figure IX–1. It must be kept in mind that there are other sources of afferent pathways to the ventromedial nucleus[14] in addition to those selected for study in these experiments.

Methods

Stimulating electrodes were usually placed in the baso-medial or central amygdaloid nucleus and in the dorsal septum at the level of the nucleus accumbens (Figure IX–2). The stainless steel, bipolar cencentric electrodes had a Teflon insulated 26-gauge outer shaft. When the effect of brain stem stimulation was being examined, a similar type of electrode was used to record from the ventromedial nucleus. In those experiments dealing with drug effects the hypothalamic electrodes consisted of a 19-gauge outer shaft which did not penetrate below the dorsal hypothalamus and through which a 26-gauge cannula or 26-gauge concentric bipolar recording electrodes could be inserted. Although several drug-injection techniques were employed, it was felt that the injection of drug in liquid form through a cannula, which was then replaced with a bipolar concentric recording electrode of matched length, was the most satisfactory.

The majority of the approximately 110 cats used in this series of experiments were acute preparations. Encéphale isolé, local anesthesia and Flaxedil immobilization, and Nembutal anesthesia were employed. It was found that barbiturates did not influence the findings in the series of animals used for the drug study, so most of the animals in this group were anesthetized with Nembutal. Barbiturates did, however, block the effects of brain stem stimulation on the hypothalamus, and the animals used in this part of the study were premedicated with Meperidine hydrochloride (3.5 mg./kg.), prepared surgically under ether anesthesia and maintained thereafter with local anesthesia, Flaxedil immobilization, and artificial respiration. It was customary to record femoral blood pressure, EKG and the electroencephalogram in this group. If indications of pain or discomfort, such as unstable blood pressure or EKG, continually aroused EEG and pupillary dilatation persisted for any length of time, the animal was given an anesthetic dose of barbiturate. All of the results described were also seen in unrestrained, conscious animals with implanted electrodes.

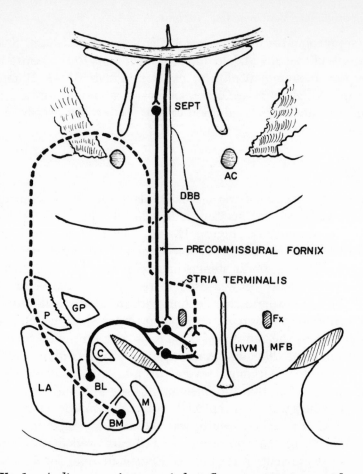

Fig. IX—1. *A diagram of some of the afferent projections to the ventro-medial nucleus from the septal region and from the amygdala. In addition to the precommissural fornix fibers passing through the septal region, a number of fibers originating in the dorsal portion of the septum follow a course into the medial forebrain bundle. They then may synapse with neurons in the lateral hypothalamus which relay to the ventromedial nucleus. The supracommissural component of the stria terminalis passes through the ventral part of the septum. The stria terminalis arises predominantly from the caudal portions of the amygdaloid basomedial nucleus and corticomedial nuclei. Some of the fibers of the stria terminalis project directly to the ventromedial nucleus while others terminate in the preoptic area and lateral hypothalamus. In addition to the stria terminalis, another group of efferent fibers from the amygdala passes ventral to the internal capsule toward the preoptic area and lateral hypothalamus where they may synapse with neurons which relay to the ventromedial nucleus.*

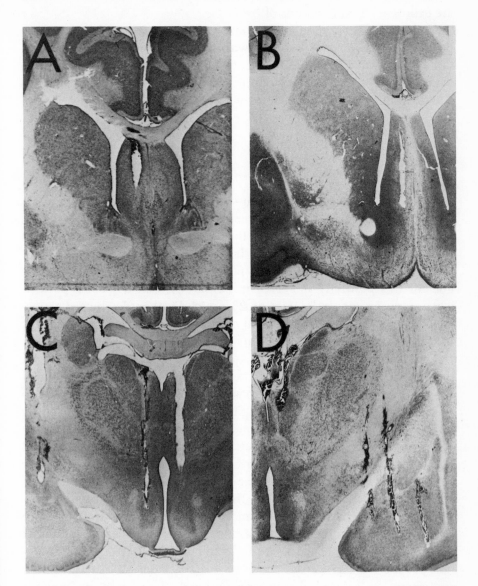

Fig. IX—2. *Photomicrographs of representative sites of stimulation and recording in these experiments. **A** shows caudal and **B** rostral septal stimulating positions. **C** shows an electrode tract in the ventromedial nucleus and one more laterally in the central amygdaloid nucleus. **D** illustrates three electrode tracts in the basomedial, basolateral and lateral amygdaloid nuclei.*

The bitartrate salts of catecholamines were used and concentrations are expressed in micrograms of free base.

At the conclusion of each experiment the animal was given an over-dose of Nembutal and perfused with saline followed by 10 per cent formol-saline-acacia solution. Twenty-five or 50 μ sections of the brain were cut with a freezing microtome and stained with thionin or by the Klüver method for the histological verification of electrode positions.

Results

IDENTIFICATION OF VENTROMEDIAL NUCLEUS RESPONSE

When stimulating electrodes are placed in the septum at the an-terior-posterior level of the nucleus accumbens, bipolar recording electrodes slowly lowered toward the ventromedial nucleus first record a single positive wave of 5 msec. latency about 1 mm. above the nu-cleus. As the recording electrode penetrates the dorsal surface of the nucleus this positivity increases in amplitude, and a second positive wave appears with a latency of 23 msec. Further downward move-ment results in a polarity reversal or turnover of both components of the response near the center of the nucleus (Figure IX–3). Within the nucleus the latency of the first component is 7 msec., while that of the second component remains the same. The relative amplitude of the first or second component depends upon the position of the stimu-lating electrodes in the septum. Stimulation dorsally in the septum just beneath the corpus callosum produces mainly the long-latency component. The shorter latency component is most prominent following stimulation ventrally in the septum just above the anterior commissure. Exploration throughout the hypothalamus shows that this bimodal evoked potential has the highest amplitude in the ventro-medial nucleus and attenuates rapidly as the electrode explores more caudal regions of the hypothalamus. Lateral to the ventromedial nucleus in the region of the medial forebrain bundle, septal stimula-tion produces a diphasic response of 4 msec. latency. In view of the anatomical features of the septum outlined in the introduction, we believe that the first component represents activation of the supra-commissural bundle of the stria terminalis which projects directly to the ventromedial nucleus. The second component is attributed to stimulation of precommissural fornix and septo-hypothalamic fibers which enter the medial forebrain bundle and terminate in the lateral hypothalamus. Lateral hypothalamic neurons then complete the pathway to the ventromedial nucleus.

Several electrophysiological observations support this interpretation.

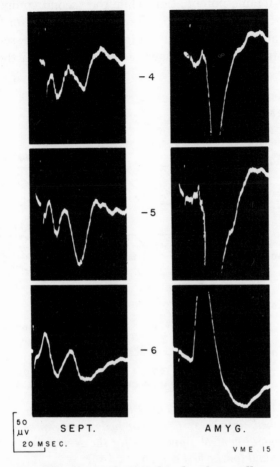

Fig. IX—3. *The left-hand column illustrates the response evoked in the ventromedial septal stimulation, the right-hand column by amygdaloid stimulation. The depth of the electrodes in Horsley-Clark coordinates are given between the two columns. The depth of H–4 corresponds to the dorsal pole of the ventromedial nucleus. Note the phase reversal of the responses as the electrode penetrates the ventromedial nucleus.*

The first component will follow 10/sec. septal stimulation without a reduction in amplitude, while the second component is attenuated greatly. Following a period of 10/sec. stimulation, the first component shows a post-tetanic potentiation while the second component usually shows a post-tetanic depression. The recovery curves for the two components are also quite different (Figure IX—4). The second component demonstrates a much longer recovery time than the first. These

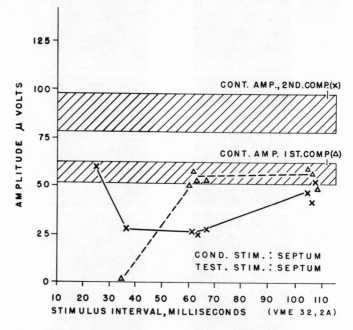

Fig. IX—4. *Recovery curve for the septal-ventromedial evoked response. Cross-hatched bars represent the range of control amplitudes for the second component* (χ) *and for the first component* (Δ).

data are consistent with the supposition that a direct pathway to the ventromedial nucleus is responsible for the first component and a plurisynaptic pathway for the second component.

Stimulation of the basal or medial amygdaloid nuclei evokes a ventromedial nucleus response which differs in several respects from that described above. This is usually a diphasic, initially positive wave when recorded from the dorsal portion of the ventromedial nucleus and reverses in polarity as the electrode is lowered. Significantly, the turnover point is usually 0.5 to 1 mm. lower than the turnover point for the potential evoked by septal stimulation. This suggests that the population of neurons within the ventromedial nucleus activated by septal stimulation is not the same as that fired by the amygdala. The latency of the amygdaloid-ventromedial response is usually 8 msec. Stimulation more laterally in the amygdala evokes ventromedial responses with latencies of 15–20 msec. However, long-latency responses have frequently been obtained with stimulation of the corticomedial portion of the amygdala. The short-latency responses have been attributed, at least in part, to activation of the stria terminalis. It should be noted that, in addition to direct projections to the ventromedial nucleus, the stria terminalis also terminates in the preoptic region and anterior hypothalamus. Both of these regions may in turn activate the ventromedial nucleus. The longer-latency responses are probably mediated by way of the longitudinal association bundle to the preoptic region and thence to the ventromedial nucleus. Interaction studies indicate that in our experiments both direct and indirect amygdaloid projections to the ventromedial nucleus are activated. Although the turnover point studies indicate that different populations of ventromedial neurons are discharged by amygdaloid and septal stimulation, interaction studies make it clear that these populations are functionally related. Amygdaloid stimulation depresses the response of the ventromedial nucleus to subsequent septal stimulation and vice versa. The latter effect is the most marked. This suppression is not a result of septal connections with the amygdala.

THE EFFECT OF SOME METABOLIC AGENTS UPON THE VENTROMEDIAL NUCLEUS

In view of the association of the ventromedial nucleus with satiety mechanisms, the action of glucose and of insulin upon septal-ventromedial and amygdaloid-ventromedial pathways was examined. Although the animals used for these experiments were usually fasted for 24 hours before they were used, control blood sugar levels were quite high (135–210 mg. per cent). This was presumably a consequence of sympatho-adrenal discharge accompanying the stress of anesthesia and surgery. The intravenous administration over a period of several minutes of 5 cc. of 5 or 10 per cent glucose-saline did not alter the septal-ventromedial response. An example is illustrated in Figure IX–5. While it might appear that the second component is slightly reduced in the postinjection records, this was not a consistent finding. The amygdaloid-ventromedial response was reduced to about

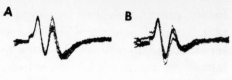

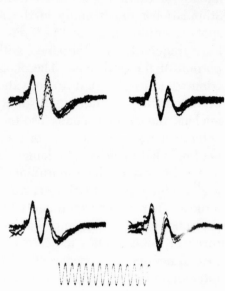

Fig. IX—5. *The effect of systemically administered glucose upon the septal-ventromedial evoked response. Each set of responses represents five superimposed sweeps. Column A, controls taken at 5-minute intervals; column B, responses taken 5, 10, and 15 minutes respectively following the intravenous administration of 5 cc. 5 per cent glucose-saline. Calibration = 50 μV. 100-cycle sweep.*

80 per cent (Figure IX—6) of its control value following glucose injection in several experiments, but this did not happen with sufficient regularity to be accepted as significant. To avoid the high blood sugar levels during the control period the experiment was repeated in a number of chronically implanted animals. Again, no clear effect of increased blood glucose levels was apparent.

The administration of large doses of insulin did have a consistent

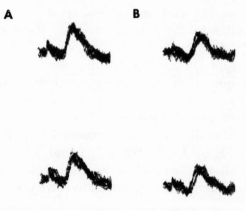

Fig. IX—6. *Superimposed traces of the amygdaloid-ventromedial evoked response. (A) controls taken at 5-minute intervals; (B) responses, 5 and 10 minutes following the intravenous administration of 5 cc. 5 per cent glucose-saline.*

effect upon the amygdaloid-ventromedial response. The intravenous administration of 40 or 80 units of insulin* produced a depression of approximately 30 per cent in the amplitude of this response (Figure IX–7). This effect was noted within 5–15 minutes of the injection. In those cases in which glucose reduced the height of the response, little or no change was noted in the recovery curve and the usual post-tetanic potentiation was seen following 10/sec. stimulation. However, following insulin the recovery curve is quite flat (Figure IX–8),

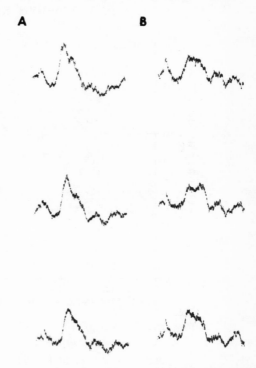

A **B**

Fig. IX—7. *Amygdaloid-ventromedial evoked response. (A) controls taken at 5-minute intervals; (B) responses taken at 5, 10, and 15 minutes respectively following the intravenous administration of 40 units of insulin.*

which suggests a decreased excitability of the amygdaloid-ventromedial pathway. The absence of post-tetanic potentiation following insulin is a further reflection of this decreased excitability. Repetition of the insulin experiments in conscious cats with chronically implanted electrodes gave similar, though less marked, results. It was clear that during the development of hypoglycemia many events were taking place in other parts of the brain. The development of seizures in the entorhinal cortex and a reduction of the amygdaloid-entorhinal-evoked response occurred. Behaviorally the animal was excited and ultimately

---

* "Iletin," Eli Lilly and Co.

showed signs of massive sympatho-adrenal discharge. Although the data on insulin is suggestive, the massive doses used and the ancillary effects of its administration make it impossible to draw any conclusions regarding any possible action upon the ventromedial nucleus.

To overcome these difficulties we studied the effects of the injection of small quantities of insulin and glucose directly into the ventromedial nucleus. After ascertaining that the injection of a one microliter volume

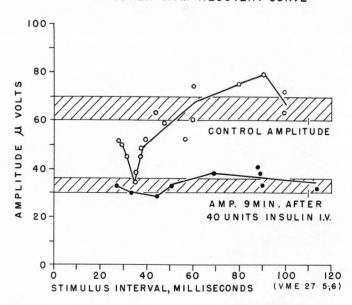

Fig. IX—8. *Recovery curve of the amygdaloid-ventro-medial response. Open circles represent the control recovery curve; closed circles, the curve obtained 9 minutes following the intravenous administration of 40 units of insulin. Hatched bars show range of amplitude of conditioning responses.*

of isotonic saline had no effect on the septal-ventromedial and amygdala-ventromedial responses, a similar volume of 5 or 10 per cent glucose-saline solution or 80 milliunits of insulin was injected into the ventromedial nucleus. No changes in ventromedial nucleus responses have been seen with these substances, and we are forced to conclude that the effects noted following systemic injection were either a consequence of an action elsewhere in the nervous system or of some agent which is secondarily mobilized. The sympatho-adrenal discharge associated with a rapidly developing hypoglycemia led us to examine the effects of catecholamines injected directly into the ventromedial nucleus.

THE EFFECT OF CATECHOLAMINES
UPON THE VENTROMEDIAL NUCLEUS

The experimental arrangement in this aspect of the study employed stimulating electrodes in the amygdaloid and septal positions described previously and the insertion of a drug-injection-recording electrode into the ventromedial nucleus. Three criteria had to be satisfied before an experiment was considered valid for an evaluation of a drug effect; demonstration of (A) turnover points of the evoked responses in the ventromedial nucleus indicating proximity to the source of the potential, (B) an inhibitory interaction between the responses evoked in the ventromedial nucleus by septal and amygdaloid stimulation, and (C) histological confirmation of electrode placements. The parameters of the responses considered were (1) amplitude following 1/sec. stimulation, (2) magnitude of post-tetanic potentiation following 10/sec. stimulation, and (3) threshold of response.

The injection of from 20 to 30 micrograms (free base) of liquid or crystalline norepinephrine or epinephrine directly into the ventromedial nucleus usually produced an immediate enhancement of the septal-ventromedial-evoked response and a concomitant decrease in the amygdaloid-ventromedial response (Figure IX–9). These changes were also reflected in the degree of post-tetanic potentiation. The septal-ventromedial response P-T-P increase ranged from 37 to 200 per cent above control values while the amygdaloid-ventromedial P-T-P varied from 32 to 100 per cent below their controls. Similar changes were noted following the intracarotid injection of 55 μg. epinephrine or norepinephrine (Figure IX–10). Although in most animals the two responses showed changes in opposite directions, the degree of enhancement of the septal-ventromedial response was seldom proportional to the amygdaloid-ventromedial depression. Depression of the amygdaloid-ventromedial response was usually the most marked change. Following injection of the drug in liquid form, the changes in the evoked responses persisted for 15–30 minutes. The septal-HVM enhancement was generally apparent within 1 minute and reached a maximum at about 5 minutes and returned to control levels sooner than the amygdala-HVM response, which appeared within 1–3 minutes and persisted for up to 30 minutes. Epinephrine and norepinephrine produced the same effects at similar doses.

When the same dose of the drug was injected in crystalline form, the time course of the effects was longer and sometimes failed to return to control amplitude. Histological examination often showed a

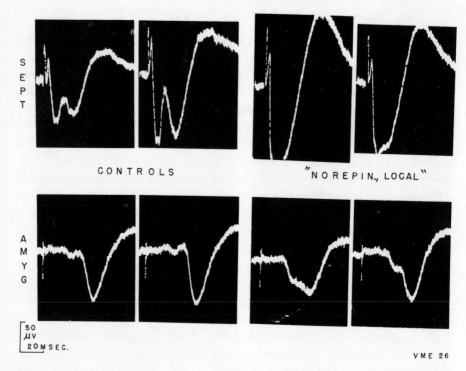

VME 26

Fig. IX—9. *Top row, septal-ventromedial response. Bottom row, amygdaloid-ventromedial response. In each pair of records the left-hand figure represents the response to single shock stimulation; the right-hand record, the post-tetanic potentiation 1 sec. following a brief period of 10/sec. stimulation. Following the injection of 55 μg. norepinephrine directly into the ventromedial nucleus, the septal-ventromedial response is increased in amplitude while the amygdaloid-ventromedial response is slightly decreased.*

ring of cell loss and pyknotic cells surrounding the site of crystalline injection (Figure IX–11). This was not seen at the sites of liquid injection, even though the dose levels were comparable.

The catecholamines seemed to produce a tachyphylaxis, for if subsequent injections are given within 90 minutes the resulting change is much less than the original. If 90 minutes or more is allowed to elapse between injections, the degree of change to the second or third injection is similar to the first. Dose levels below 20 μg. were usually without effect but in some instances depressed both responses.

The local injections of (A) isotonic saline, (B) 2 per cent hypertonic saline, (C) 20 milliunits pitressin and (D) 10 μg. sodium nitrate in isotonic saline were without effect. No changes in heart rate, pupillary dilation, or other signs of autonomic activation, such

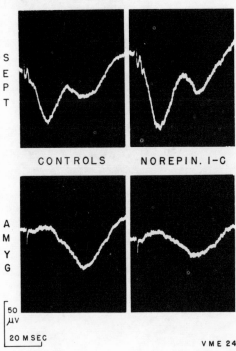

Fig. IX—10. *Top row, septal-ventromedial responses; bottom row, amygdaloid-ventromedial responses. On the right-hand side of the figure the effects of the intracarotid injection of 55 μg. of norepinephrine are seen. Note the increase in the amplitude of both components of the septal-ventromedial response and a decrease in the amplitude of the amygdaloid-ventromedial response.*

as salivation or piloerection, were noted following the injection of catecholamines into the hypothalamus.

Another adrenergic compound, D-amphetamine, was also studied and in doses of from 10 to 50 μg. depresses both responses in the ventromedial nucleus. In other structures we have examined, such as the hippocampus and the amygdala, catecholamines depress the potential evoked by septal stimulation. Ventromedial neurons responding to septal stimulation were the only ones showing an enhancement.

Our attention was now directed to other areas of the brain stem for which there is evidence of an adrenergic sensitivity.[44]

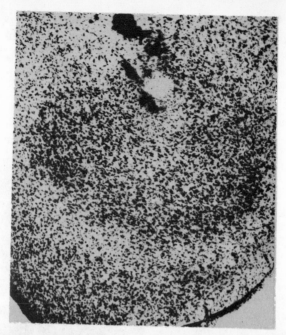

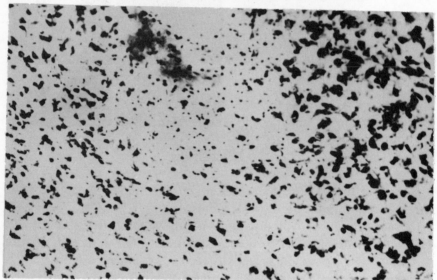

Fig. IX—11. *Photomicrographs of the site of drug injection into the ventromedial nucleus. The lower photograph shows a higher power view of the cell damage surrounding the place of injection of crystalline norepinephrine. The injection of the same dosage of norepinephrine in liquid form does not produce this cell damage.*

THE EFFECT OF RETICULAR STIMULATION
UPON THE VENTROMEDIAL NUCLEUS

High-frequency (100/sec.) stimulation of the medial portion of the mesencephalic reticular formation in locally anesthetized, Flaxedil immobilized cats produced a dissociation of responses in the ventromedial nucleus similar to that seen following local injection

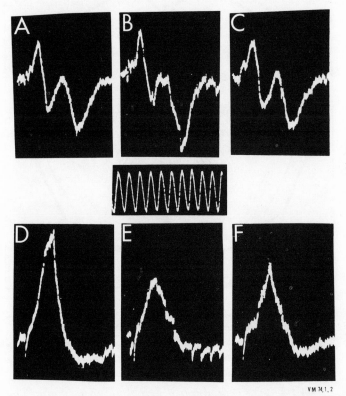

VM 74,1,2

Fig. IX—12. *The effect of medial mesencephalic reticular formation stimulation upon the septal-ventromedial response (top row) and the amygdaloid-ventromedial response (bottom row). A and D represent control responses; B and E responses during 100/sec. stimulation of the reticular formation; and C and F responses immediately following the cessation of stimulation. Note the increase in the second component of the septal-ventromedial response and the decrease in the amplitude of the amygdaloid-ventromedial response during reticular stimulation. Following stimulation the amygdaloid-ventromedial response is depressed for a few seconds while the septal-ventromedial response returns to control amplitude immediately. 50-μV. 100-cycle calibration.*

of norepinephrine (Figure IX—12). During the period of stimulation the septal-ventromedial response is larger and the amygdaloid-ventromedial response smaller. This effect is most pronounced following stimulation of the junction of the periventricular gray and reticular

Amyg – HVM   Sept – HVM

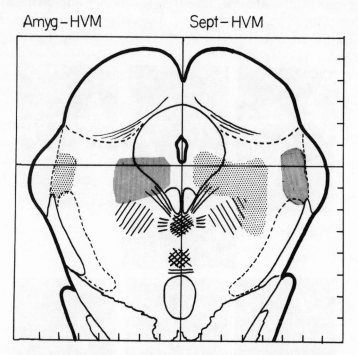

Fig. IX—13. *Diagram of the mesencephalon showing the regions which influence the ventromedial nucleus evoked responses. The stippled area represents sites in which stimulation produced increased amplitude of response; the vertical bar area the region in which stimulation produces a diminished amplitude of response. The results for the septal-ventromedial evoked response are plotted on the right-hand side of the diagram, those for the amygdaloid-ventromedial response on the left-hand side of the diagram.*

formation but may be obtained throughout the dorsomedial part of the mesencephalic tegmentum (Figure IX—13). The second component of the septal response is most markedly enhanced, while both phases of the amygdaloid response are equally depressed. Stimulation of the region just outlined also produces an increase in blood pressure and EEG arousal. However, the same blood pressure and arousal effects are seen following stimulation of other mesencephalic or diencephalic structures which do not alter the ventromedial responses. Additional evidence that the pressor response does not play a role in the changes seen is provided by the presence of the hypothalamic effect, and absence of the vascular response, during reticular stimulation in animals with a midpontine transection.

Stimulation of a smaller region in the lateral reticular formation at this same level produces just the opposite results (Figure IX–14). The septal-ventromedial response is depressed while the amygdaloid-ventromedial response is enhanced.

Septal-amygdaloid, septal-hippocampal, and fornix-mammillary evoked potentials were not influenced by reticular stimulation.

The action of the reticular formation upon the ventromedial nucleus has been duplicated in animals with chronically implanted electrodes. This effect is abolished by subanesthetic doses of barbiturate.

Discussion

The ability of catecholamines or brain stem stimulation to act upon different groups of cells within the ventromedial nucleus in opposite ways naturally leads to some consideration of the possible role of such substances in the feeding, rage, and endocrine mechanisms which have been associated with this nucleus. It is necessary to keep in mind that there has been no convincing evidence that adrenergic synapses exist in the ventromedial nucleus even though this region of the brain has a relatively high endogenous level of catecholamines[54] and that norepinephrine can modify transmission in cholinergic synapses. The catecholamines have an effect upon signal transmission in the superior cervical ganglion,[40] lumbar sympathetic ganglia,[12] and central nervous system.[37] In general, norepinephrine has been found to inhibit synaptic transmission both centrally and peripherally. Some authors have described facilitation with small doses and inhibition with larger doses,[12] while others find a postinhibitory facilitation following large intravascular doses.[38] The fact that a given dose affects the amygdaloid-ventromedial and septal-ventromedial responses differently leads us to believe the results are not related to concentration factors or secondary to vascular changes. This is further supported by the observation that medial reticular stimulation can produce the same effect as the catecholamines.

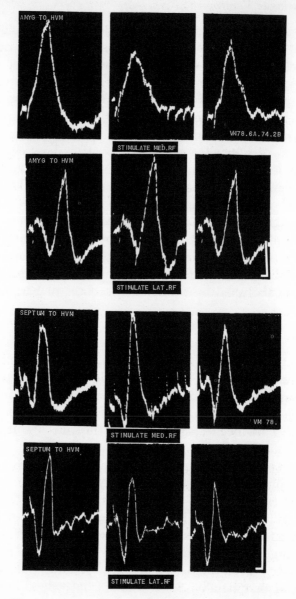

Fig. IX—14. *The effect of stimulation of the medial and lateral mesencephalic reticular formation upon septal-ventromedial and amygdaloid-ventromedial evoked responses. Note that medial reticular stimulation increases the septal-ventromedial response and decreases the amygdaloid-ventromedial response while lateral reticular stimulation produces just the opposite results. 10-msec., 50-μV. calibration.*

A number of observations suggest a relation between blood glucose levels and catecholamine secretion from the adrenal medulla. Dunér[15] found an inverse relationship between blood sugar levels and adrenal vein catecholamine levels in the intact cat, which was not seen following denervation of the adrenal. He presented further suggestive evidence that intrahypothalamic injections of 1 per cent glucose could produce a fall in catecholamine secretion while injections elsewhere in the nervous system were without effect. Armin and Grant[7] found a somewhat different relationship between blood glucose and blood "adrenaline-like" agent levels in the rabbit. Below a critical blood-glucose level of 60–70 mg. per cent, any fluctuations resulted in an increased adrenaline secretion. Increases of blood sugar above this level reduced the amount of circulating adrenaline. The work of Cannon *et al.*[13] suggests this may also be the case in the cat.

Although there is a blood-brain barrier for epinephrine[55] and norepinephrine,[57] following systemic administration of these substances the concentration found in the hypothalamus is two to five times that detected in other parts of the nervous system.

The relationship between blood-glucose levels and eating or hypothalamic electrical activity[5, 25, 41] is suggestive but as yet not unequivocal. On the other hand, it has been shown that the injection of catecholamines into the lateral hypothalamus may produce eating in rats,[22] and epinephrine may depress glucose utilization.[49]

Our own studies suggest that signal transmission in the ventromedial nucleus is not altered by glucose or insulin but is influenced by catecholamines. It remains to be demonstrated, however, that circulating catecholamines influence eating behavior.

If catecholamines are invoked in feeding mechanisms, the medial portion of the mesencephalic reticular formation, which affects the ventromedial nucleus in the same way as the catecholamines, might be expected to have some association with eating behavior. Adametz and O'Leary[1] mention that lesions in this area in cats result in markedly increased appetites.

In the sphere of aggressive behavior there also appear to be some correlations with the pattern of catecholamine release. Folkow and von Euler[17] observed that diencephalic stimulation resulted in a preponderance of either epinephrine or norepinephrine secretion from the adrenal medulla, depending upon the stimulus site. This was interpreted to indicate that separate fibers descending from the hypothalamus regulate the release of these substances.

The possibility of separate diencephalic pathways controlling epinephrine and norepinephrine release has particular significance in view of the finding that blood norepinephrine levels are elevated in a variety of affective behavioral circumstances, but epinephrine levels seem to increase only during uncertain or threatening situations.[39] Gellhorn[20] reports that high levels of adrenomedullary catecholamines decrease the excitability of the posterior hypothalamus.

Adrenergic mechanisms have also been implicated in the release of gonadotropic hormones.[46]

In summary, activation of the medial reticular formation or locally injected catecholamines can enhance the ventromedial nucleus response to septal stimulation and depress its response to amygdaloid stimulation. Just the opposite effect may be obtained with lateral reticular stimulation. It appears that there are antagonistic systems in the reticular formation acting upon the hypothalamus, much as antagonistic reticular systems located more caudally in the brain stem influence the spinal cord. Microelectrode studies of the ventromedial nucleus are needed to determine whether a change in amplitude of an evoked response signifies an increased or decreased impulse discharge by ventromedial nucleus neurons. Until these studies are completed, we do not feel it would be fruitful to speculate upon the significance of the change produced in the ventromedial nucleus by brain stem stimulation or catecholamines.

SUMMARY

The systemic or direct intrahypothalamic injection of glucose or insulin provided no evidence for an influence of these substances upon synaptic transmission in the hypothalamic ventromedial nucleus. However, direct or systemic administration of epinephrine or norepinephrine did affect this nucleus. The ventromedial response to septal stimulation was enhanced while the response to septal stimulation was suppressed. Stimulation of the medial mesencephalic reticular formation produced changes in the ventromedial-nucleus-evoked response similar to those seen following direct intrahypothalamic injections of catecholamines. Stimulation of the lateral reticular formation produced the converse effect, that is, suppression of the septal-ventromedial response and an enhancement of the amygdaloid ventromedial response. It is concluded that catecholamines can differentially affect populations of neurons within the ventromedial nucleus and that medial reticular formation may have the same influence upon the ventromedial nucleus as the catecholamines. There appear to be within the mesencephalic reticular formation antagonistic systems acting upon the ventromedial nucleus.

Acknowledgments

We are greatly indebted to Miss Nancy T. Margiotta, Miss Nancy N. Bowles, and Mrs. Fay B. Gomes for the histological preparations and technical assistance and to Mrs. Mary H. Spang for secretarial services.

References

1. ADAMETZ, J. and O'LEARY, J. L., "Experimental Mutism Resulting from Periaqueductal Lesions in Cats," *Neurology, 9*:636–642, 1959.

2. ADEY, W. R. and MEYER, M., "Hippocampal and Hypothalamic Connexions of the Temporal Lobe in the Monkey," *Brain, 75*:358–384, 1952.

3. ADEY, W. R., RUDOLPH, A. F., HINE, I. F., and HARRITT, N. J., "Glees Staining of the Monkey Hypothalamus: A Critical Appraisal of Normal and Experimental Material," *J. Anat., Lond., 92*:219–235, 1958.

4. ANAND, B. K. and BROBECK, J. R., "Hypothalamic Control of Food Intake in Rats and Cats," *Yale J. Biol. Med., 24*:123–140, 1951.

5. ANAND, B. K., DUA, S., and SINGH, B., "Electrical Activity of the Hypothalamic 'Feeding Centres' under the Effect of Changes in Blood Chemistry," *Electroenceph. clin. Neurophysiol., 13*:54–59, 1961.

6. ANDERSSON, B. and LARSSON, B., "Influence of Local Temperature Changes in the Preoptic Area and Rostral Hypothalamus on the Regulation of Food and Water Intake," *Acta physiol. scand., 52*:75–89, 1961.

7. ARMIN, J. and GRANT, R. T., "Adrenaline Release During Insulin Hypoglycaemia in the Rabbit," *J. Physiol., 149*:228–249, 1959.

8. BAN, T. and OMUKAI, F., "Experimental Studies on the Fiber Connections of the Amygdaloid Nuclei in the Rabbit," *J. comp. Neurol., 113*:245–279, 1959.

9. BRADY, J. V. and NAUTA, W. J. H., "Subcortical Mechanisms in Emotional Behavior: Affective Changes Following Septal Forebrain Lesions in the Albino Rat," *J. comp. physiol. Psychol., 46*:339–346, 1953.

10. BROBECK, J. R., "Food Intake as a Mechanism of Temperature Regulation," *Yale J. Biol. Med., 20*:545–552, 1948.

11. BROBECK, J. R., TEPPERMAN, J., and LONG, C. N. H., "Experimental Hypothalamic Hyperphagia in the Albino Rat," *Yale J. Biol. Med.*, *15*: 831–853, 1943.

12. BULBRING, E. and BURN, J. H., "An Action of Adrenaline on Transmission in Sympathetic Ganglia, Which May Play a Part in Shock," *J. Physiol.*, *101*:289–303, 1942.

13. CANNON, W. B., McIVER, M. A., and BLISS, S. W., "A Sympathetic and Adrenal Mechanism for Mobilizing Sugar in Hypoglycemia," *Amer. J. Physiol.*, *69*:46–66, 1924.

14. CLARK, W. E. LEGROS and MEYER, M., "Anatomical Relationships Between the Cerebral Cortex and the Hypothalamus," *Brit. med. Bull.*, *6*:341–345, 1952.

15. DUNÉR, H., "The Influence of the Blood Glucose Level on the Secretion of Adrenaline and Nor-adrenaline from the Suprarenal," *Acta physiol. scand.*, *28*: Suppl. *102*, 1953.

16. FERNANDEZ DE MOLINA, A. and HUNSPERGER, R. W., "Central Representation of Affective Reactions in Forebrain and Brain Stem: Electrical Stimulation of Amygdala, Stria Terminalis and Adjacent Structures," *J. Physiol.*, *145*:251–265, 1959.

17. FOLKOW, B. and VON EULER, U. S., "Selective Activation of Nor-Adrenaline and Adrenaline Producing Cells in Cat Adrenal Gland by Hypothalamic Stimulation," *Circulat. Res.*, *2*:191–195, 1954.

18. FOX, C. A., "Certain Basal Telencephalic Centers in the Cat," *J. comp. Neurol.*, *72*:1–62, 1940.

19. FOX, C. A., "The Stria Terminalis, Longitudinal Association Bundle and Precommissural Fornix Fibers in the Cat," *J. comp. Neurol.*, *79*:277–295, 1943.

20. GELLHORN, E., *Autonomic Imbalance and the Hypothalamus*, University of Minnesota Press, Minneapolis, 1947.

21. GLOOR, P., "Electrophysiological Studies on the Connections of the Amygdaloid Nucleus in the Cat. I. Neuronal Organization of the Amygdaloid Projection System. II. The Electrophysiological Properties of the Amygdaloid Projection System," *Electroenceph. clin. Neurophysiol.*, *7*: 223–242, 243–264, 1955.

22. GROSSMAN, P., "Eating or Drinking Elicited by Direct Adrenergic or Cholinergic Stimulation of Hypothalamus," *Science*, *132*:301–302, 1960.

23. HAGAMEN, W. D. and BROOKS, D. C., "Sexual Behavior of Female Cats Following Lesions of the Ventromedial Nucleus of the Hypothalamus," *Anat. Rec.*, *130*:414, 1958.

24. HAUN, C. K. and SAWYER, C. H., "The Role of the Hypothalamus in Initiation of Milk Secretion," *Acta endocr., Kbh.*, *38*:99–106, 1961.

25. HERBERG, L. J., "Hunger Reduction Produced by Injecting Glucose into the Lateral Ventricle of the Rat," *Nature, Lond., 187*:245–246, July 16, 1960.

26. HERVEY, G. R., "The Effects of Lesions in the Hypothalamus in Parabiotic Rats," *J. Physiol., 145*:336–352, 1959.

27. HESS, W. R. and AKERT, K., "Experimental Data on Role of Hypothalamus in Mechanisms of Emotional Behavior," *Arch. Neurol. Psychiat., Chicago, 73*:127–129, 1955.

28. HETHERINGTON, A. W., "The Spontaneous Activity and Food Intake of Rats with Hypothalamic Lesions," *Amer. J. Physiol., 136*:609–618, 1942.

29. HETHERINGTON, A. W. and RANSON, S. W., "The Relation of Various Hypothalamic Lesions to Adiposity in the Rat," *J. comp. Neurol., 76*:475–499, 1942.

30. HODES, R. and MAGOUN, H. W., "Autonomic Responses to Electrical Stimulation of the Forebrain and Midbrain with Special Reference to the Pupil," *J. comp. Neurol., 76*:169–190, 1942.

31. INGRAM, W. R., "Brain Stem Mechanisms in Behavior," *Electroenceph. clin. Neurophysiol., 4*:397–406, 1952.

32. JANOWITZ, H. D. and GROSSMAN, M. T., "Some Factors Affecting the Food Intake of Normal Dogs and Dogs with Esophagostomy and Gastric Fistula," *Amer. J. Physiol., 159*:143–148, 1949.

33. JOHNSTON, J. B., "Further Contributions to the Study of the Evolution of the Forebrain," *J. comp. Neurol., 35*:337–481, 1923.

34. KENNEDY, G. C., "The Role of Depot Fat in the Hypothalamic Control of Food Intake in the Rat," *Proc. Roy. Soc., B140*:578–592, 1953.

35. KOIKEGAMI, H., YAMADA, T., and USUI, K., "Stimulation of Amygdaloid Nuclei and Periamygdaloid Cortex with Special Reference to Its Effects on Uterine Movements and Ovulation," *Folia psychiat. neurol. jap., 8*:7–31, 1954.

36. MACLEAN, P. D. and DELGADO, J. M. R., "Electrical and Chemical Stimulation of Frontotemporal Portion of Limbic System in the Waking Animal," *Electroenceph. clin. Neurophysiol., 5*:91–100, 1953.

37. MARRAZZI, A. S., "The Effect of Drugs on Neurons and Synapses," in FIELD, W. S. (ed.), *Brain Mechanisms and Drug Actions,* Charles C Thomas, Springfield, Ill., 1957, pp. 45–67.

38. MARRAZZI, A. S. and MARRAZZI, R. N., "Further Localization and Analysis of Adrenergic Synaptic Inhibition," *J. Neurophysiol., 10*:167–178, 1947.

39. MASON, J. W., MANGRAN, G., BRADY, J. V., CONRAD, D. I., and RIOCH, D. McK., "Concurrent Plasma Epinephrine, Norepinephrine and 17–Hydroxycorticosteroid Levels During Conditioned Emotional Disturbance in Monkeys," *Psychosom. Med., 23*:344–353, 1961.

40. MATTHEWS, R. J., "The Effect of Epinephrine, Levarterenol and dl-Isoproterenol on Transmission in the Superior Cervical Ganglion of the Cat," *J. Pharmacol. exp. Ther.*, 116:433–443, 1956.

41. MAYER, J., "Regulation of Energy Intake and the Body Weight: The Glucostatic and the Lipostatic Hypothesis," *Ann. N.Y. Acad. Sci.*, 63:15–43, 1955.

42. MILLER, N. E., "Experiments in Motivation," *Science*, 126:1271–1278, 1957.

43. MILLER, N. E., BAILEY, C. J., and STEVENSON, J. A. F., "Decreased 'Hunger' but Increased Food Intake Resulting from Hypothalamic Lesions," *Science*, 112:256–259, 1950.

44. ROTHBALLER, A. B., "Studies on the Adrenaline-Sensitive Component of the Reticular Activating System," *Electroenceph. clin. Neurophysiol.*, 8:603–621, 1956.

45. SAWYER, C. H., "Reproductive Behavior," vol. II, FIELD, J. (ed.), *Handbook of Physiology, Sect. 1: Neurophysiology*, Williams & Wilkins Co., Baltimore, 1960, Chap. XLIX.

46. SAWYER, C. H., MARKEE, J. E., and HOLLINSHEAD, W. H., "Inhibition of Ovulation in the Rabbit by the Adrenergic Blocking Agent Dibenamine," *Endocrinology*, 41:395–402, 1947.

47. SCHREINER, L. and KLING, A., "Behavioral Changes Following Rhinencephalic Injury in the Cat," *J. Neurophysiol.*, 16:643–659, 1953.

48. SETEKLEN, J., SKAUG, O. E., and KAADA, B. R., "Increase of Plasma 17-Hydroxycorticosteroids by Cerebral Cortical and Amygdaloid Stimulation in the Cat," *J. Endocrinol.*, 22:119–127, 1961.

49. SOMOGYI, M., "Studies of Arteriovenous Differences in Blood Sugar. V. Effect of Epinephrine on the Rate of Glucose Assimilation," *J. biol. Chem.*, 186:513–526, 1950.

50. SPIEGEL, E. A., MILLER, H. R., and OPPENHEIMER, M. J., "Forebrain and Rage Reactions," *J. Neurophysiol.*, 3:538–548, 1940.

51. SUTIN, J. Unpublished observations.

52. TEITELBAUM, P. and CAMPBELL, B. A., "Ingestion Patterns in Hyperphagia and Normal Rats," *J. comp. physiol. Psychol.*, 51:135–141, 1958.

53. URSIN, H., "The Temporal Lobe Substrate of Fear and Anger," *Acta psychiat. scand.*, 35:378–396, 1960.

54. VOGT, M., "The Concentration of Sympathin in Different Parts of the Central Nervous System Under Normal Conditions and After the Administration of Drugs," *J. Physiol.*, 123:451–481, 1954.

55. WEIL-MALHERBE, H., AXELROD, J., and TOMCHICK, R., "Blood Brain Barrier for Adrenaline," *Science*, 129:1226, 1959.

56. WHEATLY, M. D., "The Hypothalamus and Affective Behavior in Cats," *Arch. Neurol. Psychiat., Chicago,* 52:296–316, 1944.

57. WHITBY, L. G., AXELROD, J., and WEIL-MALHERBE, H., "The Fate of H³-Norepinephrine in Animals," *J. Pharmacol. exp. Ther.,* 132:193–201, 1961.

58. WISLOCKI, G. B. and KING, L. S., "The Permeability of the Hypophysis and Hypothalamus to Vital Dyes, with a Study of the Hypophyseal Vascular Supply," *Amer. J. Anat.,* 58:421–472, 1936.

59. WOOD, C. P., "Behavioral Changes Following Discrete Lesions of Temporal Lobe Structures," *Neurology,* 8:215–220, 1958.

60. YAMADA, T. and GREER, M. A., "The Effect of Bilateral Ablation of the Amygdala on Endocrine Function in the Rat," *Endocrinology,* 66:565–574, 1960.

X

An Experimental Model of Temporal Lobe Epilepsy: Studies of the Convulsant Properties of Cocaine

Eduardo Eidelberg
Henry Lesse
Frederick P. Gault

A considerable amount of work has been carried out on the effects of cocaine on the nervous system, ranging from studies of its influence on neuronal membrane properties to clinical descriptions of the consequences of chronic cocainism in humans. Our interest in this drug developed from the finding of Lesse and Gault (in preparation) that cocaine induces convulsive discharges localized in the region of the amygdaloid nucleus, which may or may not be followed by generalized seizures. This localized effect of cocaine on brain activity is illustrated in Figure X—1. The experiments to be reported here represent our attempts, by means of pharmacological studies on rats, to elucidate the mechanisms involved in the generation of these convulsive phenomena.[12]

Methods

A total of 350 albino rats, of the Wistar strain, were employed. Their weight ranged from 150 to 250 g. Groups of 10 animals were used as units in each experiment, with control groups of 10 rats matched to the test groups for strain, source, sex, and weight. No animal was used in more than one experiment.

The studies described here were supported by grant K–13 from the Department of Mental Hygiene, State of California.

Crystalline cocaine hydrochloride was dissolved in saline solution and was injected intraperitoneally. The dosages employed ranged from 30 to 80 mg./kg. of the hydrochloride salt.

All other drugs employed were injected intraperitoneally unless stated otherwise. Diphenylhydantoin (Dilantin (R)) was used as the commercially available intravenous solution, diluted with saline. The same applies to phenobarbital (Luminal (R)), acetazoleamide (Diamox (R)), pyridoxine hydrochloride, chlorpromazine hydrochloride, reserpine phosphate (Serpasil (R)), phenyl-isopropylhydrazine (PIH, or Lakeside JB–516), and pyrogallol (Mallinckrodt). The dosages employed are detailed in Results, below. Dibenamine (R) was prepared as a stock 1 per cent solution in acidified propylene glycol, diluted before use with saline solution (final pH 6.0).

STATISTICAL TREATMENTS

Each experiment in this series involved the comparison of several matched groups with a comparable control group. Since the data obtained from each animal were binary (i.e., convulsion or nonconvulsion, death or no death) the assumptions for parametric statistical treatment could not be met. Hence, statistical comparisons were made by means of the Fisher Exact Probability Test.[35] In view of predicted changes (i.e., a decrease or increase in incidence of convulsions compared to control groups) the one-tailed test was utilized.

Results

As has been reported before,[10, 20] dosages of 30–40 mg./kg. of cocaine hydrochloride injected introperitoneally in rats induced a considerable degree of agitation. If left undisturbed in a large box, they circled rapidly for periods of time ranging from 5 to 30 minutes after the injection. There was also sialorrhea, mydriasis, and exophthalmos. After dosages of 50–60 mg./kg. generalized convulsions followed the initial agitated phase within 5–15 minutes after injection. The CD_{50} was 50 ± 5 mg./kg. and the CD_{100} 65 ± 5 mg./kg. At this later dose range, there was usually marked ataxia preceding convulsions. These were characterized by "freezing," quickly followed by opisthotonos and generalized clonic jerking and twitching. Often the convulsions became subintrant and ended with death of the animals.

Dosages above 60 mg./kg. shortened the agitated period preceding

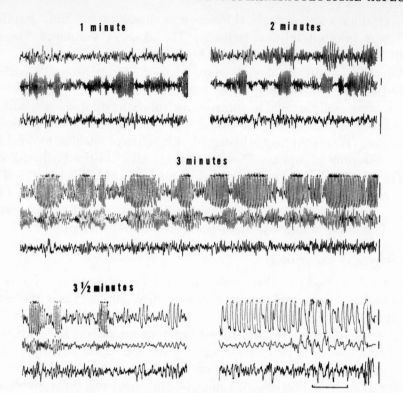

Fig. X—1. *Illustrated are samples of typical EEG records obtained from a cat with chronic indwelling electrodes after the administration of a convulsive dose of cocaine. In each sample the first tracing was obtained from the amygdaloid nucleus, the second tracing from the olfactory bulb, and the third from the neocortex. One minute after the administration of cocaine there is no significant change in electrographic activity; the cat is awake and alert. After 2 minutes, a pattern of high-voltage 40-c./sec. rhythmic activity appears in the amygdaloid region (line 1). By 3 minutes recordings show a very dramatic increase in this amygdaloid rhythmic activity but no significant change from the olfactory bulb or from the neocortex. The cat at this stage shows behavioral excitement. By 3.5 minutes recordings illustrate a clear-cut seizure pattern which is localized to the amygdala and does not involve other brain areas. The cat at this stage is extremely agitated with dilated pupils, hyperventilation, and may show circular movements. Only at the end of the 3.5-minute record do the first spike discharges begin to spread to involve the neocortex. Following this, the seizure pattern became generalized, the cat exhibited typical grand mal convulsions, and despite parenteral barbiturate medication the convulsions were fatal.*

the development of generalized convulsions and increased the probability of postconvulsive deaths.

If the generalized convulsions described above were regarded as the end point, the dose-response relationships described were quite consistent for rats of either sex and for rats obtained from three different sources. The death rate, however, varied very widely when groups of animals from different sources were compared. This made it absolutely necessary to run the experiments with parallel control groups from the same source, sex, and age as the test animals. The death rate figures are not comparable, therefore, between the experimental series illustrated in Figures X–1 and X–2.

The data summarized in Table X–1 and Figure X–1 clearly indicate that three commonly employed anticonvulsants, diphenylhydantoin, phenobarbital, and acetazoleamide, did not prevent cocaine convulsions. A drop in postconvulsive mortality in animals pretreated

Table X-1   *Incidence of Convulsions and Deaths in Saline-Injected Controls and in Animals Pretreated as Indicated.*

PREMEDICATION	NUMBER OF ANIMALS	NUMBER THAT DEVELOPED CONVULSIONS	DEATHS	PREMEDICATION	NUMBER OF ANIMALS	NUMBER THAT DEVELOPED CONVULSIONS	DEATHS
(A).	*Animals challenged with cocaine hydrochloride (60 mg./kg.)*						
Saline	10	8	7	Saline	20	14	0
Diphenylhydantoin	10	10	2°	Ethanol	10	6	1
Acetazoleamide	10	10	4	Chlorpromazine	10	1°	0
Hydroxylamine	10	2°	2°	Dibenamine	10	0°°	0
Pyridexine	10	3°	0°°	Reserpine	10	2°	0
Phenobarbital	10	7	0°°	Ergotamine Tartrate	10	7	1
(B).	*Animals challenged with cocaine hydrochloride (40 mg./kg.)*						
Saline	10	0	0	Saline	10	0	0
PIH	10	7°°	1	PIH	10	7°°	0
				Pyrogallol	10	0	0
				PIH + Pyrogallol	10	9°°	0

° P 0.05   °° P 0.01

with these drugs—which reflects the severity and duration of the generalized seizures—indicates that some protection was afforded by two of them, diphenylhydantoin and phenobarbital, but none by ace-tazoleamide. Hydroxylamine hydrochloride was effective in reducing significantly the number of animals that developed cocaine convulsions and also decreased the mortality rate. This protective effect was absent if the challenge with the cocaine was made less than 30–45 minutes after premedication with hydroxylamine. Pyridoxine hydrochloride significantly protected the treated rats against both the development of convulsions and death. This effect was short-lasting, no protection being detected if the challenge with cocaine was made later than 45 minutes after premedication with pyridoxine.

Since potentiation of "adrenergic" transmission has been postulated repeatedly as the mechanism by which cocaine exerts its peripheral

Fig. X—2. *Incidence of convulsions and postconvulsive deaths in saline-injected controls and pretreated animals, as indicated. Challenged 30–60 minutes later (see text) with cocaine hydrochloride, 60 mg./kg., intraperitoneally.*

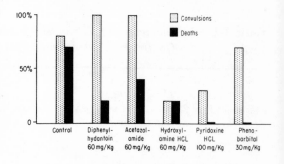

autonomic effects,[16, 17, 27, 36] a series of substances which presumably interfere with adrenergic transmission were tested for their ability to protect against cocaine convulsions. These were: (a) reserpine, which has been shown to cause depletion of serotonin, norepinephrine, and dopamine from brain tissue;[7, 23, 37] (b) chlorpromazine, which has been postulated as a central adrenergic blocking agent;[5, 6, 34] (c) Dibenamine, the prototype of synthetic adrenergic blocking agents in the peripheral autonomic nervous system,[26] with possible central effects;[15] and (d) ergotamine tartrate. It was found that reserpine, chlorpromazine and Dibenamine, injected three hours before a cocaine challenge, were all effective in preventing the development of cocaine convulsions. Ergotamine failed to offer any protection at the single-dose level employed (Figure X—2).

The results of these experiments suggested another one: determining whether a monoamino-oxidase inhibitor (in this case we employed isopropyl phenylhydrazine, or PIH)[23] would potentiate the convulsant effects of cocaine by interfering with the degradation of catecholamines or serotonin. For this a group of rats were pretreated with 20 mg./kg. of PIH and challenged two hours later with cocaine hydrochloride at a subconvulsant dose of 40 mg./kg. They were compared with a parallel control group pretreated with saline and given the same subconvulsant dose of cocaine. Figure X–3 illustrates the marked increase in number of animals that developed cocaine convulsions (70 per cent) in the PIH-treated group as compared to the saline control (0 per cent).

Inhibition by pyrogallol[24, 42, 43] of another enzyme involved in the disposition of catecholamines, catechol-O-methyl transferase,[1] failed to facilitate the development of convulsions after a challenge with cocaine

Fig. X–3. *Same procedure as described in Fig. X–2. Same challenging dose of cocaine. Note marked decrease in convulsions in animals pretreated with chlorpromazine, Dibenamine, and reserpine.*

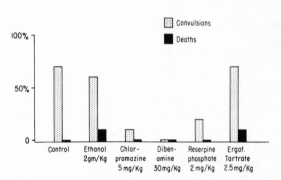

(40 mg./kg.) (Figure X–4). There was no significant difference in the number of animals that developed convulsions after the same dose of cocaine when they had been pretreated with PIH alone or with PIH together with pyrogallol.

Discussion

It is evident from the preceding data that anticonvulsants of the barbiturate or hydantoin type do not prevent the development of cocaine convulsions. While this negative finding contributes little to the explanation of the mechanisms of cocaine convulsions it may be of clinical interest, since these drugs have long been assumed to be of therapeutic value in cocaine intoxication.[20]

In contrast Dibenamine, chlorpromazine, and reserpine were most effective in protecting rats against the convulsant effect of cocaine.

It is presumed that these three substances are antagonistic to cocaine at the peripheral autonomic level. This may occur either by blocking or otherwise interfering with "adrenergic" transmission, in the case of Dibenamine[26] and chlorpromazine,[6] or by depleting nerve terminals of transmitter, in the case of reserpine.[37] Cocaine has long been thought to exert its peripheral effects by potentiation of "adrenergic" transmission. This potentiation, in the experiments of Frohlich and Loewi[16] and of Peralta and Lizarralde,[27] seemed to consist of prolongation more than actual intensification of adrenaline effects. Rothballer[29, 30] has proposed a similar potentiating effect of cocaine at the "adrenergic" receptors in the reticular activating system (see, however, Curtis and Koizumi[9]).

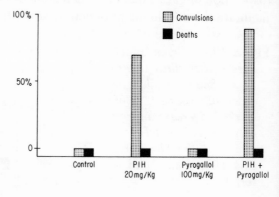

Fig. X—4. *Control animals pretreated with saline. Test animals pretreated as indicated. Two hours later a subconvulsive dose of cocaine hydrochloride (40 mg./kg.) intraperitoneally. Note the high incidence of convulsions after pretreatment with phenyl-isopropyl-hydrazine (PIH) alone, or PIH with pyrogallol, compared with controls.*

Brodie *et al.*[6] have proposed that chlorpromazine is primarily a central adrenolytic agent; this concept is still under discussion.[11, 26] Vogt[37] has shown that reserpine induces the disappearance of nordrenaline from the brain, and the same has been described by Carlsson[7] for dopamine and by Holzbauer and Vogt[22] for serotonin. On the basis of these and other observations, it has been postulated by Rothballer[29] that some form of "adrenergic" transmission does exist in the brain stem and that cocaine exerts its effects on the EEG "arousal" induced by adrenaline by a mechanism analogous to that described for its peripheral effects. In our experiments, the protection afforded to the rats pretreated by Dibenamine, chlorpromazine, and reserpine could be due to interference with a similar central "adrenergic" mechanism. If this were so, this is the only instance known to us of convulsions induced through the activity of "adrenergic" factors.

The evident synergism between PIH, an effective monoamino-oxidase inhibitor, and cocaine is also in favor of this postulation, since MAO inhibition would cause an accumulation of some substances presumed to have "adrenergic" transmitter functions. Of these noradrenaline,[14] dopamine,[7] and serotonin[25] have been suggested as likely possibilities.[19] This synergism between PIH and cocaine, it must be pointed out, is rather specific, since PIH and related substances have been shown to have anticonvulsant effects against pentylenetetrazol and EST seizures.[28]

There are several possible explanations for the protective effects of hydroxylamine and pyridoxine, since the first of these two has fairly nonspecific anticonvulsant properties[12, 31] and the second participates in a host of enzymatic sections in the brain as a coenzyme. Within the context of the data presented in this paper, however, it seems worth while to mention the fact that both of these substances—in the case of B_6, an excess of it—will interfere with the synthesis of catecholamines and serotonin at the decarboxylation step.[3, 8, 21, 32, 33, 44]

All the evidence discussed above seems to indicate that cocaine may act on the central nervous system by somehow potentiating transmission by a catecholamine or serotonin. Both are synthesized through the same decarboxylase and are degraded, at least in part, by monoamine-oxidase. Axelrod[1] has shown that catecholamines may be degraded through O-methylation by the action of catechol-O-methyl transferase (COMT). Inhibition of COMT has been achieved in vivo by administration of pyrogallol.[24, 42, 43] A test of whether the effects of cocaine are mediated by catecholamines or by serotonin is therefore possible, since in the first case pyrogallol should be as effective as a MAO inhibitor in facilitating cocaine-induced seizures and in contrast should be completely ineffective if serotonin was involved. Figure X—3 illustrates such experiments, demonstrating the ineffectiveness of pyrogallol in facilitating the appearance of cocaine-induced seizures and, therefore, the likelihood of serotonin or some other indole-amine being involved.

In view of data (Lesse and Gault, in preparation) showing the predominant involvement of the amygdala in cocaine convulsions, it is interesting to note that it has been shown[4, 18] that the amygdaloid complex contains high levels of serotonin, while its content in noradrenaline,[37] dopamine,[40] and catechol-O-methyl transferase is rather low.

Cocaine-induced convulsions have a distinctive electrographic pattern with a major participation of temporal lobe structures, plus a clinical picture that strongly resembles that of some forms of temporal lobe epilepsy. Even in their resistance to conventional anticonvulsants, these seizures are akin to those of human "psychomotor" phenomena. It may be suggested on the basis of the data presented and of these resemblances that cocaine-induced convulsions may provide a valuable model-testing situation for possible anticonvulsants for psychomotor seizures. Even more important, they may provide a lead into the biochemical and electrophysiological mechanisms responsible for temporal lobe epilepsy.

SUMMARY

Studies have been carried out on the possible neurohumoral mechanisms involved in the induction of seizures by cocaine. A series of substances have been tested for their effects on these seizures. It has been found that:

1. Conventional anticonvulsants were generally ineffective in protecting rats against the doses of cocaine employed if convulsions were regarded as the end point.

2. Dibenamine, chlorpromazine, and reserpine were highly effective in preventing cocaine seizures. Hydroxylamine hydrochloride and pyridoxine were also effective.

3. A monoamine-oxidase inhibitor (PIH) markedly potentiated the effects of subconvulsant doses of cocaine. Pyrogallol, an inhibitor of catechol-O-methyl transferase failed to produce any detectable effects.

These data suggest that cocaine may operate centrally through potentiation of the effects of serotonin or a related indole-amino.

A possible value of cocaine in future studies on temporal lobe epilepsy is discussed.

References

1. AXELROD, J., "Presence, Formation and Metabolism of Normetanephrine in the Brain, "Science, 127:754–755, 1958.

2. AXELROD, J., "The Metabolism of Catecholamines in Vivo and in Vitro," Pharmacol. Rev., 11:402–408, 1958.

3. BLASCHKO, H., "The Development of Current Concepts of Catecholamine Formation," Pharmacol. Rev., 11:307–316, 1959.

4. Bogdanski, D. F., Weissbach, H., and Udenfriend, S., "The Distribution of Serotonin, 5–Hydroxytryptophan Decarboxylase and Monoamino-Oxidase in Brain," *J. Neurochem., 1*:272–278, 1957.

5. Brodie, B. B. and Shore, P. A., "A Concept for a Role of Serotonin and Norepinephrine as Chemical Mediators in the Brain," *Ann. N.Y. Acad. Sci., 66*:631–642, 1957.

6. Brodie, B. B., Spector, S., and Shore, P. A., "Interaction of Drugs with Norepinephrine in the Brain," *Pharmacol. Rev., 11*:548–564, 1959.

7. Carlsson, A., "The Occurrence, Distribution and Physiological Role of Catecholamines in the Nervous System," *Pharmacol. Rev., 11*:490–493, 1959.

8. Clark, W. G., "Studies on Inhibition of 1–Dopa Decarboxylase *in Vitro* and *in Vivo*," *Pharmacol. Rev., 11*:330–349, 1958.

9. Curtis, D. R. and Koizumi, K., "Chemical Transmitter Substance in Brain Stem of Cat," *J. Neurophysiol., 24*:80–90, 1961.

10. Dragstedt, C. A. and Lang, V. A., "Respiratory Stimulants in Acute Cocaine Poisoning in Rabbits," *J. Pharmacol. exp. Ther., 32*:215–222, 1928.

11. Ehringer, H., Hornykiewicz, O., and Lechner, K., "Die Wirkung des Chlorpromazins auf den Katecholamin und 5–Hydroxytryptaminstoffwechsel in Gehirn der Ratte," *Arch. exp. Path. Pharmak., 239*:507–519, 1960.

12. Eidelberg, E., Baxter, C. F., Roberts, E., Saldias, C. A., and French, J. D., "Anticonvulsant Properties of Hydroxylamine and Elevation of Cerebral Gamma-Amino-Butyric Acid," *Proc. Soc. exp. Biol., N.Y., 101*:815, 1959.

13. Eidelberg, E., Lesse, H., and Gault, F. P., "Convulsant Effects of Cocaine," *Fed. Proc., 20*: 1961. Abstract.

14. Euler, U. S. von, "Autonomic Neuroeffector Transmission," in Field, J. (ed.), *Handbook of Physiology, Section 1: Neurophysiology*, vol. 1, American Physiological Society, Washington, D. C., 1959, pp. 215–237.

15. Freedman, D. X. and Giarman, N. J., "Apomorphine Test for Tranquilizing Drugs: Effect of Dibenamine," *Science, 124*:264–265, 1956.

16. Frohlich, A. and Loewi, O., "Über eine Steigerrung der Adrenalinempfindlichkeit durch Cocain," *Arch. exp. Path. Pharmak., 62*:159–169, 1910.

17. Furchgott, R. F., "The Receptors for Epinephrine and Norepinephrine (Adrenergic Receptors)," *Pharmacol. Rev., 11*:429–440, 1959.

18. Gaddum, J. N. and Giarman, N. J., "Preliminary Studies on the Biosynthesis of 5–Hydroxytryptamine," *Brit. J. Pharmacol., 11*:88–92, 1956.

19. GIARMAN, N. J., "Neurohumors in the Brain," *Yale J. Biol. Med.*, 32:73–92, 1959.

20. GOODMAN, L. S. and GILMAN, A., *The Pharmacological Basis of Therapeutics*, Macmillan, New York, 1941.

21. HOLTZ, P., "Role of 1–Dopa Decarboxylase in the Biosynthesis of Catecholamines in Nervous Tissue and the Adrenal Medulla." *Pharmacol. Rev.*, 11:317–329, 1959.

22. HOLZBAUER, M. and VOGT, M., "Depression by Reserpine of the Noradrenaline Concentration in the Hypothalamus of the Cat," *J. Neurochem.*, 1:8–11, 1956.

23. HORITA, A., "Pharmacology of JB–516 (PIH)," *Ann. N.Y. Acad. Sci.*, 80:590–595, 1959.

24. LEMBECK, F. and RESCH, H., Die Potenzierung der Adrenalinwirkung durch Cocain und Pyrogallol," *Arch. exp. Path. Pharmak.*, 240:210–217, 1960.

25. MARRAZZI, A. S., "Study of Adrenergic Cerebral Neurohumors in Relation to Synaptic Transmission Mechanisms," *Exp. Cell Res.*, Suppl. 5:370–385, 1958.

26. NICKERSON, M., "Blockade of the Actions of Adrenaline and Noradrenaline," *Pharmacol. Rev.*, 11:443–461, 1959.

27. PERALTA, B. and LIZARRALDE, E., Acción de la Cocaína sobre las Respuestas Cardíacas a la Adrenalina," *Arch. Inst. Cardiol. Méx.*, 16:34–44, 1946.

28. PROCKOP, D. J., SHORE, P. A., and BRODIE, B. B., "Anticonvulsant Properties of Monoamino-Oxidase Inhibitors," *Ann. N.Y. Acad. Sci.*, 80:643–650, 1959.

29. ROTHBALLER, A. B., "The Effect of Phenylephrine, Metamphetamine, Cocaine and Serotonin upon the Adrenaline-Sensitive Component of the Reticular Activating System," *Electroenceph. clin. Neurophysiol.*, 9:409–418, 1957.

30. ROTHBALLER, A. B., "The Effects of Catecholamines on the Central Nervous System," *Pharmacol. Rev.*, 11:494–557, 1959.

31. ROBERTS, E. and EIDELBERG, E., "Metabolic and Neurophysiological Roles of Gamma-Aminobutyric Acid (GABA)," *Int. Rev. Neurobiol.*, 2:279–332, 1959.

32. SCHMITERLOW, C. G., "The Formation *in Vivo* of Nor-Adrenaline from 3, 4–Dihydroxphenylserine (Nor-Adrenaline-Carboxylic Acid)," *Brit. J. Pharmacol.*, 6:127–134, 1951.

33. SCHOTT, H. F. and CLARK, W. G., "Dopa Decarboxylase Inhibition through the Interaction of Coenzyme and Substrate," *J. biol. Chem.*, 196:449–462, 1952.

34. SHORE, P. A. and BRODIE, B. B., "Influence of Various Drugs on Serotonin and Norepinephrine in the Brain," *Psychotropic Drugs,* Elsevier Press, Amsterdam, 1958.

35. SIEGEL, S., "Non-Parametric Statistics for the Behavioral Sciences," McGraw-Hill Publishers, New York, 1956.

36. STROMBLAD, C. R., "Effect of Denervation and of Cocaine on the Action of Sympathomimetic Amines," *Brit. J. Pharmacol.,* 15:328–332, 1960.

37. VOGT, M., "Concentration of Sympathin in Different Parts of Central Nervous System under Normal Conditions and after Administration of Drugs," *J. Physiol.,* 123:451–481, 1954.

38. VOGT, M., "Catecholamines in Brain," *Pharmacol. Rev.,* 11:483–489, 1959.

39. UDENFRIEND, S., WEISSBACH, H., and BOGDANSKI, D. F., "Biochemical Findings Relating to the Action of Serotonin," *Ann. N.Y. Acad. Sci.,* 66:602–608, 1957.

40. WEIL-MALHERBE, H. and BONE, A. D., "Intracellular Distribution of Catecholamines in the Brain," *Nature, Lond.,* 180:1050–1051, 1957.

41. WELSH, J. H., "Serotonin as a Possible Neurohumoral Agent: Evidence Obtained in Lower Animals," *Ann. N.Y. Acad. Sci.,* 66:618–630, 1957.

42. WILLIAMS, C. M., BABUSCIO, A., and WATSON, R., "In Vivo Alteration of the Pathways of Dopamine Metabolism," *Amer. J. Physiol.,* 199:722–726, 1960.

43. WYLIE, D. W., ARCHER, S., and ARNOLD, A., "Augmentation of Pharmacological Properties of Catecholamines by O-Methyl Transferase Inhibitors," *J. Pharmacol. exp. Ther.,* 130:239–244, 1960.

44. YUWILER, A., GELLER, E., and EIDUSON, S., "Studies on 5–Hydroxytryptophan Decarboxylase," *Arch. Biochem.,* 80:162–173, 1959.

XI

Comments on Neuropharmacological Studies of EEG and Behavior

José M. R. Delgado

The study of correlations between electrical activity of the brain and behavior was the starting point of electroencephalography and recently has been the subject of symposia in Marseilles, 1957, and in Moscow, 1960. Most of the research in this area has been concentrated on electrical signs of conditioning, perhaps because of the relative simplicity of the problem and the objectivity of the experimental approach. In the present work, however, conditioning is being considered minimally, and other trends in research are presented. Still another field, namely, the study of correlations between electrical activity of the brain and spontaneous behavior is practically unexplored, in spite of its obvious interest. We think that this field is very promising and that it will expand rapidly, thanks to recent methodological developments. Objective recording of individual and social spontaneous behavior is possible with the aid of time-lapse photography, which permits precise qualification and quantification of behavioral categories.[3] As shown in Figure XI–1, radio receivers have been used to stimulate the brain of completely free animals and make possible the investigation of cerebral structures which play a role in specific patterns of behavior. The combination of these techniques with telemetering of biological data, including EEG, will

These comments are a discussion of papers presented by the authors of the three preceding chapters. Some of the investigations mentioned in this report were supported by grants from the Office of Naval Research and the United States Public Health Service.

allow the analysis of correlations between free behavior and electrical activity of determined areas of the brain.

The amygdala has been the subject of investigation in two of the previous chapters. Drs. Eidelberg, Lesse, and Gault describe a specific effect of cocaine upon the amygdala which could be responsible for the onset of the typical seizures which appear in cocaine intoxication. In this interesting study, the specificity of the effect perhaps should be investigated further and the following questions and comments come to mind.

Fig. XI—1. *With radio-controlled stimulation of the brain of completely free animals, we investigated the cerebral areas which influence individual and social behavior. Recordings of spontaneous and induced behavior were taken by time-lapse photography.*

Rhythmic bursts of high-voltage activity synchronous with respiration have been described in the olfactory apparatus by Adrian[1] and have been recorded in the amygdala by MacLean and Delgado.[6] Is there a correlation between these spontaneous bursts and cocaine-induced electrical activity? Can cocaine increase the sensitivity of the olfactory apparatus?

The hippocampus is one of the cerebral areas with a low threshold for electrical after-discharges, and we have demonstrated that electrical stimulation of some parts of the limbic system—for example, the septum—may evoke a hippocampal after-discharge with a small disturbance at the site of stimulation. In other words, stimulation within a system may be triggered by areas of low threshold located far from the stimulated point.

As shown in Figure XI–2, after-discharges recorded in the amygdala may be of two types: (a) when the pattern is similar to that of other discharging areas of the brain, the electrical disturbance of the amygdala should be considered only as *propagated;* (b) in other cases the amygdala after-discharge has a typical pattern of about 6 c./sec., which may also be evoked by its direct stimulation and which indicates an active and direct participation of the amygdala

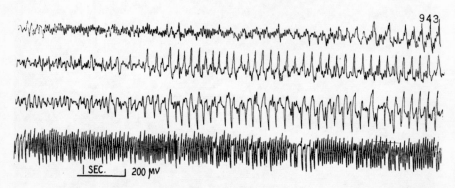

Fig. XI—2. *Transition from* propagated *to* reactive *after-discharges is seen in the second and third channels. First channel is the left amygdala; second channel the right amygdala; third, left to right amygdala; fourth, left hippocampus.*

accompanied by clinical symptoms such as ipsilateral facial contractions. In this case the after-discharge is considered *reactive.* The activity evoked by cocaine is reminiscent rather of hippocampal activity than of the typical amygdala pattern. However, in the records of Drs. Eidelberg, Lesse, and Gault, the hippocampal activity is atypical and without clear seizure activity.

Perhaps the previous comments also bear some relation to the chapter by Drs. Sutin, Van Orden, and Tsubokawa, in which the amygdala and septum were electrically stimulated. In addition, I was impressed by the fact that locally injected catecholamines have a different effect on the response of the ventromedial nucleus of the hypothalamus to septal and to amygdaloid stimulation. Perhaps we should not be too surprised, because it is well known that in the vascular system adrenaline may reverse its action, depending on the target, on the functional state of the target, and on the presence of other drugs. The beautiful and precise work of Dr. Sutin and collaborators shows the tremendous complexity of the problem. To understand the role of cerebral neurohumors it would perhaps be necessary to study the effect of each substance on each structure, in relation to each impulse coming from each area of the brain—a task which seems formidable in spite of all the computers at our disposal. Concrete data, however, may help to solve concrete questions, and, for example, in the regulation of food intake, only a few cerebral structures are apparently involved. There is a question whether these experiments suggest a relative independence of septum and amygdala, or if their feeding functions must be carried out through the hypothalamus. In our opinion, the inhibition of alimentary reactions produced by amygdala stimulation is not necessarily mediated through the feeding and satiation hypothalamic centers. We favor the hypothesis of an amygdala-septal-caudate system which would be related to, but not completely dependent on, the ventral-lateral hypothalamic system.[3] The importance of behavioral, biochemical, and temporal factors in the interpretation of results has been mentioned by Dr. Freedman. In complete agreement with his comments, I would like to emphasize the importance of social factors. Most psychopharmacological investigation is carried out on individual animals. However, most animal life and certainly most human activities are performed in a social medium with a continuous series of stimuli which may modify the reactivity of each individual. These social factors are often overlooked and deserve greater attention. I have seen, for example, that the presence or absence of one monkey in a colony of six may change the sexual behavior of all the other members of the group. In our opinion, generalization of behavioral results induced by drug administration requires the experimental study of social effects.

Dr. Freedman's demonstration that LSD–25 induces a small but significant elevation of serotonin located in the particulate fraction of the brain is of great interest. I was impressed by the fact that serotonin in the medial thalamus increased 50 per cent (54 per cent in the controls and 78 per cent in the LSD–25-treated dogs), while in the lateral thalamus there was no change (34 per cent and 36 per cent respectively). The interpretation of results is handicapped by our lack of knowledge of the functions of serotonin in brain physiology, but it may have a functional significance. I would like to add a comment about the interpretation of chemical studies. We often have an anatomical deformation of our concepts, presuming that a well-defined structure should be uniform in its functions, while this is not usually the case. The hippocampus, for example, may have after-discharges in its rostral part without involvement of its caudal part. The hypothalamus is a most complex conglomeration of neurons with a tremen-

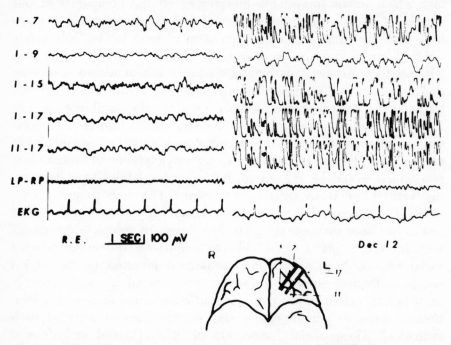

Fig. XI—3. *In humans, after-discharges of the frontal lobes may go on for minutes without any detectable symptoms. Observe that the convexity scalp leads LP–RP (left to right parietal) do not show the disturbance.*

dous variety of functions. Why, then, should we expect uniformity in the biochemical behavior of these areas? In general, we may have two types of chemical modification: one which affects large areas of the brain, such as the depletion of serotonin produced by reserpine, and the other which is restricted to very small structures, such as the liberation of acetylcholine during synaptic transmission. The location of cerebral structures responsible for specific biochemical-functional changes is of great interest, and the use of techniques to perfuse local areas of the brain in unanesthetized animals may give important clues in this study. Gaddum[4] is investigating this problem with his "push-pull" cannula, and, in collaboration with Drs. Simhadri and Apelbaum, we are also studying this type of problem with our chemitrodes.

In the analysis of electroencephalographic and behavioral correlations, we find general changes in the electrical activity affecting most of the brain, and also localized modifications of activity, which may pass undetected by scalp recordings but have great behavioral repercussions. I agree with the comments of Dr. Fink about the need to improve our electronic instrumentation to make the frequency analyses more helpful and reliable than in the past. In the interpretation of behavioral-electroencephalographic correlations there is a surprising contrast between after-discharges evoked in humans by electrical stimulation of the frontal lobes (Figure XI–3), which may go on for one or two minutes without any detectable symptomatology, and the clear manifestations in other cases with very localized after-discharges in the temporal lobe.[2]

The correlation suggested between increased synaptic activity, cholinergic effect, EEG hypersynchronization, clinical sedation, and euphoria is very interesting and could perhaps be reinforced if we could more precisely determine its generalization and its exceptions. Among the latter, we know that hallucinations may be evoked by a local hypersynchrony produced by electrical stimulation of the temporal lobe, and we also know that hypersynchrony of some areas will give excitatory or inhibitory effects, depending on their neuronal structure.

References

1. ADRIAN, E. D., "The Electrical Activity of the Mammalian Olfactory Bulb," *Electroenceph. clin. Neurophysiol.*, 2:377–388, 1950.

2. DELGADO, J. M. R. and HAMLIN, H., "Direct Recording of Spontaneous and Evoked Seizures in Epileptics," *Electroenceph. clin. Neurophysiol.*, 10: 463–486, 1958.

3. FONBERG, E. and DELGADO, J. M. R., "Avoidance and Alimentary Reactions During Amygdala Stimulation," *J. Neurophysiol.*, 24:651–664, 1961.

4. GADDUM, J. H., "Push-Pull Cannulae," *J. Physiol.*, *155*:1P, 1961.

5. JASPER, H. H. and SMIRNOV, G. D., "The Moscow Colloquium on EEG of Higher Nervous System," *Electroenceph. clin. Neurophysiol.*, Supp. *13*, 420 pp., 1960.

6. MACLEAN, P. D. and DELGADO, J. M. R., "Electrical and Chemical Stimulation of Fronto Temporal Portion of Limbic System in the Waking Animal," *Electroenceph. clin. Neurophysiol.*, 5:91–100, 1953.

EPILEPSY AND BEHAVIOR DISORDERS

XII

EEG and Ictal
and Postictal Behavior

Eli S. Goldensohn

In the past three decades great strides in understanding the clinical manifestations of epilepsy have been made through electroencephalography. It is used as a method of classifying epilepsy,[10, 11, 24] and its influence on the concept of seizures has been so great that the term "cerebral dysrhythmia" derived from electroencephalography is used by some as a definition or synonym for epilepsy.[12, 17] Often the epileptic nature of puzzling symptoms is demonstrated only through the use of electroencephalography.[13] The great value of electroencephalography in confirming the diagnosis of convulsive disorders as well as the fact that clear-cut changes in the EEG are usually seen at some time during a seizure has tended to obscure the fact that there is limited temporal or qualitative correlation between the clinical events of an epileptic seizure and the simultaneously occurring electrical activity recorded from the scalp. This report deals particularly with such limitations in correlation and inquires into their meaning.

The following patients and their records demonstrate aspects of the variable relationships between the electrical activity of the brain and clinical seizure phenomena. The first patient demonstrates the following features: (a) the paucity of EEG changes which accompany auras, (b) prominent interictal paroxysmal activity found at the surface of the cortex which cannot be seen in the EEG, and (c) ictal states signaled by the electrocorticogram which are not recognized on the EEG. C. F. is a 22-year-old female who at the age of nine years during convalescence from a siege of measles, mumps, and whooping

This work was supported in part by National Institute of Mental Health Research Grant M–3166, United States Public Health Service.

293

cough had her first generalized seizure. At the age of 14 years, the attacks began with sensations of "closing of the left ear," numbness of the left side of the face, and "seeing circles out of the left corner of the eye," which were followed by unconsciousness and falling with generalized tonic and clonic movements. At 16 years she spent several weeks in a mental hospital for the treatment of a psychosis apparently precipitated by Primidone. By the time she reached the age of 18, the generalized major component of her attacks had become infrequent, and psychomotor attacks occurred which began with "scary feelings" or a sense of floating or "awareness of breathing rapidly" or more rarely the feeling of "closing of the ear" or of hearing of a distant sound. Rarely too, she experienced forced ideas intruding from outside her normal stream of thought. These auras were followed by automatic behavior for which she was amnesic. Once, following a short attack in a theater, she noticed that her legs were cold. A companion told her that she had removed her stockings and put them in her purse. In spite of prolonged and strenuous efforts at medical control she continued to have two to five attacks daily until the time of temporal lobectomy. In the resting state, a mild slow-wave abnormality was present in the right temporal region (Figure XII–1a). One of the patient's usual auras was precipitated by the intravenous injection of Metrazol. In spite of the subjective manifestations only a slight increase in the right-sided slowing without paroxysmal activity was evident (Figure XII–1b). At operation, which was performed under local anesthesia, many spikes were seen in the corticogram (Figure XII–1c) in spite of the absence of any paroxysmal activity at the scalp on numerous examinations. Chewing movements and depression of responsivity were noticed during parts of periods in which a marked increase in spiking from the cortex occurred and independent spiking was recorded from the amygdala (Figures XII–1d and XII–1e). This demonstrates that paroxysmal electrical activity which does not appear at the scalp can nevertheless be present at the surface of the brain during simple automatisms and subtle interference with perception and thought processes.

Patient 2 (C. K.) incidentally also demonstrates the paucity of EEG changes during auras and shows (a) that a seizure may be well under way before the occurrence of EEG changes which reveal the ictal nature of the experience, (b) the importance of psychological influences on the content of the ictal hallucinations, and (c) that affective and experiental changes of ictal quality are not accompanied by EEG

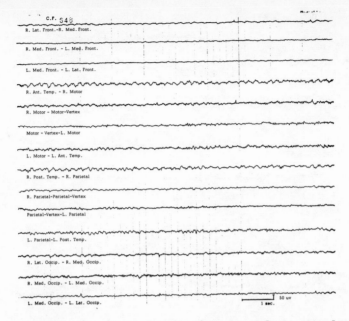

Fig. XII—1a. *Control EEG showing right temporal slow-wave focus.*

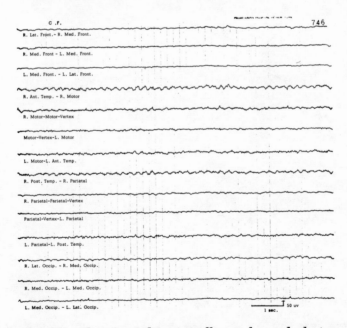

Fig. XII—1b. *Record practically unchanged during aura induced by Metrazol.*

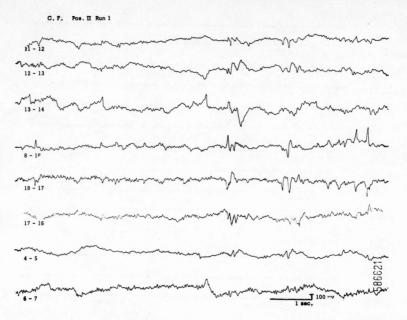

Fig. XII—1c. *Corticogram showing high-voltage spikes which were not seen in scalp recording.*

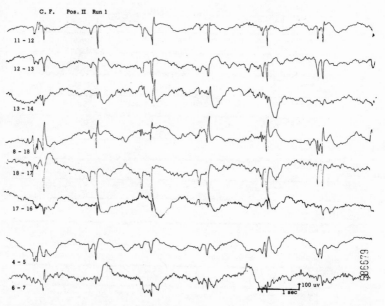

Fig. XII—1d. *Corticogram showing increased spiking during period of chewing movements and depressed responsiveness.*

changes. C. K. is a 35-year-old woman who, following a febrile illness, began to experience feelings of depersonalization and unreality. She stated that she felt that "life has a dreamlike quality" and that she was "like a spectator." She felt as though it was not actually she who was in the hospital and that when she touched her face she was not touching herself. These feelings of detachment lasted from minutes to as long as several hours. She also experienced sensations of nausea, vertigo, and *déjà vu*. She described hallucinations in which she saw a shrouded figure coming toward her, who she believed might have been her husband, who had died a few years before. She also ex-

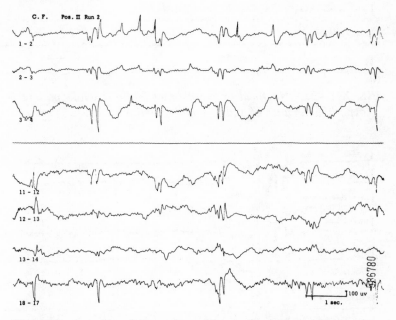

Fig. XII—1e. *Depth recording. Electrode 1 shows independent spiking from region of amygdala. Electrodes 11 to 18 are on the cortex.*

perienced auditory hallucinations. A spontaneous seizure occurred during a routine EEG examination. The seizure began with an auditory aura in which she heard her daughter calling to her (Figure XII—2a). There was no significant change in the EEG. Shortly after this she exclaimed "Oh" (Figure XII—2b) and became less responsive; then a sharp wave focus of increasing intensity and amplitude appeared in the left anterior temporal area (Figure XII—2c). Complete con-

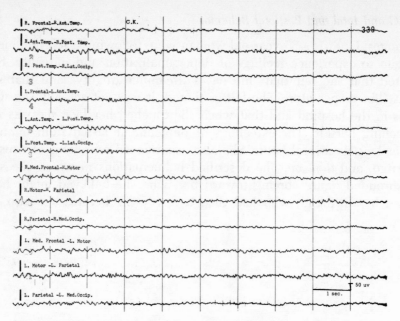

Fig. XII—2a. *No focal or paroxysmal features while patient is experiencing aura of auditory hallucinations.*

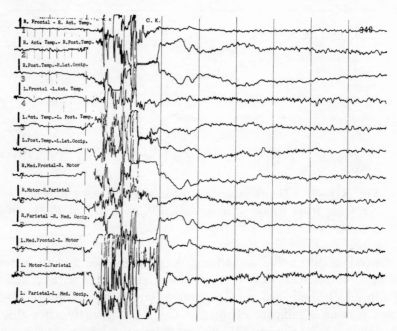

Fig. XII—2b. *Ten seconds later, no significant change in the background EEG as patient becomes partly unresponsive. Movement of patient causes prominent artefact.*

sciousness was never lost. A slow-wave abnormality in the same area persisted after she was again fully aware. During periods of depersonalization and detachment, prolonged recordings revealed no EEG changes. This patient is of exceptional interest because the content of her auditory and visual hallucinations were partly related to psychological trauma.

Patient 3 (J. T.) is an example of a seizure in which complicated psychomotor activity including emotional display occurs before significant changes appear in the EEG. Figure XII–3 shows the onset

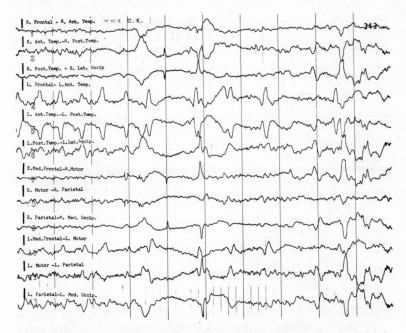

Fig. XII—2c. *Thirty seconds later a sharp wave focus of high intensity has developed in the left temporal area as partial unresponsiveness continues.*

of a Metrazol-activated seizure in which this patient attempted to get up, smiled, chewed, and voiced repetitive syllables in a singing fashion. His attack began with no other change than voltage depression. Later during further episodes of laughing and smiling 1–2/sec. waves appeared in the right frontal-motor area.

Patient 4 (B. J.) demonstrates that unresponsiveness may be accompanied by unilateral EEG abnormality. Previously occurring slow spikes (Figure XII–4a) became very frequent but remained unilateral (Figure XII—4b). The increased unilateral discharging was accompanied by a sharp sigh, confusion, terror, screaming, and unresponsiveness for a few moments followed by confused speech. This type of unilateral abnormality was also noted in Patient 2 who, however, remained partially responsive throughout her seizure. The recording directly from the cortex (Figure XII—4c) at operation showed many rapid spikes which were not present in the regular scalp run, a feature also seen in Patient 1.

The wide range of EEG activities seen during a single behavioral

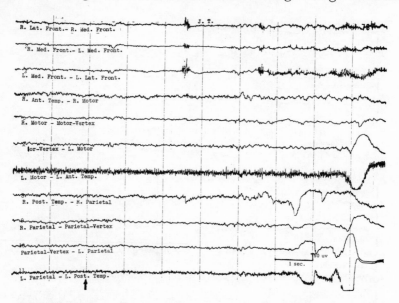

Fig. XII—3. *Arrow points at onset of seizure, which is accompanied by voltage depression. Patient smiles and makes automatic movements. Movement of patient causes high-voltage artefacts.*

characteristic demonstrates the lack of specificity of the EEG for types of ictal behavior. Patient 3, referred to before, showed smiling and laughing in association both with enhancement of local slow-wave activity and with voltage depression. Patient 5 (J. M.) (Figure XII—5a and XII—5b) also showed laughter twice during the seizure. At one time laughter was accompanied by high-voltage generalized spike-and-wave activity; at the next time, the same laughter occurred shortly after electrical evidence of the seizure was over and there was slowing but no paroxysmal activity.

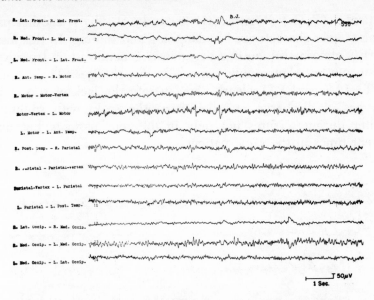

Fig. XII—4a. *A few sporadic right fronto-temporal sharp waves are seen before the onset of the seizure.*

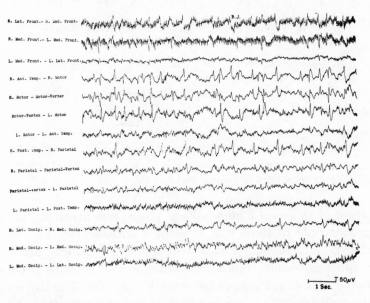

Fig. XII—4b. *Frequent unilateral sharp waves appear during seizure in which patient is momentarily unresponsive. Frontalis muscle artefact obscures the recording in the first two channels.*

Patient 6 (P. G.) (Figures XII–6a and XII–6b) is another patient
having attacks characterized by laughing and smiling. In this instance
the EEG abnormality on one occasion is generalized and paroxysmal
but on another shows only minor specific changes. The recordings
on J.T., J.M., and P.G. clearly demonstrate the lack of specificity of
the types of discharge recorded from the scalp with smiling and
laughter during seizures not only in different patients but also at
different times in the same patient.

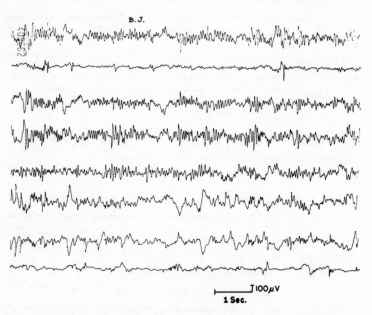

Fig. XII—4c. *Corticogram reveals rapid spikes in fronto-*
temporal area. A cystic region is responsible for the voltage
depression seen in lines 2 and 8.

In spite of prolonged high-voltage paroxysms involving all of the
cortex accessible to the EEG, awareness and memory can be maintained. Although most patients with bursts of typical high-voltage
3/sec. spike-and-wave complexes lasting several seconds become unresponsive, this is not always the case. Figure XII–7 is the record of
a 14-year-old boy (E. N.) who had a period of continuous spike-and-
wave discharges lasting for six hours which was finally terminated
with intravenous paraldehyde. During the prolonged 3/sec. spike-
and-wave discharging, he responded at all times, and was able to

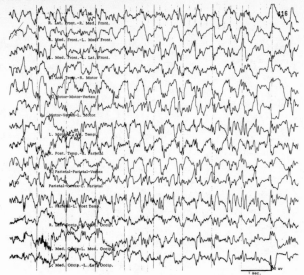

Fig. XII—5a. *Continuous high-voltage spikes and 2-per-second spike and wave discharges accompanied by laughter.*

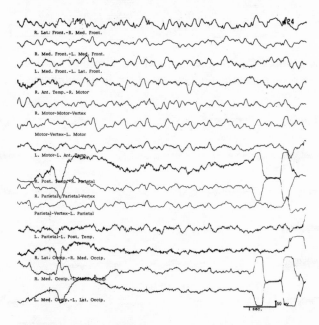

Fig. XII—5b. *Eighty seconds later during the same clinical seizure, nonparoxysmal slow activity is now accompanied by laughter.*

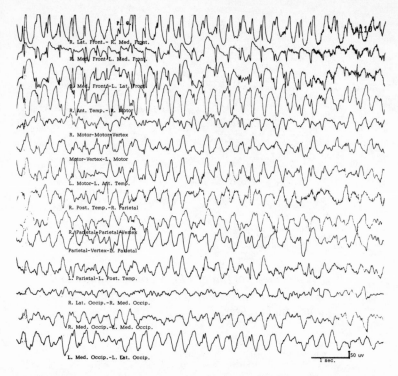

Fig. XII—6a. *Continuous atypical 3-per-second spike and wave discharges accompanied by laughter in spontaneous seizure.*

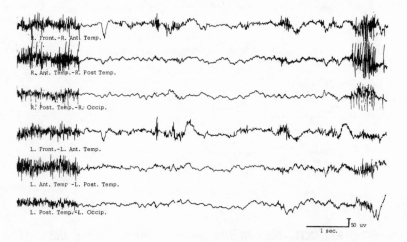

Fig. XII—6b. *Voltage depression and movement and muscle artefact accompanied by laughter in Metrazol-induced seizure.*

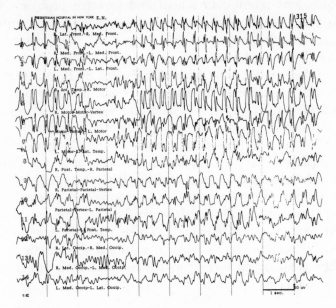

Fig. XII—7a. *Continuous discharging of 3-per-second spike and wave complexes for many hours, during which high degree of intellectual function is maintained.*

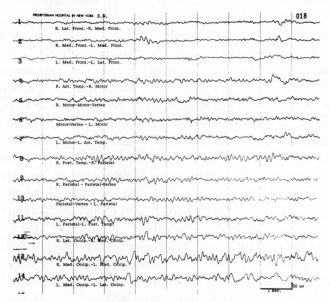

Fig. XII—7b. *Control record.*

answer questions relating to school and to solve problems in arith-
metic. At times he showed some disinhibition by moving about and
being unreasonable about wanting to pull off the electrodes. Most
of the time, however, he was agreeable and friendly. He was amnesic
for most of the events of the six hours. Patient 8 (R. A.) Figure XII–
8) had similar continuous discharges over a still longer period which
were associated with abdominal pain and vomiting and a display of
hostility toward her family. She was partly amnesic. Patient 9 (E. S.)
(Figure XII–9), with somewhat similar bilaterally synchronous paroxysms, displayed complex automatic behavior and was abusive. He
had complete amnesia for the attacks. Patient 10 (J. R.) (Figure
XII–10) simply recognized that things appeared somewhat out of
focus and that she was slower than usual in solving her problems at
school. Memory was not impaired. These patients demonstrate that
prolonged bilaterally synchronous generalized discharges may occur
with either great or no loss of awareness and with either complete
amnesia or intact memory.

Discussion

The material presented demonstrates the frequent lack of correspondence between the electrical activity recorded from the scalp
and the clinical events during seizures. Although changes from the
resting record appear in most instances at some time during an attack,
the examples shown clearly indicate that there is no obligatory relationship between the type of EEG activity encountered and the
clinical symptomatology including auras, subjective distortions, or
hallucinations, types of automatisms, and levels of awareness. In addition we have found no clear-cut consistent relationship between the
time of appearance of EEG changes and the onset or termination
of the clinical seizure. We have not attempted such correlations in
terms of grand mal or focal motor attacks where closer relationships
with both time of occurrence and quality of EEG change may exist.

For many years it has been known that clinical seizures may begin
before changes in the EEG are evident[16, 18] and that regularly recurring interictal EEG abnormalities frequently cease or are arrested during a clinical seizure.[16] It has also been recognized that entire seizures
of various types may occur without significant change in the EEG
or with only suppression of the resting rhythms.[3, 21] It is therefore not
surprising to find that between 10 per cent and 45 per cent of

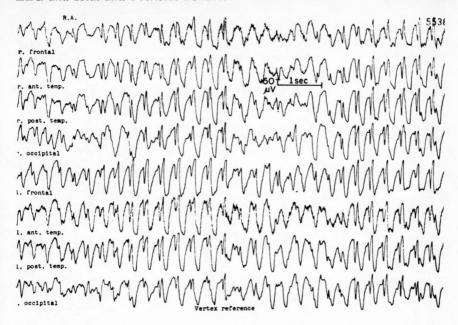

Fig. XII—8a. *Continuous spike and wave discharges for many hours associated with abdominal pain, vomiting, and hostile behavior.*

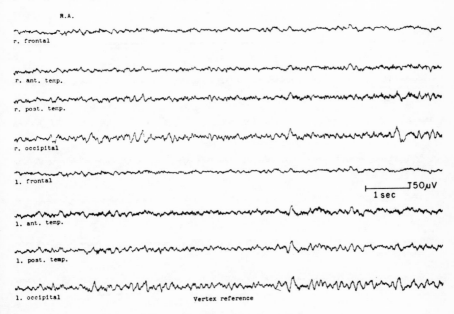

Fig. XII—8b. *Control record.*

E. S.   711

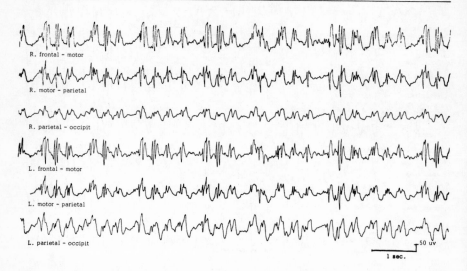

Fig. XII—9a. *Bilaterally synchronous multiple spike and slow-wave discharges associated with automatic behavior and amnesia.*

E. S.   **740**

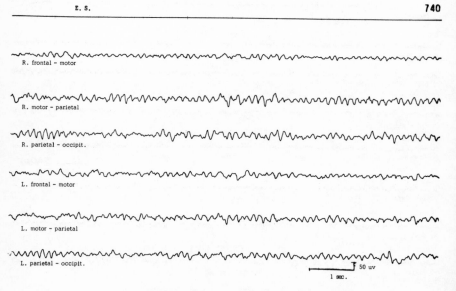

Fig. XII—9b. *Control record.*

J.R.

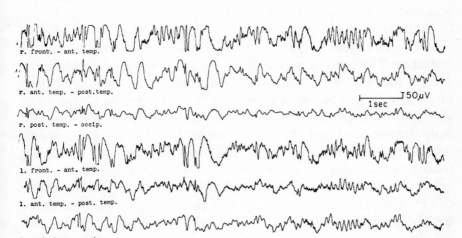

r. front. - ant. temp.

r. ant. temp. - post.temp.

50μV
1 sec

r. post. temp. - occip.

l. front. - ant. temp.

l. ant. temp. - post. temp.

l. post. temp. - occip.

Fig. XII—10a. *Prolonged high-voltage 9–10 paroxysms with bifrontal accentuations and spike and wave discharges associated with intellectual slowing, retained consciousness, and memory.*

J.R.

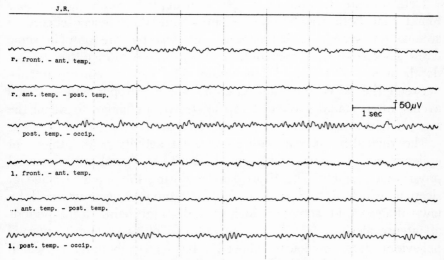

r. front. - ant. temp.

r. ant. temp. - post. temp.

50μV
1 sec

post. temp. - occip.

l. front. - ant. temp.

..., ant. temp. - post. temp.

l. post. temp. - occip.

Fig. XII—10b. *Control record.*

Metrazol-activated seizures of several clinical types were not accompanied by significant or appreciable EEG changes[3] and that the most complex characteristic clinical events in a seizure sequence often occurred after the electrical activity had ceased to be paroxysmal.[3, 8] In 31 patients studied by Ajmone-Marsan and Abraham,[2] the onset of clinical attacks and of EEG changes were simultaneous in only 12 instances. The attacks appreciably preceded any EEG evidence in 11 and followed it in eight. Their experience in a smaller number of patients with electrodes implanted into the depths of the brain was similar. Significant change in the electrical activity from the scalp seldom occurred during the aura. This finding is of special interest because auras often have a greater clinical value in locating pathology than other manifestations of seizures. Presumably the aura reflects the beginning of the attack when abnormal functioning is still limited to a local damaged area of the brain which is responsible for the convulsive disorder. With complex automatic behavior, only one-third of Ajmone-Marsan and Abraham's patients[2] showed simultaneous EEG changes of any type which could be correlated with the onset or characteristic phases of the automatisms. They also showed that in seven of nine cases evidence of clinical seizures continued when the EEG signs of the seizures "seemed definitely over." Gastaut and Vigouroux,[9] in an analysis of five hundred records taken during psychomotor seizures, found half of their cases to be unclassifiable in EEG terms.

Delgado and Hamlin,[5] in studies with depth recordings, have also found that both spontaneous seizures and the clinical effects of stimulation, such as hallucinations and *déjà vu,* are only in some cases associated with recognizable electrical changes either in the depth or at the surface of the brain. The lack of correspondence between the EEG and the aura, the seizure proper and postictal events, often makes it difficult to use electrical changes to signal the time of beginning or end of a clinical seizure.

The difficulties in correlating electrical activity with attacks of epilepsy are not unique and extend into both normal and abnormal physiological states. The EEG pattern during dreaming, a stage of sleep in which it is difficult to obtain arousal, is characterized by low-voltage rapid activity which is indistinguishable from periods of intense alertness.[6, 20] This is an example of two opposite normal behavioral states previously believed to be electrically different, which are characterized by practically identical electroencephalograms. A similar paradoxical finding is the presence of normal or practically normal records in some cases of deep coma.[7, 19]

What is the nature of the processes which allow EEG changes to be very different from case to case or to be absent in the face of even such profound cerebral dysfunction as coma or generalized major seizures? A partial answer lies in the fact that EEG registers attenuated and distorted information derived mainly from changes in the postsynaptic potentials of a limited neuronal population (i.e., the available cortex) and that overactivity or hypersynchronization of this population is not a requisite for abnormal behavior.

The postsynaptic graded potentials recorded in the EEG are not directly related to nerve impulses themselves but rather represent changes in excitability which may inhibit or facilitate "all-or-none" activity in the form of nerve impulses.[22] The direction of the potential sign of a fluctuation in the EEG does not necessarily signify whether primarily inhibitory or facilitory influences are dominant because each EEG wave is the algebraic sum of numerous inhibitory and excitatory postsynaptic potentials acting in different portions of the dendritic processes and cell bodies at various depths in the cerebral cortex. Although gamma-amino butyric acid (Gaba) reverses the polarity of simple superficial cortical or transcallosal surface-negative responses,[23] the complexity of the sources generating EEG seizure discharges is demonstrated by the action of Gaba on spontaneous spike discharges recorded directly from the human epileptic cerebral cortex. In this instance the topical application of Gaba, which presumably inhibits excitatory influences at the synapse, causes a variety of changes (Figure XII–11) in which the second negativity seen before Gaba is now replaced by a prolonged third negativity at the same time that the initial positivity is enhanced. Such analyses in conjunction with the complexity of the histology of the cortex do not lead us to expect simple correlations between the sign of the EEG potentials and inhibition or excitation and prepare us on several accounts to recognize that at best only rough correlations between the EEG and ictal behavior are possible in the patient with epilepsy.

Another reason for the failure of the EEG to show a high correlation with ictal symptoms is that behavior triggered by cortically induced seizures may occur mainly from activation of lower centers in the diencephalon and brain stem. In at least some instances the electrical changes at the cortex which are roughly coincident with motor manifestations of seizures have been shown not to be causally related to them.[4] Van Buren and Ajmone-Marsan[25] in pointing out that the occurrence of ictal autonomic manifestations and automatisms do not correlate with EEG changes, also suggest that the areas responsible for these manifestations may be confined to the diencephalon and brain stem which are not accessible to present surface or depth recording techniques. Still another cause for the frequent failure of the EEG to correlate with clinical seizures was illustrated in Figure XII—1c and has been remarked on in other studies.[1, 14, 26] For reasons which are so far not understood, records at the scalp often fail to reflect paroxysmal activity which may be present at very high amplitude on the surface of the cortex.

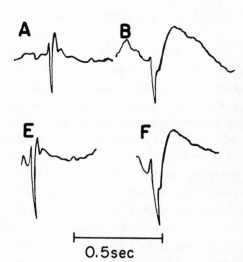

Fig. XII—11. *Spontaneous spikes from cortex in human epilepsy. A and E control. B and F effects of Gaba.*

0.5sec

CONCLUSION

Are there predictable scalp EEG correlates for consciousness? It appears not. For interference with memory? It appears not. What are the scalp EEG correlates for ictal hallucinatory and other psychic and mood experiences? Practically none. Is there a characteristic type of scalp EEG discharge during psychomotor attacks? No, not always. When does a seizure start? When does it end? The scalp EEG frequently does not tell us. The answers to these questions are generally negative because the attenuated postsynaptic potentials that are found at the cortex are only approximate and incomplete indications of the underlying cerebral dysfunction which is responsible for ictal and postictal behavior.

References

1. ABRAHAM, K. and AJMONE-MARSAN, C., "Patterns of Cortical Discharges and Their Relation to Routine Scalp Electroencephalography," *Electroenceph. clin. Neurophysiol.*, 10:447, 1958.

2. AJMONE-MARSAN, C. and ABRAHAM, K., "A Seizure Atlas," *Electroenceph. clin. Neurophysiol.*, Suppl. 15, 1960.

3. AJMONE-MARSAN, C. and RALSTON, B. L., *The Epileptic Seizure*, Charles C Thomas, Springfield, Ill., 1957.

4. DAWSON, G. D., "The Relation Between the EEG and Muscle Action Potential in Certain Convulsive States," *J. Neurol. Neurosurg. Psychiat.*, 9:5, 1946.

5. DELGADO, J. M. R. and HAMLIN, H., "Direct Recording of Spontaneous and Evoked Seizures in Epileptics," *Electroenceph. clin. Neurophysiol.*, 10:463, 1958.

6. DEMENT, W. and KLEITMAN, N., "Cyclic Variations in EEG During Sleep and Their Relation to Eye Movements, Body Motility, and Dreaming," *Electroenceph. clin. Neurophysiol.*, 9:673, 1957.

7. FISHGOLD, H. and MATHIS, P., "Obnubilations, Comas, et Stupeurs," *Electroenceph. clin. Neurophysiol.*, Suppl. 11, 1959.

8. GASTAUT, H., *The Epilepsies: Electro-Clinical Correlations* (BRAZIER, M. A. B., trans. from French), Charles C Thomas, Springfield, Ill., 1954.

9. GASTAUT, H. and VIGOUROUX, M., "Electro-Clinical Correlations in 500 Cases of Psychomotor Seizures," in BALDWIN, M. and BAILEY, P. (eds.), *Temporal Lobe Epilepsy*, Charles C Thomas, Springfield, Ill., 1958.

10. GIBBS, ERNA L., FLEMING, M. M., and GIBBS, F. A., "Diagnosis and Prognosis of Hypsarhythmia and Infantile Spasms," *Pediatrics*, 13:66–73, 1954.

11. GIBBS, F. A., DAVIS, H., and LENNOX, W. G., "The Electroencephalogram in Epilepsy and in Conditions of Impaired Consciousness," *Arch. Neurol. Psychiat.*, Chicago, 34:1133–1148, 1935.

12. GIBBS, F. A., GIBBS, ERNA L., and LENNOX, W. G., "Epilepsy: a Paroxysmal Cerebral Dysrhythmia," *Brain*, 60:377–388, 1937.

13. GOLDENSOHN, E. S. and GOLD, A. P., "Prolonged Behavioral Disturbances as Ictal Phenomena," *Neurology*, 10:1, 1960.

14. GOLDENSOHN, E. S., O'BRIEN, J. L., and RANSOHOFF, J., "Electrical Activity of the Brain in Patients Treated with Hemispherectomy or Extensive Decortication," *Arch. Neurol.*, Chicago, 5:210, 1961.

15. GOLDENSOHN, E. S., PURPURA, D., and HOUSEPIAN, E., "Analysis of Cortical Surface Evoked Activity and Paroxysmal Discharges in Familial Myoclonus Epilepsy," *Electroenceph. clin. Neurophysiol., 13*:318, 1961.

16. LENNOX, M. and BRODY, B. S., "Paroxysmal Slow Waves in the Electroencephalogram of Patients with Epilepsy and with Sub-Cortical Lesions," *J. nerv. ment. Dis., 104*:237, 1946.

17. LENNOX, W. G., *Epilepsy and Related Disorders,* vol. 2, Little, Brown & Co., Boston, 1960.

18. LENNOX, W. G., GIBBS, E. L., and GIBBS, F. A., "Effect on the Electroencephalogram of Drugs and Conditions Which Influence Seizures," *Arch. Neurol. Psychiat., Chicago, 36*:1236, 1936.

19. LOEB, C., "Electroencephalographic Changes During the State of Coma," *Electroenceph. clin. Neurophysiol., 10*:589, 1958.

20. MORUZZI, G., in *CIBA Foundation Symposium on the Nature of Sleep, London, 1960,* Little, Brown & Co., Boston, 1961, pp. 392–394.

21. PENFIELD, W. and JASPER, H., *Epilepsy and the Functional Anatomy of the Human Brain,* Little, Brown & Co., Boston, 1954, 896 pp.

22. PURPURA, D., "Nature of Electrocortical Potentials and Synaptic Organizations in Cerebral and Cerebellar Cortex," *Int. Rev. Neurobiol., 1*:47, 1959.

23. PURPURA, D., GIRARDO, M., and GRUNDFEST, H., "Components of Evoked Potentials in Cerebral Cortex of Cat," *Electroenceph. clin. Neurophysiol., 12*:95, 1960.

24. SYMONDS, C., "Classification of Epilepsies," *Brit. med. J., 1*:1235–1238, 1955.

25. VAN BUREN, J. M. and AJMONE-MARSAN, C., "A Correlation of Autonomic and EEG Components in Temporal Lobe Epilepsy," *Arch. Neurol., Chicago, 3*:683, 1960.

26. WILLIAMS, D. and PARSONS-SMITH, G., "Cortical Rhythms Not Seen in Electroencephalogram," *Brain, 73*:191–202, 1950.

XIII

Positive Spike Discharges in the EEG and Behavior Abnormality

Charles E. Henry

The deliberate emphasis of this paper is on a review and synthesis of the existing published clinical and experimental data rather than a display of our own original material. My task is to present the material dealing with that curiously complex configuration in the electroencephalogram only approximately described as 6 and 14/sec. positive spiking, together with a congeries of clinical correlates, in a meaningful and challenging fashion. It is not necessary that one be persuaded that the inferences drawn from the data are convincing or even entirely plausible, but it is hoped that the facts will suggest the urgent need for further and vigorous psychiatric participation in this intriguing research area.

Furthermore, it is not really necessary to present new data on over 1,200 cases from our own laboratories. There already exists a considerable body of evidence (not always well organized or clearly written up) from a number of workers in various laboratories. Some of this was recapitulated at the 1961 Orthopsychiatric meetings in New York City, along with new material. To my knowledge the literature dealing with 6 and 14/sec. positive spiking has not been critically and systematically reviewed in print; there has in fact been a puzzling lack of attention to the phenomenon. Practical clinical aspects will be emphasized in this present review.

The initial disclosure by Gibbs and Gibbs in 1951 appeared in an early issue of the journal, *Neurology*, "Electroencephalographic Evidence of Thalamic and Hypothalamic Epilepsy."[19] They reported that this pattern was found in 2 per cent of a group of 300 control subjects and in 6 per cent of a group of 5,000 epileptics or suspected epileptics.

They noted the frequency variation, the regional differentiation over the head, and the imperative necessity for sleep recording. The positive spike discharges were not found to correlate highly with other types of seizure discharge or even with epilepsy, since most of these patients had normal waking EEGs. They were impressed by the age distribution with maximal incidence through the adolescent and young adult years and with the atypical ictal features which were really more epileptoid than epileptic, with attacks of pain, rage, and vegetative symptomatology. They also regarded the positivity of the discharge as suggesting a subcortical origin, although the neurophysiological grounds upon which such reasoning is based have been criticized.[5]

In retrospect one wonders if the "thalamic" adjective applied to this highly deviant form of "epilepsy" has not contributed to the difficulty in getting to a rational discussion of the pattern. Perhaps the Gibbses were already aware of the two positive spike cases with intracranial neoplasm, reported in the same journal a few months later by W. A. Stephenson.[96] Six of his 32 positive spike cases (out of 2,500 adult patients) showed neurological findings with possible brain stem involvement, two with verified deep nuclear invasion. Taken together with the more psychiatric aspects of their clinical behavior, one might infer that these cases had a considerable bearing on the controversial terminology of "thalamic or hypothalamic epilepsy."

The following year saw only a single major publication, but it received very wide distribution since it was Chapter 13 of Volume 2 of the second edition of Gibbs and Gibbs' *Atlas*.[29] The electrographic features were expanded and illustrated and the number of cases increased to 427. They pointed out that psychiatric disorder was more common in this positive-spike group than with any other type of epilepsy except the anterior and mid-temporal lobe focal disturbance, with the main feature being a behavioral disturbance. Again there was a very long list of associated clinical complaints with some emphasis on pain, paresthesias, and rage attacks; as in their first paper, they mentioned the unique fact that four of these patients had committed murder. Etiology remained uncertain except that 21 per cent of the patients had experienced severe head trauma and another 9 per cent encephalitis. Again they mentioned the favorable results obtained by the common anticonvulsants in maximal tolerated dosage. Of some historical interest is Grossman's early note[33] dealing briefly with the clinical significance and experimental manipulation of the pattern which he, perhaps more appropriately, termed "positive bursts."

In 1953 Schwade and colleagues[82, 86] reported two cases of murder in teen-age boys with 6 and 14/sec. positive spiking and stated that they had similar EEG abnormality on 46 cases with impulsive amnestic behavior. The case of (probable multiple) homicide is a vivid example of the clinical behavior exhibited by some of these patients. The authors clearly indicate their assumption of a causal relationship between the inferred thalamic disorder and its electrographic and clinical expression. A possible relationship to peptic ulcer was also suggested;[51, 52] no subsequent work on this was encountered.

In the next year, Millen[66, see also 64] had a paper reporting 22 cases of 14 and 6/sec. positive spiking in 547 EEGs; since only 98 of these were sleep tracings the real proportion is actually high. The clinical relationships involved head injury, convulsive disorder, and behavior problems, and there was further speculation about the probable deep origin of the discharge. Gibbs *et al.*[20] discussed the disappearance and migration of epileptic foci in children in a review article appearing in the pediatric literature, mentioning that positive spike activity tended to occur in new cases of epilepsy among adolescents and presenting material showing the gradual onset of this discharge. Furthermore, they had already learned[31] what we later discovered for ourselves: despite the many clinical forms under which the positive spike pattern may masquerade, the clinical picture is so characteristic that the EEG findings are often predictable. Even without the benefit of historical perspective, it is clear that Hill's[38] rejection of the validity of the positive spike pattern was not justified.

The experiments reported by Grossman[34] in 1954 appear to have been overlooked by other workers. He verified his earlier finding of depressed evoked activity in sleep on the side of the lesion and noted a characteristic *distortion* of both spontaneous and evoked activity from posterior head regions in patients with episodic aggressive behavior. The distortion occurred as marked reduction of the negative half of the fast 14/sec. activity and exaggeration of the positive phase; both 7 and 14/sec. activity were observed and illustrated. Either biphasic or predominantly negative barbiturate spindle activity was converted to positive bursts following local cocainization of cat cortex; similar changes were reported during the recovery cycle of spreading depression and other conditions of reduced cortical activity. He inferred that the positive bursts in (especially the younger) human EEGs were distorted sleep spindles resulting from laminar blocking in superficial layers of association cortex, with associated clinical manifestations a release phenomenon.

Most of the material on 6 and 14/sec. positive spiking in the next several years was in the form of brief notes and abstracts. The Gibbs laboratories had collected 2,000 cases.[24] They reported the incidence of this pattern in cerebral palsy (6 per cent of 441 patients);[73] one case with phenylpyruvic oligophrenia;[15] and, curiously—this pattern was the single abnormality in a series of 129 cases of breathholding—a single case.[59] An exhibit from Schwade and Geiger[83] dealt with over 500 children and young adults with clinical histories of impulsive violent behavior, all showing 14 and 6/sec. positive spiking in their EEGs. Presumably this is the same series of cases reported more extensively the following year[84] as 453 cases between 1.5 and 18 years of age, including five "bizarre, impulsive-compulsive" murderers. Of interest is their inclusion of possible amygdaloid abnormality and their statement that they had recognized the association between behavior disorder and 6 and 14/sec. positive spiking in 1949.

Eventually, reports of this pattern appeared from other than the Chicago area. From St. Louis, Mills[68] added another teen-age murderer to the list of those with positive spiking and proclaimed a psychodynamic "sin of omission" when such neurophysiological data are ignored. Kellaway[43] reported the pattern as a common late sequel of head injury in children, but not closely related to severity of injury. There was a one-page informative abstract[76] from the Bergen (Norway) laboratory, this study appearing in detail several years later.[79] Silverman[92, 93] mentioned the discharge as seen during sleep activation. With adequate technique being required, the description of this by Garneski and Green[18] was timely but not really convincing. A series of unfortunate compounded errata further complicated understanding of this already difficult matter. Most unusually, comments of the editorial referees and the authors' replies were included as part of the article. Although this allowed (presumably) Denis Hill to agree that the spike phenomena were real, probably of cerebral origin, and perhaps even of positive polarity, there was a confusing error in numbering of the figures. The editorial discussion almost certainly contains another figure reference error beyond that subsequently identified. Climactically, the erratum listing in the table of contents of the next issue of the *Journal* was to the wrong page.

Many other studies dealing with the EEG in childhood, as well as others dealing with abdominal epilepsy, were published without reference to positive spiking. A paper in *Lancet*[3] contrasted 131 children with and 133 children without recurrent abdominal pain; there were no electrographic differences; the authors seemed unaware of the necessity for sleep recording. An abstract[61] in *The EEG Journal* dealt with the recurrent syndrome in children; by history one would have confidently predicted a high incidence of 6 or 14/sec. positive spiking in the population of 52 cases. Seconal sleep was mentioned as being used in a single case; four children recorded during one of their recurrent episodes of abdominal pain or headache did not show the discharge; presumably no sleep was obtained. A quotation from Gibbs at that time is only slightly less apposite at present: "The clinical investigator has two responsibilities: (1) to gain significant information and (2) to convince others of its significance. Failure to perform the second function reduces the value of the first."[25]

By the time of the Fourth International EEG Conference in Brussels we had seen several hundred cases of 6 and 14/sec. positive spiking, and in a Discussion[36] emphasized the apparent relationship to behavior disorders. Presthus *et al.*[77] again mentioned the great variety of clinical symptoms shown by such patients, and Shimoda[88] noted autonomic, emotional, and conscious disturbances. Another abstract from Japan[69] reported the beneficial effect of anticonvulsant treatment in such patients. Nicholson and Knott[70] found a 2–3-fold higher incidence of 6 and 14/sec. positive spiking in psychiatric vs. other patients. The first abstract from R. Walter's laboratory[100] dealt with a patient developing 14 and 6/sec. positive discharges following an anesthetic accident. The technique of recording provoked lively discussion.[47]

In 1958 Poser and Ziegler contributed a condensed[74] and extended[75] report on the clinical significance of positive spiking. A nose reference electrode was found valuable, with again the abnormality being occipito-temporal in distribution and more often seen in the younger ages. They were impressed with the incidence of epileptic equivalents, migraine attacks, and behavior disturbance; over half of their 136 patients also showed other types of EEG abnormality. They felt that EEG examination was more important for children with behavior disturbance than for those with idiopathic grand mal epilepsy, and agreed with Gibbs and Low[31] that the clinical story is sufficiently characteristic that 14 and 6/sec. positive spiking can often be predicted on clinical grounds. They noted in some cases a dramatic disappearance of the episodic behavioral disturbance and improved EEG in association with anticonvulsant therapy.

Garneski[16] very briefly reported on this pattern in juvenile behavior problems—with very little further elaboration in an almost equally terse note two years later.[17] There were two matched groups of 48 juveniles each, with the sole known relevant variable being that of behavior problem; the pattern showed with an incidence of 8 per cent in the nonbehavior group and 23 per cent in the behavior problem group. In Gibbs' brief chapter in the volume *Temporal Lobe Epilepsy*[27] and again in the ARNMD volume *The Brain and Human Behavior*,[26] he described the developmental history of this pattern, regarded as the most characteristic temporal lobe discharge seen in adolescents. (See also reference 30.) Many studies dealing with age factors were reviewed in the Spiegel *Progress* volume covering 1958;[37] a number of these dealt with behavior disorder without this complex being mentioned by the contributors to this area. The abstracts from the Symposium on Childhood Convulsions from the French EEG Society,[98] appearing in *The EEG Journal,* contained no mention of this in the 22 papers given; in contrast, 98 cases of 6 and 14/sec. positive spiking were reported in the Japanese literature.[54]

In the Nationwide Symposium on Convulsive Disorders published in the *Medical Clinics of North America,* 1958, a volume which few EEGers seem to see, chapters by Kellaway and Conn[44] and by Druckman[14] dealt specifically with the syndrome of convulsive equivalent state. The full-blown syndrome, associated with 6 and 14/sec. positive spiking, includes episodic headache, abdominal pain, vomiting, pallor, limpness, weakness, dizziness, and temperature change, followed by sleep. Patients show some variability from attack to attack with not all features being consistently present; headache is almost universally mentioned. Electrographically, positive spiking was the most consistent, but not universal, feature. The matter of paroxysmal abdominal pain received brief but specific discussion with relationship to 14 and 6/sec. positive spiking (as well as spontaneous paroxysmal slow activity and marked response to overbreathing) in the book by Chao et al., *Convulsive Disorders in Children,*[8] they again mention the good response to Dilantin, with diamox and meprobamate also effective. The pattern was reported present in nine of ten children with pseudohypertropic muscular dystrophy and in some of the mothers, although the illustrative material is not always convincing.[104]

In 1959 papers dealing with positive spiking began to appear in the pediatric journals. Kellaway and colleagues[45] elaborated on the specific EEG correlate of convulsive equivalent disorder[42] in children, by which the authors meant one or more of three particular types of complaint—attacks of headache or abdominal pain associated with autonomic disturbance, behavioral disturbances, and seizures in the form of simple unconsciousness and generalized convulsions. Of 550 cases showing the pattern of positive spiking, more than half had histories of paroxysmal attacks of headache and/or abdominal pain or other autonomic disturbance. When the sample was further restricted to cases showing positive spiking as the only abnormality in the record, again more than half had such clinical complaints. Other EEG abnormalities were of nonspecific nature, often too much occipital slowing or a pronounced or prolonged response to hyperventilation, and it was suggested that these two features are often associated with the presence of the positive spike discharge. It is difficult to determine the proportion of cases with positive spiking who showed no symptoms, but the authors mentioned that during serial study following head injury or encephalitis the pattern had been noted to develop following the clearing of the acute diffuse early disturbance and that subsequently many patients developed the clinical symptomatology. Generally, a specific etiology was not determinable but 21 per cent had a history of some type of head injury and 18 per cent had a history of encephalitis; the cerebral insult might be subtle; heredity did not appear important. Of great interest are their reported 2.3 per cent incidence of this pattern in a control group of 1,000 normal children and a 10.2 per cent incidence for all children referred to that laboratory because of symptoms referable to the central nervous system. In marked contrast, there was an 0.53 per cent incidence in their series of 14,000 adult patients. Although the pattern tended to disappear in a few years without treatment, clinical symptoms of a paroxysmal nature responded well to anticonvulsant therapy, whereas those of a more continuous or chronic type did not show such a good response. These workers make the very important point that the 14 and 6/sec. positive spike pattern is not itself a seizure discharge in the sense that a 3/sec. wave-and-spike complex is a discharge with obvious associated clinical manifestations. They subscribe to the assumption of the origin of these discharges in some deep midline structure, apparently in part because of the topographic distribution of the configuration. (See also reference 47.)

The Eleventh Western Institute on Epilepsy[78] held in Milwaukee in September, 1959 (Proceedings available in mimeographed format), devoted a session to the clinical and electrographical aspects of 6 and 14/sec. positive spiking; criminal and aggressive behavior was emphasized. The contribution of Metcalf is of particular interest for his suggestion that the limbic system is a likely site of origin of positive spiking and for his reference to an unpublished case of Walker and Marshall which failed to show positive spikes from implanted electrodes in thalamus and hypothalamus. Still another Midwestern laboratory[32] found an incidence of 139 records showing positive spiking out of 1,000 consecutive routine sleeping EEGs; the briefly listed clinical correlates merely confirmed previously published work. Another case of matricide was reported.[105, 106] Metcalf[63] described the developmental sequence of the pattern in one child. A pair of identical twins showed concordant positive spiking and clinical complaints.[65, 67]

In 1960 there was a flowering of both clinical and experimental interest in 14 and 6/sec. positive spiking, including papers from South America[1] and the Scandinavian[79] countries. The latter, by Refsum and colleagues, is an elaboration of their earlier brief abstracts and gives both a fair summary of the literature and a presentation of new data. They reported on 72 patients with this pattern as the only seizure-type abnormality, nearly two thirds of the patients being above 15 years of age. They noted the wide variety of paroxysmal-type symptoms from such patients, many of whom had more than one complaint. Head injury seemed the most common etiological factor; most patients showed no neurological abnormality. There were two tumor cases, one in the posterior fossa and another deep in the left hemisphere. They mentioned specifically that many of the symptoms under discussion were not necessarily of diencephalic origin but might involve the limbic system.

Hughes[39] suggested that this frequency complex might better be described as 14 and 7/sec. positive spiking (cf. Grossman[34]) and gave statistical and neurophysiological reasoning for this. Other workers have commented on frequency characteristics, and all must have noted the considerable variability in the pattern. Indeed, a perceptive recordist may hear this acute complex being scribed by well-sharpened pens before it is actually seen. Strict conformation of frequency is less important than the quite characteristic configuration and its geometric distribution over the head.

To date, few studies have included adequate control populations, being largely dependent on other types of cases referred to the same laboratory. Walter *et al.*[101] quite properly criticized the traditional retrospective type of approach that had generally been used. They elected an intensive clinical and EEG study of a small group of control and positive spike patients between the ages of five and 20 years. Since all cases had been referred to the laboratory for an evaluation of suspected CNS involvement, there were groups with normal EEGs, abnormal EEGs, a pure 14 and 6 group, and a 14 and 6 group which also had other EEG abnormality. With a total number (N) of 74 and group Ns ranging from 13 to 23, they were able to make a detailed neurological and psychological evaluation, the latter relying largely on psychological tests. Having computer facilities available, the 263 rated items were grouped into five clusters which appeared to have relevance to the symptoms given in the previous literature. These were classified as (1) aggressive behavior, (2) organic symptomatology, (3) emotional symptomatology, (4) disturbed mother syndrome, and (5) disturbed family syndrome. When compared with the EEG findings only two differences were statistically significant: (a) the 13 children with a pure 14 and 6/sec. positive spike abnormality had a significantly lower score than either the normal or abnormal EEG groups on emotional symptomatology; (b) the mixed 14 and 6/sec. positive spike group had significantly higher scores on the aggressive behavior cluster than did the normal or abnormal EEG groups. The complaints of headache, abdominal pain, and vertigo were not significantly different in distribution among the four groups. They were unable to confirm the association of electrographic positive spiking and clinical autonomic phenomena; they speculated that this was due to a combination of descriptive and semantic disagreement and a function of the type of case which tended to be referred to various laboratories.

Thus, in the first of the reasonably well-controlled studies, the expected relationship failed to appear. It should be noted, however, that the comparison was between children with positive spike abnormality and other children referred to the EEG laboratory, rather than with children from the general population. This work has not been done in our own laboratory, nor has search of the literature revealed such a control population. Still another problem[53] is the clear identification and formulation of the presumptive clinical complex. As one reads through the now extensive literature on this topic one becomes aware of an overriding obligato of clinical conviction that there is some (causal?) connection between the electrographic complex and the clinical behavior. It is obvious that many workers in this area become convinced through seeing the day-to-day accumulation of cases; unfortunately, a rigorous demonstration is rarely attempted.

Other recent studies have received critical summary comment.[56] A group of 19 cases with paroxysmal abdominal pain, often with other episodic complaints as well, were reported[87] to have 14 and 6/sec. positive spiking as the most common EEG abnormality; the exact number is not determinable from the presented data—the interpretation of which received later pediatric protest.[12] Stehle[95] reported 30 cases with the positive spike discharge, all showing severe aggressive behavior and affective defect; the behavior of two patients resulted in death of a family member, two others severe physical injury, and two suicide attempts, plus other examples of extreme property damage. He commented specifically on the psychic indifference of such patients with lack of remorse, or guilt, or self criticism. Schwade and Geiger[85] related this type of discharge to the "irresistible impulse" and emphasized the need for psychotherapy in association with anticonvulsant therapy. A discursive paper dealt with this pattern in relation to reading disability.[80] Gibbs et al. found a substantial incidence of 14 and 6/sec. positive spiking as a nonspecific abnormality in a large series of patients with cerebral palsy[22] and mental retardation.[21]

A definitive paper formulating a specific electroclinical syndrome was contributed to the Lennox Festschrift by Kellaway et al.[46] They present a group of 459 children with primary complaint of headache and/or abdominal pain, all of whom had 14 and 6/sec. positive spiking in their sleep EEGs. The autonomic nervous system was regarded as strongly involved but the pathophysiological basis as yet undemonstrated. Numerous case histories and the results of therapy with Dilantin and diamox are given. They advise that a child with such clinical complaints should be suspected of a paroxysmal CNS disorder; if his EEG shows 6 and 14/sec. positive spiking such a diagnosis is the most likely explanation of the symptoms. To establish this, four initial criteria must be fulfilled: (1) the presence of the primary symptoms of headache and/or abdominal pain, often with associated pallor, sweating, temperature alteration, and so on, (2) the repeated and stereotyped paroxysmal character of the complaint, (3) the presence of 14 and 6/sec. positive spiking, and (4) the absence of specific disease of abdominal or intracranial structures; they suggest a fifth criterion for final confirmation, viz., a favorable result with anticonvulsant therapy. Their presentation of the evidence for this specific electroclinical syndrome is sufficiently complete and convincing that it is required reading for anyone interested in the problem or concerned with children.

Although behavior disorder was not even mentioned in the above study, Hughes *et al.*[40, 41] recently reported an approximate two-thirds incidence of behavior disorder or autonomic dysfunction in 115 cases exhibiting positive spike discharges; the combined incidence reached 90 per cent. Their finding of a right-sided predominance and a tendency to show slowing through posterior temporal regions in the waking state is in agreement with our experience. Noteworthy is their matched group of cases with similar clinical symptomatology but no positive spiking; EEGs of this group were generally less abnormal. The apparent absence of positive spiking in Kennard's[48] recent paper is explicable only if sleep studies were never done, as the group of over 200 predominantly male 6 to 16-year olds was selected on the basis of disturbed behavior in every case. However, an abstract[49] suggests a relationship between positive spiking and frontal fast activity; the tendency for positive spiking to be associated with myoclonic jerking in sleep is probably just an example of how the pattern is brought out by any alerting procedure. Two recent studies from England[2, 72] fail to mention positive spiking in populations where one would expect a high incidence of the pattern; the apparent failure to include sleep tracings is a persisting fault in many European laboratories. The eminently sensible book by Kiloh and Osselton[50] does contain a cautious evaluation of the phenomenon; interestingly, their illustration (of positive spiking) taken from the Gibbs *Atlas* is one of the only two EEG samples that are not original with the authors.

Among the final papers appearing in the period covered by this review is a full report (in German) from the Iowa City laboratories[71] dealing with 343 cases; the highest proportion of positive spiking occurred in psychiatric patients. A relatively high incidence was also found in schizophrenic patients[81] and in emotionally disturbed asthmatic children.[6] A verified case of hypothalamic tumor showed 14 and 6/sec. dysrhythmia.[4] A few papers mention the results of anticonvulsant therapy.[9, 103] Three contributions by Shimoda *et al.*[89, 90, 91] list an extraordinary variety of clinical features; diphenhydramine was reported selectively useful as an activating agent. Finally, there has been increasing reference to positive spike abnormality in the clinical psychiatric literature[10, 55, 58, 99] and in professional advertising media.[13, 97] Inevitably, an analytically oriented account of two teen-age murderers[107] reached the popular press[94] with immediate rebuttal by Gibbs,[28] who denied relationship between murder and 6 and 14/sec. positive spiking.

With the exception of an early reference by Knott *et al.*[57] to positive spiking in cats with large hypothalamic lesions and the neglected work of Grossman,[34] the only experimental production of this pattern was described in a recent paper by Hehman *et al.*[35] Serotonin-injected chicks showed plausible discharges of positive spikes independently from either hemisphere. There has been a surprising paucity of animal experiment work on this problem, for neither negative nor "positive" results were otherwise found in the literature.

UPSHOT

It will be obvious from this review that each investigator has seen the problem from a slightly different perspective. Each has been impressed with certain aspects of the clinical correlates, probably reflecting the type of clinical population referred to that laboratory. Variously, head and belly pain, autonomic dysfunction, atypical epilepsy, and malevolent aggression have all been emphasized. All of these have intimate ramifications into psychiatry, neurology, and pediatrics and involve difficult diagnostic problems. Any independent laboratory assistance would seem to be a blessing. There are so few predictable events in psychiatry that any indications of such should be vigorously exploited by many workers. The word "predictable" is used literally and advisedly, for a brief clinical history or even the judgment of a perceptive technician observing the patient during application of electrodes may be enough to suggest strongly the likelihood of positive spiking if a sleep tracing is obtained. The discharge is more reliably predicted from history than is, for example, the wave-and-spike complex of classical petit mal epilepsy. We have also noted a strong tendency for positive Aschheim-Zondek tests to be associated with positive spiking in teen-age acting-out unmarried girls.

As of this writing the real clinical significance of this pattern, *if there be any*, is anything but clear. There is a surfeit of possible clinical relationships, too often resulting from uncontrolled studies,[53] but almost nothing is known of the basic neurophysiological substrate that might produce such an unorthodox discharge. And even if one chooses to ignore the cases not predicted by history and the apparent normals with such activity, there is the problem of causal vs. casual relationship between clinical and EEG data. Some type of causal association is frankly assumed or at least implicit in most papers. Our own laboratory experience suggests that bursts of positive spiking might be regarded as a neurophysiological handicap, the importance of which varies as a function of the environment of the patient. A child subjected to the dual stress of 6 and 14/sec. positive spiking and a poor behavioral environment may well react with an unacceptable clinical response that would not be elicited if he lived in a less stressful situation. The strictures set forth in a recent review[56] are still pertinent.

Why, then, do so few laboratories report the presence of 6 and 14/sec. positive spiking? We have repeatedly seen it in patients with reports of negative EEG findings from other laboratories. First of all, sleep is imperative. We have only three patients with 6 and 14/sec. positive spiking in the waking record, a rare phenomenon but also reported by others. Light sleep—whether natural or induced—is usually the critical stage. The pattern is most clearly derived from the posterior temporal regions. Laboratories omitting an electrode in this area are seriously handicapped. And, since even 16-channel equipment does not permit optimal recording of all leads simultaneously, a montage must be designed to "trap" the pattern most effectively. The following figures are included to illustrate variations in pattern with particular reference to various electrode combinations; we have found simultaneous recording to ipsilateral and contralateral ears to be especially useful. Although the reporting of the discharge is the responsibility of the electroencephalographer, the detection and clear demonstration of it is uniquely the responsibility of the recording technician. The performance of the latter directly reflects the degree to which the former has been willing and able to share his knowledge. Ultimately, success depends on the technician who has the motivation and skill to select the optimal montage at the critical stage of sleep, not forgetting that the easiest way to demonstrate the pattern is by gradually alerting the patient from sleep into lighter stages of drowsiness.

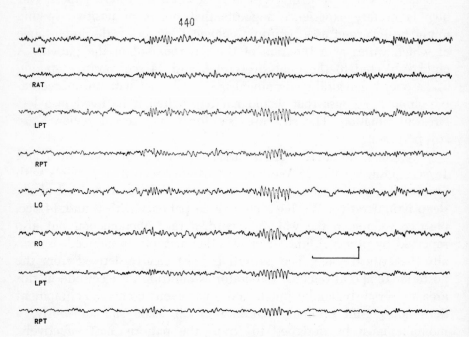

440

Fig. XIII—1. *Twenty-six-year-old woman with behavior disorder, excess alcohol, and some depression, with previous EST. This shows 14/sec. positive bursts in simple form, bilaterally but with higher voltage on the left side. The two bottom channels are to ipsilateral ear; others to contralateral ear. In this and other figures, calibration equals 1 sec. at 50 μV. L = left, R = right, AT = anterior temporal, PT = posterior temporal, O = occiput.*

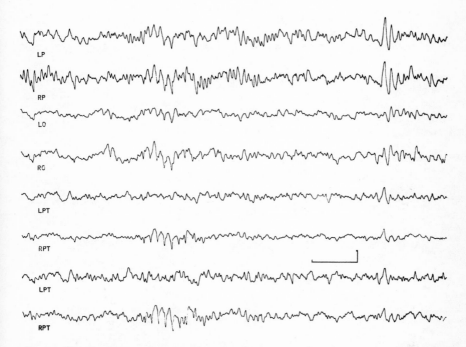

Fig. XIII—2. *Adolescent boy with severe behavior disorder; identical twin had similar record. 6/sec. positive spikes mostly on right side. Note voltage difference against contralateral ear (two bottom channels) as compared to ipsilateral ear on other channels. P = parietal; other abbreviations as in Figure 1.*

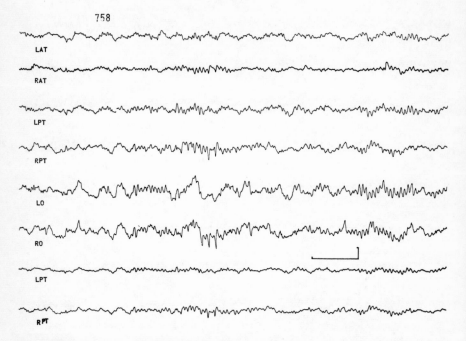

Fig. XIII—3. *Adolescent girl with history of severe headache. Intermixture of approximately 6 and 14/sec. positive activity on right side, seen better against controlled contralateral ear (six top channels) than against ipsilateral ear (two bottom channels).*

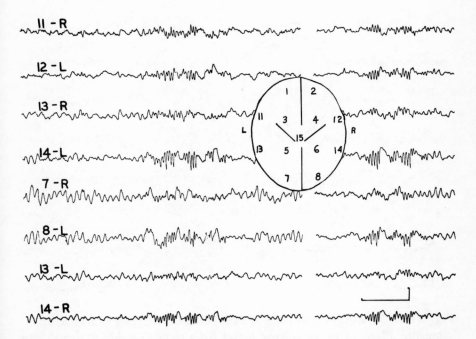

Fig. XIII—4. *Record from adolescent boy who attacked sister with knife and remembered nothing of episode. This illustrates the rapidity with which 14/sec. positive spiking may occur as normal alpha rhythm is depressed in drowsiness; latter section shows similar pattern in deeper sleep. There is better definition of right-sided discharge in recordings against the contralateral (left) ear; note right ear contribution from grid 2, best seen in channel 1.*

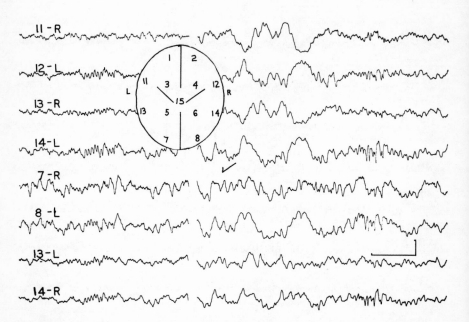

Fig. XIII—5. *Fifteen-year-old girl with behavior difficulty in school. Spontaneous 14/sec. positive spiking better from right side during deep sleep and in a more complex discharge appearing several seconds after slight auditory stimulus (check-mark). This procedure of gradual alerting is often critical in demonstration of such activity; inadvertant or uncontrolled environmental noise may at times be put to advantage.*

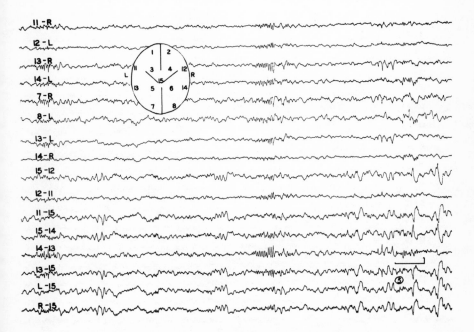

Fig. XIII—6. *Figures 6 through 9 are all from the same record of a nine-year-old girl, made three months before removal of posterior fossa medulloblastoma. Waking records showed occipito-temporal slow activity over a wide range of frequencies, but mostly at 3–4/sec. and worse on the left side. All pre- and postoperative records showed much 14 and 6/sec. positive spiking bilaterally and independently, with a posterior temporal maximum. Figure 6 shows predominantly left-sided 14 and 6/sec. positive bursts in a montage especially useful for detecting these discharges. Note higher voltage from posterior temporal referred to contralateral as compared to ipsilateral ear. When the same left posterior temporal lead is run in the usual 1-grid 2 linkage against vertex, the relatively unfamiliar pattern of spikes "pointing away" from adjacent channels (e.g., 13 and 14) indicates recorded positivity of the discharge.*

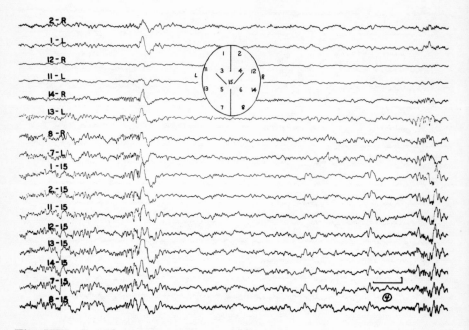

Fig. XIII—7. *This montage is somewhat less sensitive to the display of positive spiking. Note simultaneous presence of 14/sec. positive bursts from right side and 6/sec. positive bursts from left, referred to ipsilateral ear lead. Patterns are less characteristic when referred to vertex, tending to be "lost" in vertex sleep activity.*

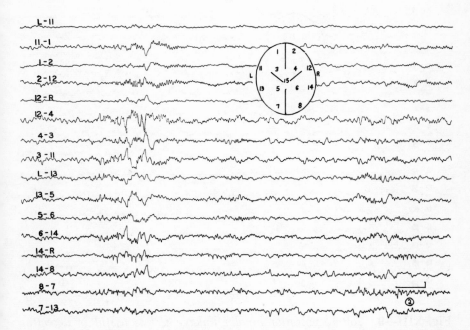

Fig. XIII—8. *This transverse montage allows easy differentiation of normal bilateral spindling from positive spiking. Note complex intermixture of frequencies and hemispheric independence.*

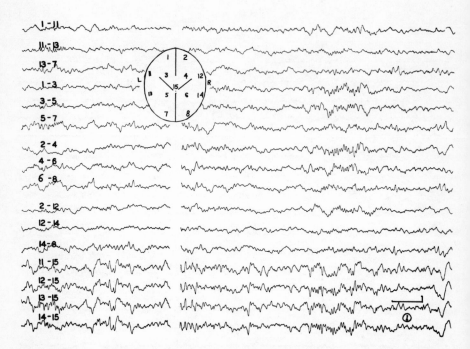

Fig. XIII—9. *Antero-posterior bipolar linkage is less useful in detecting positive spiking (shown in the first section) than in detecting bilateral spindling (shown in the second half).*

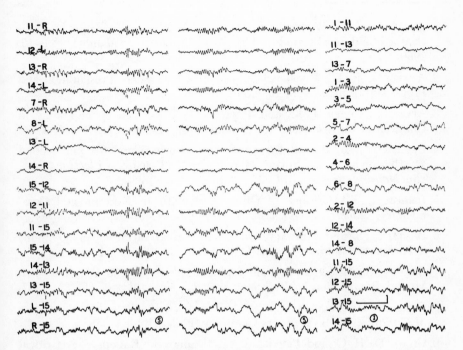

Fig. XIII—10. *Ten-year-old boy with history of premature birth, several days in oxygen, and fainting spells, thought to be "functional," associated with breath-holding attacks. Previous EEG two years earlier was abnormal with very high voltage negative sharp wave discharges broadly through the right temporal, even more active in natural sleep, during which stage he also showed predominantly right-sided posterior temporal 14–16/sec. positive spiking. The present waking record is improved (never any anti-convulsant treatment) with only a little residual right temporal slowing and fragments of negative sharp activity. In sleep there are normal bilateral spindling and abundant 16 and 6/sec. positive spike discharges, as before. Samples illustrate predominantly 14/sec. positive bursts shifting from side to side. Note effect of "active" contralateral ear reference lead in yielding fragments of mirror image discharge; the preservation of some ipsilateral ear reference is therefore useful to readily identify polarity. Widely spaced derivations reveal discharges better than closely spaced linkage. Note the clear independence of positive spiking and normal spindles. Lead placement as in Figures 6 through 9.*

References

1. ALBERNAZ, J. G., "Aspectos Electroencefalográficos das Espículas Positivas a 14 e 6 por Segundo," *Arch. Neuro-psiquiat.* (*S. Paulo*), *18*:3–18, 1960.

2. ANNESLEY, P. T., "Psychiatric Illness in Adolescence: Presentation and Prognosis," *J. ment. Sci.*, *107*:268–278, 1961.

3. APLEY, J., LLOYD, J. K., and TURTON, C., "Electroencephalography in Children with Recurrent Abdominal Pain," *Lancet*, *1*:264–265, 1956.

4. BEVILACQUA, A. R. and LITTLE, S. C., "Fourteen and Six per Second Dysrhythmia with Proven Hypothalamic Disease," *Electroenceph. clin. Neurophysiol.*, *13*:314–315, 1961.

5. BISHOP, G., "A Critique of Gibbs' Law with an Experimental Commentary," *Electroenceph. clin. Neurophysiol.*, *2*:91–92, 1950.

6. BLATMAN, S. and METCALF, D. R., "Abnormal Electroencephalograms in Asthmatic Children," *Amer. J. Dis. Child.*, *102*:531, 1961.

7. BRANDT, S., "Electroencephalographic Findings in 200 Children with Mental Retardation," *Electroenceph. clin. Neurophysiol.*, *9*:735, 1957.

8. CHAO, D. H., DRUCKMAN, R., and KELLAWAY, P., *Convulsive Disorders of Children*, W. B. Saunders Company, Philadelphia, 1958.

9. CHAO, D. H.-C. and PLUMB, R. L., "Diamox in Epilepsy," A Critical Review of 178 Cases," *J. Pediat.*, *58*:211–218, 1961.

10. CHODOFF, P., "The Problem of Psychiatric Diagnosis: Can Biochemistry and Neurophysiology Help?" *Psychiatry*, *23*:185–191, 1960.

11. CONDON, J. V., BECKA, D. R., and GIBBS, F. A., "Electroencephalographic Abnormalities in Hyperthyroidism," *J. clin. Endocr. 14*:1511–1518, 1954.

12. Correspondence, *J. Pediat.*, *57*:634–635, 1960.

13. "Distinctive EEG Pattern Tied to Behavior Problems," *Scope*, *5*, January 27, 1960.

14. DRUCKMAN, R., "Pain and Autonomic Disturbances in Convulsive Equivalent States," in KELLAWAY, P. and CONN, H. F. (eds.), *The Medical Clinics of North America*, W. B. Saunders Company, Philadelphia, 1958, pp. 475–479.

15. FOIS, A., ROSENBERG, C., and GIBBS, F. A., "The Electroencephalogram in Phenylpyruvic Oligophrenia," *Electroenceph. clin. Neurophysiol.*, *7*:569–572, 1955.

16. GARNESKI, T. M., "Increased 6 and/or 14 per Second Spike Dysrhythmia in Juvenile Behavior Problems," *Electroenceph. clin. Neurophysiol., 10*:358, 1958.

17. GARNESKI, T. M., "Six and Fourteen per Second Spikes in Juvenile Behavior Disorders," *Electroenceph. clin. Neurophysiol., 12*:505, 1960.

18. GARNESKI, T. M. and GREEN, J. R., "Recording the Fourteen and Six per Second Spike Phenomenon," *Electroenceph. clin. Neurophysiol., 8*: 501–505, 1956.

19. GIBBS, E. L. and GIBBS, F. A., "Electroencephalographic Evidence of Thalamic and Hypothalamic Epilepsy," *Neurology, 1*:136–144, 1951.

20. GIBBS, E. L., GILLEN, H. W., and GIBBS, F. A., "Disappearance and Migration of Epileptic Foci in Childhood," *Amer. J. Dis. Child., 88*: 596–603, 1954.

21. GIBBS, E. L., RICH, C. L., FOIS, A., and GIBBS, F. A., "Electroencephalographic Study of Mentally Retarded Persons," *Amer. J. ment. Defic., 65*:236–247, 1960.

22. GIBBS, E. L., RICH, C., PERLSTEIN, M., and GIBBS, F. A., "The Predictive Value of EEG as Regards Epilepsy in Cerebral Palsy," *Electroenceph. clin. Neurophysiol., 12*:756, 1960.

23. GIBBS, F. A., "Value of Electroencephalography," *Mod. Med., 75*–82, 1954.

24. GIBBS, F. A., "Subjective Complaints and Behavior Disturbances Associated with Fourteen and Six per Second Positive Spikes," *Electroenceph. clin. Neurophysiol., 7*:315, 1955.

25. GIBBS, F. A., "Clinical Correlates of 14 and 6 per Second Positive Spikes (1865 Cases)," *Electroenceph. clin. Neurophysiol., 8*:149, 1956.

26. GIBBS, F. A., "Abnormal Electrical Activity in the Temporal Regions and its Relationship to Abnormalities of Behavior," *Res. Publ. Ass. nerv. ment. Dis., 36*:278–294, 1958.

27. GIBBS, F. A., "Differentiation of Mid-Temporal, Anterior Temporal and Diencephalic Epilepsy," in BALDWIN, M. and BAILEY, P. (eds.), *Temporal Lobe Epilepsy*, Charles C Thomas, Springfield, Ill., 1958, pp. 109–117.

28. GIBBS, F. A., "6 & 14 (Letters to the Editor)," *Time, 79*, January 19, 1962.

29. GIBBS, F. A. and GIBBS, E. L., "Thalamic and Hypothalamic Epilepsy," in *Atlas of Electroencephalography*, vol. 2, *Epilepsy*, Addison-Wesley Press, Cambridge, Mass., 1952, pp. 329–345.

30. GIBBS, F. A. and GIBBS, E. L., "Changes in Epileptic Foci with Age," *III Int. Congr., Electroenceph. clin. Neurophysiol., 233*–234, 1953.

31. GIBBS, F. A. and LOW, N. L., "Symposium on Laboratory Tests and Special Procedures; Electroencephalography in Children," *Pediat. Clin. N. Amer.* 2:291–303, 1955.

32. GLENN, C. G. and KNUTH, R., "Incidence of Fourteen and Six per Second Positive Spike Discharges in Routine Sleeping EEG's," *Dis. nerv. Syst.*, 20:340–341, 1959.

33. GROSSMAN, C., "The Relationship of 'Positive Spikes' to 'Spontaneous' Activity and Cortical Excitability," *Electroenceph. clin. Neurophysiol.*, 4:381, 1952.

34. GROSSMAN, C., "Laminar Cortical Blocking and its Relation to Episodic Aggressive Outbursts," *Arch. Neurol. Psychiat., Chicago, 71:*576–587, 1954.

35. HEHMAN, K. N., VONDERAHE, A. R., and PETERS, J. J., "Effect of Serotonin on Behavior, Electrical Activity of the Brain, and Seizure Threshold of the Newly Hatched Chick. With a Note on the Production of Seizures Presenting 14-per-Second and 6-per-Second Positive Spikes," *Neurology, 11:*1011–1016, 1961.

36. HENRY, C. E., "Discussion," *IV int. Congr., Electroenceph. clin. Neurophysiol.*, 29–30, 1957.

37. HENRY, C. E. and KNOTT, J. R., "Electroencephalography," *Progr. Neurol. Psychiat.*, 14:270–297, 1959.

38. HILL, D., Book review of *Atlas of Electroencephalography, Electroenceph. clin. Neurophysiol.*, 5:139–143, 1953.

39. HUGHES, J. R., "The 14 and 7 per Second Positive Spikes—A Reappraisal Following a Frequency Count," *Electroenceph. clin. Neurophysiol.*, 12:495–496, 1960.

40. HUGHES, J. R., GIANTURCO, D., and STEIN, W., "Electro-Clinical Correlations in the Positive Spike Phenomenon," *Electroenceph. clin. Neurophysiol.*, 13:599–605, 1961.

41. HUGHES, J. R., GIANTURCO, D., STEIN, W., CURTIN, M. J., and BROWN, V. P., "Electro-Clinical Correlations in the Positive Spike Phenomena," *Electroenceph. clin. Neurophysiol.*, 13:496, 1961.

42. KELLAWAY, P., "Convulsive Equivalent Disorders," *Electroenceph. clin. Neurophysiol.*, 5:130, 1953.

43. KELLAWAY, P., "Head Injury in Children," *Electroenceph. clin. Neurophysiol.*, 7:497–502, 1955.

44. KELLAWAY, P. and CONN, H. F., "Electroencephalography in the Diagnosis and Management of the Epilepsies," in KELLAWAY, P. and CONN, H. F. (eds.), *The Medical Clinics of North America*, W. B. Saunders Company, Philadelphia, 1958, pp. 439–460.

45. KELLAWAY, P., CRAWLEY, J. W., and KAGAWA, N., "A Specific Correlate of Convulsive Equivalent Disorders in Children," *J. Pediat.*, 55:582–592, 1959.

46. KELLAWAY, P., CRAWLEY, J. W., and KAGAWA, N., "Paroxysmal Pain and Autonomic Disturbances of Cerebral Origin: A Specific Electro-Clinical Syndrome," *Epilepsia*, 1:466–483, 1960.

47. KELLAWAY, P., MOORE, F. J., and KAGAWA, N., "The '14 and 6 per Second Positive Spike' Pattern of Gibbs and Gibbs," *Electroenceph. clin. Neurophysiol.*, 9:165–166, 1957.

48. KENNARD, M. [A.], "Paroxysmal Behavior and its EEG Correlates," *Epilepsia*, 1:484–492, 1960.

49. KENNARD, M. A., "EEG Changes Occurring with Drowsiness in Emotionally Disturbed Children," *Electroenceph. clin. Neurophysiol.*, 13:305–306, 1961.

50. KILOH, L. G. and OSSELTON, J. W., *Clinical Electroencephalography*, Butterworths, London, 1961.

51. KIRSCHBAUM, W. R. and STEHLE, H. C., "Electroencephalographic Studies of Patients with Peptic Ulcer and Functional Gastric Disorders," *Electroenceph. clin. Neurophysiol.*, 4:380, 1952.

52. KIRSCHBAUM, W. R. and STEHLE, H. C., "Electroencephalographic Studies of Patients with Peptic Ulcer and Functional Gastric Disorders," *Electroenceph. clin. Neurophysiol.*, 5:513–524, 1953.

53. KOEGLER, R. R., COLBERT, E. G., and WALTER, R. D., "Problems in the Correlation of Psychopathology with Electroencephalographic Abnormalities," *Amer. J. Psychiat.*, 117:822–824, 1961.

54. KOIZUMI, A., YAMAMASU, T., MORISHITA, T., IWAI, H., and SHIMODA, Y., "A Statistic Observation of 14 and 6 CPS Positive Spikes," *Electroenceph. clin. Neurophysiol.*, Suppl. 12:29, 1958.

55. KNOTT, J. R., "EEG and Behavior," *Amer. J. Orthopsychiat.*, 30:292–297, 1960.

56. KNOTT, J. R. and HENRY, C. E., "Electroencephalography," *Progr. Neurol. Psychiat.*, 16:254–282, 1961.

57. KNOTT, J. R., INGRAM, W. R., WHEATLEY, M. D., and SUMMERS, T. D., "Hypothalamic Influence on Cortical Activity," *Electroenceph. clin. Neurophysiol.*, 3:102, 1951.

58. KOUPERNIK, C., "Epileptic Paroxysms of a Vegetative and Anxious Nature in Children: Two Case Histories," *J. Child Psychol. Psychiat.*, 1:146–155, 1960.

59. LOW, N. L., GIBBS, E. L., and GIBBS, F. A., "Electroencephalographic Findings in Breath Holding Spells," *Pediatrics*, 15:595–599, 1955.

60. LYKETSOS, G., BELINSON, L., and GIBBS, F. A., "Sleep Recordings on Psychotic Patients With and Without Psychomotor Seizures," *Electroenceph. clin. Neurophysiol., 4*:379, 1952.

61. MACKEITH, R. C. and PAMPIGLIONE, G., "The Recurrent Syndrome in Children: Clinical and Electroencephalographic Observations in 52 Cases," *Electroenceph. clin. Neurophysiol., 8*:161, 1956.

62. MATSUMOTO, Y., SUZUKI, A., SASANI, S., NAKAJIMA, S., and KURITA, T., "EEG Studies on Abdominal Epilepsy of Children," *Electroenceph. clin. Neurophysiol.,* Suppl. *18*:65, 1959.

63. METCALF, D. R., "On the Development of 6 and 14 per Sec. Spikes," *Electroenceph. clin. Neurophysiol., 11*:616–617, 1959.

64. MILLEN, F. J., "A Study of Fourteen-and-six per Second Dysrhythmia in Children," *Electroenceph. clin. Neurophysiol., 5*:128, 1953.

65. MILLEN, F. J., "Abdominal Epilepsy," *Arch. Neurol., Chicago, 4*:119, 1961.

66. MILLEN, F. J. and WHITE, B., "Fourteen and Six per Second Positive Activity in Children," *Neurology, 4*:541–549, 1954.

67. MILLEN, F. J. and WINTERS, K., "Fourteen and Six per Second Positive Spike Activity in the EEG of Identical Twins and Family," *Electroenceph. clin. Neurophysiol., 11*:845, 1959.

68. MILLS, W. B., "Paroxysmal 14 and 6/sec. Spike Discharges and Clinical Cases, Including a Teenage Murderer," *Electroenceph. clin. Neurophysiol., 8*:344, 1956.

69. NAOI, T., SHINOZAKI, T., and HIROSAWA, M., "On '14 and 6 per Second Positive Spikes,'" *Electroenceph. clin. Neurophysiol.,* Suppl. *9*:59, 1957.

70. NICHOLSON, J. M. and KNOTT, J. R., "Sleep EEGs in Psychiatric Patients," *Electroenceph. clin. Neurophysiol., 9*:375–376, 1957.

71. NIEDERMEYER, E. and KNOTT, J. R., "Über die Bedeutung der 14 und 6/sec-positiven Spitzen im EEG," *Arch. Psychiat. Nervenkr., 202*:266–280, 1961.

72. NUFFIELD, E. J. A., "Neuro-physiology and Behaviour Disorders in Epileptic Children," *J. ment. Sci., 107*:438–458, 1961.

73. PERLSTEIN, M. A., GIBBS, E. L., and GIBBS, F. A., "The Electroencephalogram in Infantile Cerebral Palsy," *Amer. J. phys. Med., 34*:477–496, 1955.

74. POSER, C. M. and ZIEGLER, D. K., "Clinical Significance of the 14 and 6 per Second Positive Spike Complex," *Trans. Amer. neurol. Ass.,* 170–172, 1958.

75. POSER, C. M. and ZIEGLER, D. K., "Clinical Significance of 14 and 6 per Second Positive Spike Complexes," *Neurology, 8*:903–912, 1958.

76. PRESTHUS, J., REFSUM, S., SKULSTAD, A., and ÖSTENSJÖ, S., "Fourteen and

Six per Second Positive Spikes. An Electroencephalographic and Clinical Study. Preliminary Report," *Acta psychiat. scand., 31*:166, 1956.

77. PRESTHUS, J., REFSUM, S., SKULSTAD, A., and ÖSTENSJÖ, S., "Clinical Correlates of the Fourteen and Six per Second Positive Spikes. An Electroencephalographic and Clinical Study. Preliminary Report," *IV int. Congr., Electroenceph. clin. Neurophysiol.,* 128–129, 1957.

78. Proceedings, *Eleventh Western Institute on Epilepsy,* Milwaukee, Wisconsin, 1959.

79. REFSUM, S., PRESTHUS, J., SKULSTAD, A. A., and ÖSTENSJÖ, S., "Clinical Correlates of the 14 and 6 Per Second Positive Spikes. An Electroencephalographic and Clinical Study," *Acta psychiat. scand., 35*:330–344, 1960.

80. ROBERTS, A. C., METRICK, S., and ROWLEY, J., "Factors in Behavior of Certain Epileptic Children," *Dis. nerv. Syst., 21*:669–677, 1960.

81. SCHMIDT, H. O. and ANDREWS, R. C., "Notes on the 6- and 14-Positive Spikes in the EEG," *Psychol. Rep., 9*:399–400, 1961.

82. SCHWADE, E. D. and GEIGER, S. G., "Matricide with Electroencephalographic Evidence of Thalamic or Hypothalamic Disorder," *Dis. nerv. Syst., 14*:18–20, 1953.

83. SCHWADE, E. D. and GEIGER, S., "Behavior Disorders of the Impulsive-Compulsive Type with Consistent Abnormal EEG Findings," *Electroenceph. clin. Neurophysiol., 7*:473–474, 1955.

84. SCHWADE, E. D. and GEIGER, S. G., "Abnormal Electroencephalographic Findings in Severe Behavior Disorders," *Dis. nerv. Syst., 17*:307–317, 1956.

85. SCHWADE, E. D. and GEIGER, S. G., "Severe Behavior Disorders with Abnormal Electroencephalograms," *Dis. nerv. Syst., 21*:616–620, 1960.

86. SCHWADE, E. D. and OTTO, O., "Homicide as a Manifestation of Thalamic or Hypothalamic Disorder with Abnormal Electroencephalographic Findings," *Wisconsin med. J., 52*:171–174, 1953.

87. SHEEHY, B. N., LITTLE, S. C., STONE, J. J., McAVOY, M., and RHEA, E., "Abdominal Epilepsy," *J. Pediat., 56*:355–363, 1960.

88. SHIMODA, Y., "On Primary Thalamic and Hypothalamic Epilepsy," *IV Int. Congr., Electroenceph. clin. Neurophysiol.,* 194, 1957.

89. SHIMODA, Y., "The Clinical and Electroencephalographic Study of the Primary Diencephalic Epilepsy or Epilepsy of Brain Stem," *Acta neuroveg., 23*:181–191, 1961.

90. SHIMODA, Y., KOIZUMI, A., and TANAKA, K., "Electroencephalographic Activation of 'Diencephalic Epilepsy' with Diphenhydramine," *Yonago Acta med., 4*:99–102, 1960.

91. SHIMODA, Y., KOIZUMI, A., YAMAMASU, T., YOSHINO, Y., NANBA, M., and

TANAKA, K., "Statistical Observation of Six and Fourteen per Second Positive Spikes," *Yonago Acta med.*, 5:102–108, 1961.

92. SILVERMAN, D., "Sleep as a General Activation Procedure in Electroencephalography," *Electroenceph. clin. Neurophysiol.*, 8:317–324, 1956.

93. SILVERMAN, D. and MORISAKI, A., "Re-evaluation of Sleep Electroencephalography," *Electroenceph. clin. Neurophysiol.*, 10:425–431, 1958.

94. "6 & 14 Syndrome," Medicine, *Time*, 79, January 5, 1962.

95. STEHLE, H. C., "Thalamic Dysfunction Involved in Destructive-Aggressive Behavior Directed Against Persons and Property," *Electroenceph. clin. Neurophysiol.*, 12:264–265, 1960.

96. STEPHENSON, W. A., "Intracranial Neoplasm Associated with Fourteen and Six per Second Positive Spikes," *Neurology*, 1:372–376, 1951.

97. "Storm in the Brain," *The Laboratory*, 29:2–7, 1961.

98. "Symposium on Childhood Convulsions," *Electroenceph. clin. Neurophysiol.*, 10:338–343, 1958.

99. WALKER, A. E., "Murder or Epilepsy?" *J. nerv. ment. Dis.*, 133:430–437, 1961.

100. WALTER, R. D., "Some Clinical Correlation of 14 and 6 per Sec. Spiking Activity," *Electroenceph. clin. Neurophysiol.*, 9:377, 1957.

101. WALTER, R. D., COLBERT, E. G., KOEGLER, R. R., PALMER, J. O., and BOND, P. M., "A Controlled Study of the Fourteen- and Six-per-Second EEG Pattern," *Arch. gen. Psychiat.*, 2:559–566, 1960.

102. WINFIELD, D. L., "Emotional Disturbances of the Brain-Damaged Child with Reference to the Electroencephalogram," *Memphis mid-S. med. J.*, 36:403–406, 1961.

103. WINFIELD, D. L. and AIVAZIAN, G. H., "Librium Therapy and Electroencephalographic Correlates," *J. nerv. ment. Dis.*, 133:240–246, 1961.

104. WINFIELD, D. L., BRITT, L. P., and RASKIND, R., "EEG Findings in Pseudohypertrophic Muscular Dystrophy," *Sth. med. J.*, 51:1251–1259, 1958.

105. WINFIELD, D. L. and OZTURK, O., "Electroencephalographic Findings in Matricide: A Case Report," *Electroenceph. clin. Neurophysiol.*, 9:570, 1957.

106. WINFIELD, D. L. and OZTURK, O., "Electroencephalographic Findings in Matricide. A Case Report," *Dis. nerv. Syst.*, 20:176–178, 1959.

107. WOODS, S. M., "Adolescent Violence and Homicide: Ego Disruption and the 6 and 14 Dysrhythmias," *Arch. gen. Psychiat.*, 5:528–534, 1961.

XIV

Interictal Psychosis in Psychomotor-Temporal Lobe Epilepsy: An EEG-Psychological Study

Gilbert H. Glaser
Richard J. Newman
Roy Schafer

The concept of a psychomotor-temporal lobe seizure state has developed over the past one hundred years with gradual delineation particularly by Jackson,[17] Penfield and Jasper,[24] Gibbs,[11] Lennox,[19] and Gastaut.[9] The seizures are usually characterized by auras of anxiety and visceral symptoms, followed by alterations in consciousness associated with many varied complex feeling and thinking states and automatic somatic and autonomic motor behavior. These phenomena are associated with at least a partial amnesia. During the seizure repetitive stereotyped automatisms occur, such as swallowing, sucking, or chewing and movements of the arms and legs. This phase usually is followed by a period of automatic action of varying complexity with semipurposeful, inappropriate, and bizarre behavior involving an interplay with the environment and determined in part by psychological factors. The activities in this phase often may appear to merge into normal behavior. Electroencephalographic correlates of these seizures are usually unilateral or bilateral temporal lobe discharges, especially from anterior regions; but occasionally more diffuse abnormality may occur, including bilaterally asynchronous and synchronous spike-wave discharges. The temporal lobe aspects of the seizure state are emphasized in patients with olfactory hallucinations, the uncinate seizures of Jackson and the occurrence of occasional dysphasic disturbances as part of the seizure complex. However, persistent neurological disorder such as dysphasia is exceptional in the interictal period. It is felt that in some instances, particularly those with bilateral EEG abnormality, seizure discharging originating in a subcortical, upper brain stem-diencephalic region may spread through a temporal lobe, accumulating thereby more characteristic symptoms.[8, 9, 12, 20] With this background it is felt preferable to use the more generic term, psychomotor seizure state.

A relatively high incidence of interictal psychological abnormality has been found in patients with psychomotor-temporal lobe seizures. These are characterized in varying fashion as personality disorders, psychoneurotic disturbances—especially hysterical and obsessive-compulsive—and psychotic states with schizophrenic episodes.[2, 6, 10, 11, 15, 25, 27, 28] In some patients an alternation between seizures and overt psychosis has been observed, especially in relation to anticonvulsant therapy.[11, 15] A fluctuating behavioral disturbance other than seizure, therefore, can occur and be differentiated. Often, however, it has been difficult to separate an ictal psychic episode from an interictal state, and acute epileptic psychoses actually have been recognized as components of the seizure complex since their first description by the French neuropsychiatrists of the mid-nineteenth century.[7, 23]

In recent years the electroencephalogram has enabled more effective evaluation of these patients and a conference at Marseilles, held in 1956 and reported in 1959,[5] considered the clinical and electroencephalographic manifestations of psychotic episodes in epileptics between clinical seizures. Patients with psychomotor epilepsy, in contrast to those with centrencephalic seizures, were reported to have episodes of long duration, often ending in a seizure and characterized by a disturbance of affect, but not often confusion. Confusional states were much more common in patients with centrencephalic seizures. The electroencephalogram during these episodes in patients with psychomotor seizures showed either unmodified rhythms, desynchronization, "forced normalization" with disappearance of abnormal discharges,[18] or reinforced temporal abnormality. Rarely did slow-wave dysrhythmia occur, and continuous spike-wave discharging was reported never to appear in this group. Lorentz de Haas and Magnus,[21] however, emphasized the association of bilaterally synchronous spike-wave complexes in addition to bilateral baso-temporal foci in patients with psychomotor epilepsy and schizophrenic psychosis. They had the impression that subcortical genesis of seizure states was relatively common in epileptic patients who had schizophrenic-psychotic features.

Pond[25] described a group of patients with temporal lobe epilepsy and psychotic states, the latter often developing as the seizures diminish. The psychotic symptoms included paranoid ideas, hallucinations, and thought disorders in a setting of warm and appropriate affect, in contrast to "true" schizophrenia.

The investigation herein described attempts to present the first phase of an evaluation of interictal personality and behavior in patients with psychomotor-temporal seizures, with special consideration being given to those factors relating to psychosis. This report is not concerned directly with such important related matters as dynamic psychopathology of the patient and his seizure content, emotional stress as a precipitating factor, and the role of drugs and psychotherapy in the development of these phenomena.

Method

The study was carried out at The Yale–New Haven Medical Center with 22 patients from the In and Out Patient services of the Neurology and Psychiatry units. To achieve some homogeneity of certain psychological aspects, this group of patients consisted of females only, between the ages of 17 and 45. All had seizures diagnosed as psychomotor-temporal. Eight also had infrequent generalized seizures. All of the patients had experienced one or more clearly defined clinical episodes of psychosis not considered to be actually part of the seizure complex, each episode lasting one to many days. All were receiving anticonvulsant drugs (diphenylhydantoin, phenobarbital, and primidone) in varying combinations and moderate dosage.

Electroencephalograms were recorded in all patients with a 21 lead international system electrode placement and Grass apparatus. Recordings were taken during the waking state, sleep, hyperventilation, and photic stimulation. All patients were evaluated fully neurologically in order to rule out a remediable cerebral lesion, and none was present in any of the cases. Psychiatric evaluation was performed during a series of interviews. All patients were given a battery of psychological tests including the Rorschach, Thematic Apperception, object sorting, Bender-Gestalt, and Wechsler. In addition to actual scoring, great attention was paid to the details of the patient's performance during the test. The psychologists knew of the diagnosis of epilepsy but did not know the specific nature of the seizures.

Results

The electroencephalograms were performed with the patient in an interictal state with regard to overt seizures and occasionally during a period of prolonged deviant or psychotic behavior.

Characteristically, the patients with psychomotor seizures showed focal temporal theta activity or spikes in ten instances which, however, were not clearly localized in any particular portion of the temporal region, although often the anterior regions were emphasized; bilateral temporal theta discharges in four instances; diffuse theta activity in four; and bilateral 3–5 c./sec. spike-waves discharging with bilateral temporal preponderance in three instances. The electroencephalogram was normal in one case. Correlations with the intensity of interictal psychological disorder were not clear. In four patients there was an intensification of temporal theta and spiking discharge and in one bilateral spike-wave disturbances were more in evidence.

Psychiatric Evaluation and Psychological Test Results

All the patients had experienced significant interictal psychiatric disturbance reaching psychotic proportions and lasting from one to many days. The reactions were characterized as paranoid, depressive, confusional, hallucinatory (mainly auditory), and containing bizarre behavior. One patient had frequent episodes of self-mutilation. There were no indications of withdrawal or atavistic mechanisms. More characteristic details are presented in the case reports. The psychological tests showed a distinct similarity of pattern in all instances, varying mainly in the intensity of the deviations. The most characteristic abnormality was that described as a fluidity of thought processes associated with indications of confusion. This was manifest as a loss of trains of association and word-finding and tracking difficulties during the testing. There were indications of a waxing and waning of alertness and fluctuations in the accuracy of perceptions. Looseness of associations without bizarre content or modes of thought was common. There were occasional indications of concreteness. There were no indications of autism or withdrawal; actually, there were continued rational attempts to be in contact with reality. There were no signs of archaic thinking or autistic fantasy elaboration. The immediate memory seemed to be normal. The intelligence quotients ranged from 67 to 134. There were no significant correlations between the test results and anticonvulsant drug dosage. Illustrative case reports follow.

Case Reports

L.R. Age 33. This woman's history of seizures began in infancy, when at the age of six weeks she had a generalized convulsion following an abdominal operation for volvulus. Recurrent attacks, however, began at the age of 12, when she started to experience occasional generalized convulsions and frequent psychomotor seizures. She did moderately well in school and graduated from high school with good grades. However, she was seclusive and asocial from the age of 14. Her seizures were under only moderately good control with anticonvulsant drugs, the seizure frequency varying from rarely one per day to one every several weeks. She became preoccupied with religious matters during adolescence, and this gradually became intense. At the age of 20 she indicated increasing conflict between herself, God, and the devil, and there was a break with reality. She became delusional, extremely tense, ran away from home and attempted suicide. During the past 13 years her psychosis has been under only fair control with frequent flare-ups requiring hospitalization. At times her tensions build up and lead into an actual seizure. Occasionally the psychosis becomes prominent with hallucinations, both auditory and visual, marked religious preoccupations, and obsessional acts related to religious practices. In association with these symptoms she becomes involved in impulsive, compulsive eating. She has regarded this as producing her seizures. When the patient's anger responses achieve a certain intensity, seizures occur, preceded by more severe projective mechanisms and excessive religiosity. Her regression is to an oral level of sexuality during which she describes excessive eating as a "rotten habit" and is guilt-ridden about her aggressive indulgency and oral-sadistic and incorporative fantasies. The psychotic episodes appear to be attempts to fend off hostile impulses and project them to others. The excessive religiosity and compulsive eating represent further conflicts between conscience structure and impulse life. The patient is frequently disorganized, circumstantial, inappropriate, and amnestic. She is bothered by an inability to concentrate and has stated that "my mind stutters frequently." Her electroencephalograms have shown a consistent spike focus and paroxysmal theta discharges appearing from the left temporal region, especially the middle area rather than the anterior (Figure XIV–1). The intensity of the electroencephalographic abnormality has not been found to vary according to the severity of the patient's psychosis.

Psychological tests showed a Verbal IQ of 96 and a Performance IQ of 84. There were many striking abnormalities of psychological

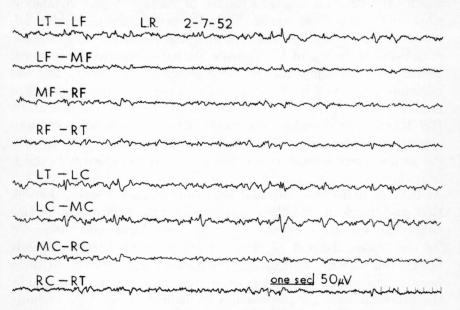

Fig. XIV–1. *Electroencephalogram of patient L.R., taken at age 24. A left middle temporal spike focus was present.*

function which were not regarded characteristic or suggestive of a schizophrenic picture. There were lapses of time perspective, of visual motor functioning, and of immediate verbal recall, as well as concreteness and tendencies toward looseness of association. Confusional tendencies were prominent: she manifested obvious fluidity of thought with variable disruptions having a waxing and waning quality. The patient was always quite concerned with the clarity of her thinking and made significant efforts to control, restrict, and contain her emotions and actions in order to be clear, accurate, and realistic. She did not tend to become bizarre, and her misperceptions and arbitrary thought processes involved relatively benign, neutral content rather than showing features of autistic elaboration. The theme of religiosity runs through the tests. However, efforts toward realistic conventional modes of thought were prominent, and she seemed to maintain a good hold on conventional ways of approaching problems. A certain degree of word-finding difficulty was also apparent. In the Rorschach test there were indications of ideational endeavor and intellectual functioning higher than that measured in the Wechsler Scale. Many of the responses in the tests indicated her conflictful hostile feeling toward her mother and sister, feelings which were developed within the context of her psychotic aberrations.

F.F. Age 44. This woman has had a history of psychomotor seizures since the age of 18. During the seizure she would, in a stereotyped way, stroke or pat articles of furniture or curtains, salivate, groan, and clutch her mouth, as well as occasionally wander about in automatic fashion. She was frequently preoccupied with inadequate feelings concerning running her home, taking care of her family, and having social relationships. Frequent episodes of paranoid psychosis appeared with delusions of reference and persecution, particularly concerning her neighbors. The patient suffered from severe feelings of inadequacy from the time of puberty; these were enhanced by her overcritical husband and then projected during her psychosis. Of interest was the greater occurrence of these psychotic reactions when her diphenylhydantoin medication was increased in an attempt to control the seizures better. However, there was not always good seizure control in association with the development of the psychotic reaction. When she was severely paranoid her sensorium generally was clear. This patient's electroencephalogram always contained spiking and sharp wave discharges from the right and left middle and anterior temporal regions, particularly the middle temporal (Figure XIV–2). These appeared during the waking state and sleep and did not vary in intensity in association with the psychotic reaction or in response to drug therapy.

The patient's psychological tests show prominent characteristics of confusion, involving fluidity of thinking along with clouding of consciousness which fluctuated in degree, never being absent. The tests were performed with the patient in an interseizure state while she was not having any obvious psychotic manifestations. There was marked limitation in her ability to perceive experience accurately, to analyze its individual components, and to integrate or synthesize them. There were weaknesses of spatial orientation and fluctuating motor incoordination. Reality testing was less than adequate, and at times behavior was clearly inappropriate. However, she showed steady and strenuous efforts to cut through the fog that surrounded her, to hold on to or create some degree of contact and clarity and stability of perception. Her Verbal IQ was 92 and Performance IQ 83. Emotionally, she seemed to devote a major portion of her energy to maintaining touch with reality and to be continually alert and checking in order to maintain emotional equilibrium. She expressed feelings of perplexity, impotence, inadequacy, stupidity, disconnected-

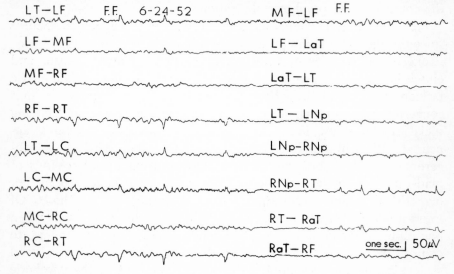

Fig. XIV—2. *Electroencephalogram of patient F.F., taken at age 35. Bitemporal spiking discharges were present.*

ness, fragmentation, being malformed, awkward, and incomplete. It was felt that these responses were markedly different from those of schizophrenics, particularly in the rational efforts to keep in contact with reality and in adherence to logical premises. She did not show archaic thinking and autistic fantasy elaboration.

B.W. Age 39. This is a woman with a six-year history of psychomotor seizures. The seizures have an auditory-hallucinatory aura of familiar pleasant voices from the past, and are characterized by automatic, often aggressive, behavior along with disturbed consciousness. There was total amnesia for the content of the actual seizures. In addition, in between these spells she would experience episodes of increased aggressive impulses with feelings of being "nasty" and desiring to throw things in a setting of paranoid delusions and hallucinations. Somnambulism also was frequent. She was aware of feelings of euphoria, a sense of familiarity with her surroundings and sensations "as if in a world all by myself." Psychiatric evaluation indicated that the patient's denial of anal-sadistic impulses produced intense anxiety which led into the psychotic, hallucinating episodes. When aggressive impulses became more conscious and were acted

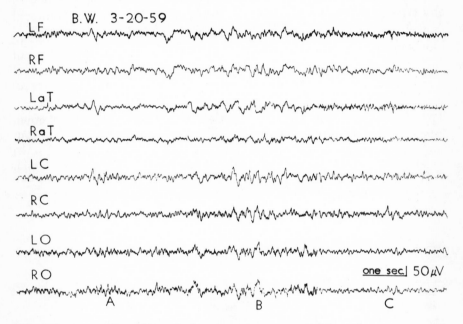

Fig. XIV—3. *Electroencephalogram of patient B.W., taken at age 37. Paroxysmal theta discharges were frequent throughout.*

out the somnambulism, for example, occurred less often. Her electroencephalograms have shown diffuse paroxysmal high-amplitude theta discharges with occasional predominance from the left temporal region, but no well-defined focus or spiking discharge (Figure XIV—3). These abnormalities did not vary in relation to the intensity of the actual seizures or the interseizure behavioral disorder.

The psychological tests indicated confusion and variability of intellectual functioning with weakness of abstract thinking and occasional disturbances around the intake of perceptual and auditory material, as well as in the expression of verbal material. There were defects in visual motor coordination and a tendency to rotate perceptual material. Particular difficulty in arithmetical computations was prominent. However, conventional judgments were well maintained and relatively well developed. Intellectual functioning was in the average range with Verbal IQ of 92 and Performance IQ of 96, with indication that her potential level may have been as much as 15 points higher. The patient showed attempts to deal with her confusion and weakness of intellectual control by conscious suppression. Expression of affect was relatively stable. There were no indications of the presence of any type of schizophrenic reaction. Repressive efforts were prominent as well as the rich use of fantasy. There were indications of marked blocking around sexual aggressive material.

F.D. Age 19. This girl was admitted to the hospital with a three-week history of a confused delusional state with bizarre behavior. Two weeks previously she had experienced a head injury of unknown intensity. Following this she began to experience spells during which

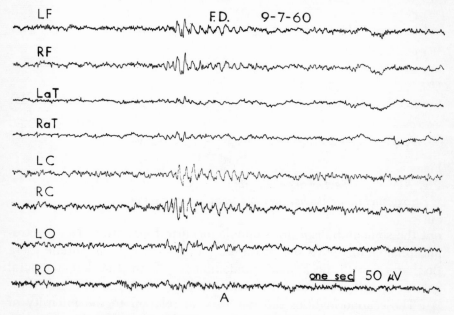

Fig. XIV—4. *Electroencephalogram of patient F.D., age 19, performed during episode of disturbed, psychotic behavior. Bilateral, paroxysmal theta and spike-wave complexes are present, particularly from the fronto-central regions.*

she "went off," making bizarre movements, after which she "came back" and stated that she then was feeling all right and just having difficulty breathing. The neurological examination was essentially normal. Psychiatric evaluation and history revealed that three months previously the patient suffered rejection in a love affair, and at the same time her identical twin became pregnant and married soon after. Factors of guilt, loss of identity, and escape from reality were manifest in the content of the psychotic episodes.

The electroencephalogram on admission (Figure XIV—4) contained diffuse paroxysmal abnormality with sharp, slow spiking waves in the theta range and atypical spike-wave complexes, especially from the fronto-central regions bilaterally in right-sided preponderance. The temporal regions were relatively clear. Because of the marked disturbed behavior, the patient was treated with electroconvulsive therapy. This rapidly produced a resolution of the bizarre hyperactive disorder, with relaxation of agitation, limitation of delusions and hallucinatory activity, and cessation of such behavior as running about and taking off her clothes. Prior to the electroconvulsive therapy, the electroencephalogram had shown a spontaneous im-

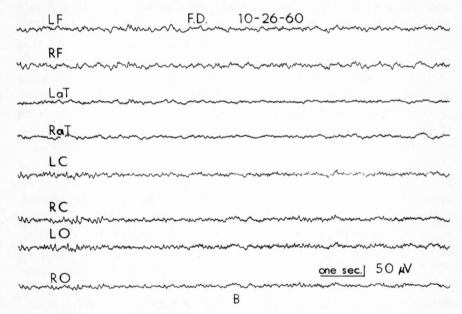

Fig. XIV—5. *Electroencephalogram of patient F.D., age 19, performed after improvement in mental state and behavior. Only small amounts of diffuse theta activity are present.*

provement (Figure XIV–5), with only small amounts of diffuse theta activity, no paroxysmal discharging or lateralizing preponderance, and no build-up during hyperventilation which had been prominent previously. One month after the cessation of ECT and the maintenance of distinctly improved behavior aside from the persistence of a moderate confusional state, the patient began to have a series of psychomotor seizures characterized by olfactory aura at onset, staring, experiences of dizziness, and automatic behavior with wandering about the room and being out of contact for about one minute. These seizures were somewhat different from the patient's previous behavioral disorder, were self-limited but occurred frequently during the following months. They were completely controlled by anticonvulsant medication.

The electroencephalogram performed two weeks after the onset of the psychomotor seizures showed a recurrence of more distinct epileptiform abnormality with sharp waves and slow spike discharges appearing in a generalized way but particularly from the left parietal and occipital regions (Figure XIV–6).

The psychological tests were performed on this patient two and one half months after the onset of psychomotor seizures and one and one half months after the control of seizures by medication. The test results indicated tendencies toward fluidity involving repetition of verbalization and the forgetting of percepts and questions, word-finding difficulties, and variability in the capacity for abstract thinking and in visual motor and memory efficiency. There were peculiar verbalizations, disruptions of perceptual experience, and indications of development of fantasies suggesting the capability of odd, even projective, delusional-like ideations. These abnormalities indicated a susceptability to psychotic ideation, but the findings were not those of a schizophrenia. Although odd thoughts were expressed often illogically, there was not the introduction of the degree of bizarre, autistic elaboration and morbid primitive content which would be expected in a schizophrenic picture. Rather, the patient showed strong efforts to repress and contain diffuse, unmodulated affective reactions and to orient her ideas in the direction of adherence to realistic consideration, orderliness, and conventionality. The disruptions of functioning were sporadic, and the struggle to maintain reality was obvious. There were suggestions of concern with the clarity of perceptual experience, spatial orientation, body balance, and physical motility. She expressed depressive feelings of being an unlucky, unfortunate person who was badly put together. There were certain impairments of functioning, particularly memory deficits and defects in verbal concept formation more indicative of organic brain damage. Yet even these impairments fluctuated in degree. The patient obtained a Verbal IQ of 79 and a Performance IQ of 81. It was felt that her intellectual capacities were at least 10 points higher and that some of the deficits in intellectual functioning might have been a residual of the electro-

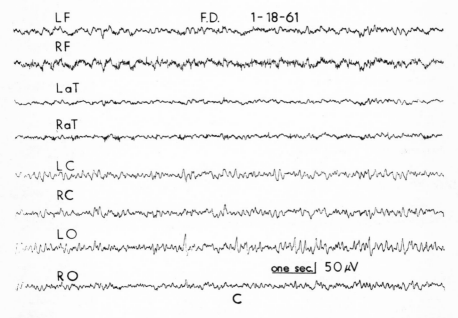

LF   F.D.   1-18-61

RF

LaT

RaT

LC

RC

LO

one sec.| 50 μV

RO

C

Fig. XIV—6. *Electroencephalogram of patient F.D., age 19, after onset of more typical, distinct psychomotor seizures. Sharp waves and slow spike discharges appear diffusely but particularly from the left parietal and occipital regions.*

convulsive therapy which had been administered over three months previously.

P.P. Age 17. This schoolgirl was admitted to the hospital with symptoms of lethargy, fatigue, withdrawal, and dissociated thinking which had developed during the previous two and one half months. She thought that germs were invading her body, which had to be emptied out. Prior to onset, there had been the immediate stress of heavy traveling and difficulties in interpersonal relationships. Conflicts with parental figures were in the background as well as a recent initial love affair. A pregnancy fantasy seemed overwhelming. At the time of admission the patient was acutely disorganized and had bizarre verbalizations and many somatic delusions in a setting of an incoherent thought disorder. She was oriented, but a memory impairment was present as well as some difficulty in attention and concentration. Her behavior remained in this state with occasional periods of more extreme confusion and fluctuating delusional reactivity. An

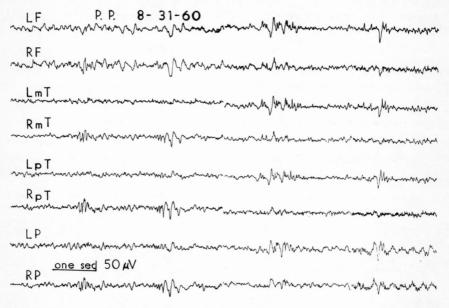

Fig. XIV—7. *Electroencephalogram of patient P.P., age 17, during period of psychotic, disturbed behavior. Episodes of slow spikes, sharp waves, and atypical spike-wave complexes are present, mainly from the temporal regions bilaterally.*

electroencephalogram performed the day after admission showed a distinct abnormality with monophasic and diphasic slow spikes and atypical spike-wave complexes, the latter at a frequency of 4–5 c./sec., mainly from both temporal regions (Figure XIV–7). These discharges increased during light sleep. Dilantin therapy was started, and within three days the patient showed more appropriate speech and behavior which persisted for some weeks although fluctuation did occur. The electroencephalogram, performed two weeks after admission, was markedly improved with only a mild generalized theta abnormality. Relapse occurred after one month associated with increased confusion, loose associations, and somatic delusions. Continued psychotherapy, pharmacotherapy with Prolixin and anticonvulsants, gradually produced a relative clearing. There was no change in the EEG in association with the relapse. The electroencephalogram remained improved and within two months was probably within the normal range, containing only small amounts of random 5–7 c./sec. theta activity (Figure XIV–8).

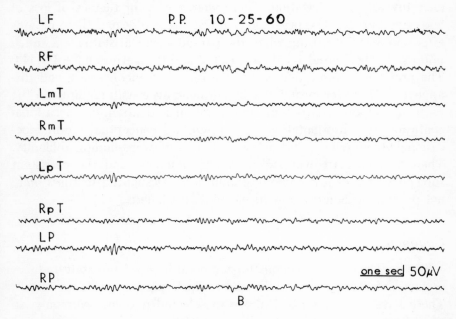

Fig. XIV—8. *Electroencephalogram of patient P.P., age 17, after clinical improvement. The record is within the normal range for this age with but small amounts of random, diffuse theta activity.*

A battery of psychological tests, performed during the first week of the patient's hospitalization, showed devastated functioning in all areas. There were indications of contamination, self-references, and feelings of depersonalization and unreality. Preoccupation with sexual, anal, oral, and religious issues was present with ruminations concerning ideas of world destruction. Preferred defenses were projection and withdrawal. Many paranoid elements were present in terms of projection of thoughts and feelings onto external stimuli. Preoccupation with fear of the parents was present, but organized delusions of persecution were not indicated. There were despairing features seen in concern with death and loneliness. Some psycho-motor retardation was present. Verbal IQ was 93 and Performance IQ 99. However, potential functioning was regarded to be much higher, probably within the bright-normal to superior range. The intellectual functioning was lowered by thought disorganization, difficulty in abstract thinking, and concreteness. Considerable confusion was manifest with impairment of attention, concentration, and memory. Bender-Gestalt designs were adequate grossly, but with a tendency toward primitivization. There were persistent themes of loss of body equilibrium. The psychological tests were repeated three months after admission at a time when the patient's clinical status was much improved. The Verbal IQ then was 112 and the Performance IQ 114. The previous extreme degree of confusion and incoherency had disappeared. However, prominent impairments were still manifest in the form of temporary lapses in concentration and attention, occasional confusion and disorientation, perceptual and conceptual fluidity, occasional concreteness, and a few instances of word-finding difficulty. There was concern over lack of body intactness and the persistent subjective fear of loss of body equilibrium. Despairing features were not prominent. Some paranoid elements remained.

Comment

The presence of a psychomotor-temporal lobe seizure state induces certain defects in cerebral function which predispose to psychosis. These have been described above in selected patients. Not only do psychic symptoms appear ictally in this disorder, but alterations in personality and behavior develop in the apparent interictal periods.

The present study was not designed to determine the incidence of these reactions. Its purpose was to characterize, in detail, features relevant to the interictal psychological disorder appearing in psychomotor epileptics. In some patients, these psychological disturbances are impulsive, aggressive, unstable states or obsessive-compulsive disorders and excessive preoccupations with religious activities. This complex of reactions is rather similar to the previously described epileptic personality and represents merely a nonspecific personality disorder appearing in all groups of seizure patients.[3] Other patients, as in the present series, develop psychotic reactions which occasionally resemble a schizophrenic disorder.[6, 11, 15, 25, 27, 28] As indicated, however, the basic disturbance is different, there being in the patients with psychomotor seizures a fluctuating disorder of mental functioning with fluidity of thought processes, manifested in loss of trains of associations and word-finding and tracking difficulties, along with continued rational efforts to be in contact with reality. Subtle difficulties in verbal, cognitive functions are important.[26] Inappropriate behavior, misinterpretation of situations with paranoid reactions, hallucinatory activity, and denial and religiosity may occur but are secondary phenomena. There were no significant signs of autism, archaic thinking, withdrawal, or symbolic processes such as would be expected in schizophrenia. These reactions, therefore, resemble those described by Pond.[25]

The onset of the psychotic reaction does not appear to be related clearly to psychological trigger mechanisms in all instances, but in many it does follow increasing build-up of tension and anxiety. In other instances, however, gradual confusion and intellectual disorganization, often subtle at first, seem to initiate the process. Often it is difficult to distinguish these manifestations from the prodromes or auras which actually precede a seizure. Gastaut and others[10] have discussed this in terms of a preictal excitation, and the concept of "continuous prodrome or aura" has developed.[29] The interictal behavior disorders and psychotic states in part, therefore, could be the result of preictal or mere subictal excitation, the latter if actual seizure does not occur. The known involvement of deep temporal, pararhinal, and diencephalic structures, in psychomotor seizure states, can account for the development of both affective disturbances and confusional states with minor alterations of consciousness. These would be the anatomical and physiological substrates of such reactions.

It would be more helpful in these considerations if electroencephalographic correlates were absolute. However, only occasionally is there a significant EEG correlate with these reactions. In the present series an infrequent increase of paroxysmal seizure activity, localized or generalized, occurred and diminished as the psychotic reaction cleared, but not in a very distinct time association. More often, there were no related changes in the scalp EEG. A "forced normalization" as described by Landolt[18] was not observed, although in at least two instances an increase or relapse in psychotic reaction did occur at a time when the electroencephalographic abnormality had improved and was remaining minimal. It is well known, though, that abnormal electrical activity in the nature of paroxysmal seizure discharges may be recorded from deeper structures, such as the amygdala, involved in these seizure states in both man and experimental animal, without transmission or development into activity recorded from the surface electroencephalogram.[1, 4]

In some contrast to the study reported by Dongier,[5] we have observed in our patients with psychomotor epilepsy occasionally prominent confusion as well as disturbances of affect. The EEG abnormalities, albeit infrequently, did consist of spike-and-wave discharges, as well as slow-wave dysrhythmia. Some of these clinical EEG correlates resemble those of "centrencephalic" epileptics, but the confusion is less intense, more continuous, and associated with more complex psychological disturbances. This is not the picture of a petit mal status. However, the problem of EEG specificity in psychomotor epilepsy has been considered in the last several years,[8, 9, 12, 20] and it is recognized that certain distinct psychomotor seizure states may originate in the subcortical structures involved in the limbic system and be associated with bilaterally synchronous and asynchronous discharges in the EEG. Our experience is similar to that of Lorentz de Haas and Magnus,[21] who report the relatively common association of psychotic states with schizophrenic features in patients with psychomotor epilepsy and bilaterally synchronous spike-wave complexes in their electroencephalograms, suggesting subcortical genesis. It may be that grouping or classification of these seizure disorders still is best on the basis of clinical manifestations rather than electroencephalographic abnormality, since the latter may be nonspecific, variable, and fluctuating. Mirsky and his colleagues[22] were not able to differentiate clearly between patients with focal and nonfocal epilepsy, selected by EEG criteria, using a battery of psychological tests and scored results, except for suggestive impairment of attention in patients with "centrencephalic" electroencephalograms.

The clinical entity discussed here is regarded to be a psychosis occurring in a setting of psychomotor-temporal lobe epilepsy with only a superficial resemblance to schizophrenia apparent in but some instances. However, in this context it might be worth while to consider how this disorder might relate to that occurring in patients diagnosed as having schizophrenia with "epileptic discharges" in their electroencephalograms.[13, 14] It has been stated that up to 20–25 per cent of schizophrenic patients, particularly catatonic, show paroxysmal abnormalities in their electroencephalograms with bilaterally synchronous spikes, fast spike-and-wave complexes or slow-wave bursts.[14] Some, however, do experience epileptic clinical phenomena spontaneously, particularly at onset or termination of a psychotic episode, during insulin therapy or if they have a familial predisposition for seizures. Hill[14] emphasized that these epileptic discharges consist of paroxysmal slow waves and spike-and-wave forms of faster frequencies (greater than 4 c./sec.) than is usually found in clinical epileptic cases. Further evaluation of these cases with regard to their basic diagnosis of schizophrenia might be made. Hoch has regarded this type of reaction as a symptomatic schizophrenia in epilepsy.[16] They could represent, therefore, the type of schizophrenic-like disorder considered in the present study—that is, one which is really based upon a psychomotor-temporal lobe seizure state.

SUMMARY

Certain disorders in cerebral function have been described in patients with psychomotor-temporal lobe epilepsy which predispose to interictal psychosis. These are predominantly a fluidity of thought processes, loss of trains of associations, word-finding difficulties, and fluctuations in the accuracy of perceptions. The psychotic states which may develop include inappropriate, bizarre behavior, paranoid and depressive reactions, hallucinatory activity, denial and excessive religiosity. The continued efforts to be in contact with reality and lack of autism, archaic thinking, withdrawal, or peculiar symbolism differentiate these reactions from a schizophrenic process.

Electroencephalographic correlates with interictal psychotic episodes are only occasional and then consist of more intense focal temporal or bilateral paroxysmal discharge. At times the EEG is normal during a psychotic state. However, it is possible that these interictal personality and behavior disturbances may be due at least in part to subictal cerebral excitation.

References

1. ABRAHAM, K. and MARSAN, C. A., "Patterns of Cortical Discharges and Relation to Routine Scalp Electroencephalography," *Electroenceph. clin. Neurophysiol.*, 10:447–461, 1958.

2. BINGLEY, T., "Mental Symptoms in Temporal Lobe Epilepsy and Temporal Lobe Gliomas," *Acta psychiat. scand.*, vol. 33, Suppl. *120*, 1958.

3. DELAY, J., PICHOT, P., LAMPÉRIÈRE, T., and PERSE, J., *The Rorschach and the Epileptic Personality*, Logos Press, New York, 1958.

4. DELGADO, J. M. R. and HAMLIN, H., "Direct Recording of Spontaneous and Evoked Seizures in Epileptics," *Electroenceph. clin. Neurophysiol.*, 10:463–486, 1958.

5. DONGIER, S., "Statistical Study of Clinical and Electroencephalographic Manifestations of 536 Psychotic Episodes Occurring in 516 Epileptics Between Clinical Seizures," *Epilepsia*, 1:117–142, 1959. See also: *Rev. neurol.*, 95:587–616, 1956.

6. ERVIN, F., EPSTEIN, A. W., and KING, H. E., "Behavior of Epileptic and Non-epileptic Patients with Temporal Spikes," *Arch. Neurol. Psychiat.*, Chicago, 74:488–497, 1955.

7. FALRET, J., *De l'État Mental des Épileptiques*, Asselin, Paris, 1861.

8. FUSTER, B., CASTELLO, C., and RODRIGUEZ, B., "Psychomotor Attacks (Primary Automatisms) of Subcortical Origin," *Arch. Neurol. Psychiat.*, Chicago, 71:266–472, 1954.

9. GASTAUT, H., "So-called 'Psychomotor' and 'Temporal' Epilepsy—A Critical Study," *Epilepsia*, 2:59–76, 1953.

10. GASTAUT, H., MORIN, G., and LESEVRE, N., "Étude du Comportement des Épileptiques Psychomoteurs dans l'Intervalle de Leurs Crises," *Ann. méd.-psychol.*, 1:1–27, 1955.

11. GIBBS, F. A., "Ictal and Non-ictal Psychiatric Disorders in Temporal Lobe Epilepsy," *J. nerv. ment. Dis.*, 113:522–528, 1951.

12. GLASER, G. H. and GOLUB, L. M., "The Electroencephalogram of Psychomotor Seizures in Childhood," *Electroenceph. clin. Neurophysiol.*, 7:329–340, 1955.

13. HILL, D., "EEG in Episodic Psychotic and Psychopathic Behavior," *Electroenceph. clin. Neurophysiol.*, 4:419–442, 1952.

14. HILL, D., "Electroencephalogram in Schizophrenia," in: RICHTER, D. (ed.), *Schizophrenia. Somatic Aspects*, Pergamon Press, London, 1957, pp. 33–51.

15. HILL, D., POND, D. A., MITCHELL, W., and FALCONER, M. A., "Personality Changes Following Temporal Lobectomy for Epilepsy," *J. ment. Sci.*, 103:18–27, 1957.

16. HOCH, P. H., "Clinical and Biological Interrelations Between Schizophrenia and Epilepsy," *Amer. J. Psychiat.*, 99:507–512, 1943.

17. JACKSON, J. H., *Selected Writings of John Hughlings Jackson*, vol. I, *On Epilepsy and Epileptiform Convulsions*, TAYLOR, JAMES (ed.), Hodder & Stoughton, London, 1931.

18. LANDOLT, H., "Über Verstimmungen, Dammerzustande und schizophrene Zustandbilder bei Epilepsie," *Schweiz. Arch. Neurol. Psychiat.*, 76:313–321, 1955.

19. LENNOX, W. G., *Epilepsy and Related Disorders,* Little, Brown & Co., Boston, 1960.

20. LICHTENSTEIN, R. S., MARSHALL, C., and WALKER, A. E., "Subcortical Recording in Temporal Lobe Epilepsy," *Arch. Neurol., Chicago,* 1:288–302, 1959.

21. LORENTZ DE HAAS, A. M. and MAGNUS, O., "Clinical and Electroencephalographic Findings in Epileptic Patients with Episodic Mental Disorders," in LORENTZ DE HAAS, A. M. (ed.), *Lectures on Epilepsy,* Elsevier, Amsterdam, 1958, pp. 134–167.

22. MIRSKY, A. F., PRIMAC, D. W., MARSAN, C. A., ROSVOLD, H. E., and STEVENS, J. R., "A Comparison of the Psychological Test Performance of Patients with Focal and Non-focal Epilepsy," *Exp. Neurol.,* 2:75–89, 1960.

23. MOREL, B. A., *Traité des Maladies Mentales,* Masson et Cie, Paris, 1860.

24. PENFIELD, W. G. and JASPER, H. H., *Epilepsy and the Functional Anatomy of the Human Brain,* Little, Brown & Co., Boston, 1954.

25. POND, D. A., "Psychiatric Aspects of Epilepsy," *J. Indian med. Prof.,* 3:1441–1451, 1957.

26. QUADFASEL, A. F. and PRUYSER, P. W., "Cognitive Deficit in Patients with Psychomotor Epilepsy," *Epilepsia,* 4:80–90, 1955.

27. RODIN, E. A., DE JONG, R. N., WAGGONER, R. W., and BAGCHI, B. K., "Relationship Between Certain Forms of Psychomotor Epilepsy and 'Schizophrenia,'" *Arch. Neurol. Psychiat., Chicago,* 77:449–463, 1957.

28. RODIN, E. A., MULDER, D. W., FAUCETT, R. L., and BICKFORD, R. G., "Psychologic Factors in Convulsive Disorders of Focal Origin," *Arch. Neurol. Psychiat., Chicago,* 74:365–374, 1955.

29. SCOTT, J. S. and MASLAND, R. L., "Occurrence of Continuous Symptoms in Epilepsy Patients," *Neurology,* 3:297–301, 1953.

XV

Behavior Disorder Associated with Seizure States: Pharmacological and Psychosocial Management

Thomas Detre
Robert G. Feldman

The management of behavioral and emotional disorders associated with seizures remains a poorly understood aspect in the over-all treatment of epileptic patients. Often the nature of the psychological disturbance may go unrecognized, or it may be considered a part of the seizure discharge and be treated with more anticonvulsant drugs. We are beginning to realize, however, that even when adequate control of seizures has been achieved by pharmacological means, the associated emotional and behavioral manifestations may continue to create difficult problems.

Clinics usually deal with the patient's need for emotional support by scheduling periodic visits for renewal of prescriptions and only brief discussions of his problems. This kind of assistance might be quite useful for those patients who have no major behavioral symptoms and whose over-all functioning has been adequate; but there are others whose social adjustment is poor and in whom seizure activity has significantly interfered with personality development since childhood. Many of these patients manage to live on the outside but would probably be institutionalized if it were not for the willingness of their families and social agencies to provide emotional and financial help. Others, whose families are less supportive, periodically end up in institutions and return to their homes after each crisis without much long-term gain. While it is true that on the basis of our present knowledge a fundamental cure for these patients

366

does not exist, undoubtedly therapy is required which includes measures which alleviate the discomfort of the seizure experience and assist in the over-all adaptation within the family and environment, providing optimal social integration and rehabilitation.

A combined psychotherapeutic and pharmacological approach need not be a controversial matter provided that the psychogenic factors are considered in their proper context. Even though an unfavorable interpersonal climate may precipitate or aggravate seizure mechanisms, one must keep in mind that a nervous system which is capable of producing an ictal discharge has certain peculiar characteristics.

Behavioral manifestations may be a reflection of the area of the brain involved during the seizure. Psychomotor-temporal lobe seizures are often preceded by auras of anxiety and visceral symptoms, followed by alterations in awareness, with many varied feelings and distorted thinking states. There may be at least a partial amnesia. There is a period of recovery during which the patient may show semipurposeful and sometimes inappropriate behavior involving an interplay with the environment. Although a relatively high incidence of psychological abnormality has been found during the postictal and interictal periods, electroencephalographic correlations which may be made (Chapters XII and XIV) are sometimes absent, and indeed the electroencephalogram may be normal. The direct ictal behavior usually follows a repetitive pattern, and this often consists of a rather well-defined, simple sequence of characteristic actions, such as head turning, unintelligible speech, or aphasia, purposeless movements, or bizarre body positioning, specific visceral sensations, and hallucinatory phenomena. In other instances, behavioral disturbances may be more complex, and range from loss of impulse-control and ictal depression to neurotic or psychotic syndromes. The differential diagnosis on clinical grounds is usually difficult, especially in the absence of a history of recurring episodes of a behavioral disorder. Serial electroencephalograms and extensive psychological testing may be necessary for the documentation of an underlying seizure disorder.

It is generally agreed that adequate criteria for the classification of the various psychiatric manifestations of seizure disorders are not yet available.[18] This, of course, does not exclude the validity of certain observations which may lead to the correct diagnosis. For example, the depressive affect associated with seizure disorders is rarely as persistent as that seen with psychotic depressions. Dysphoria and irritability, however, are usually prominent and are accompanied by some degree of confusion. Similarly, while short manic-like episodes may occur, they resemble hebephrenic silliness rather than the true mood elevation seen in the manic-depressive psychosis. Patients with brief catatonic-like reactions characteristically show more passive than active negativism with immobility or catalepsy. Predominance of primitive visceral and somatic hallucinations is another important differential diagnostic criterion. Although these perceptual disturbances may occur in "functional" psychoses, they are usually transient and are quickly replaced by a more organized type of auditory hallucination. In paroxysmal psychoses, auditory hallucinations are seldom seen, but when present they are brief, stereotyped, and rarely feed into the further development of the presenting delusional system. Visual hallucinations, in contrast, are very frequent and are much more elaborate and picturesque than those found in functional psychoses. Interestingly, these hallucinations, which usher in the full-blown picture of an organic psychosis in seizure disorders, quickly disappear once the patient expresses delusional thoughts. Oneiroid syndromes associated with temporal lobe seizures may last for several weeks with lucid periods occurring when stimulated verbally or otherwise. It should be re-emphasized that early differentiation between the "process" type of schizophrenic reaction and the psychosis of epilepsy starting with schizophrenic-like syndromes is difficult. Paranoid states may be seen: though they are generally lucid, they are frequently accompanied or preceded by crepuscular states. While orientation to place and person does not seem to be grossly disturbed, impairment in time orientation can often be demonstrated by detailed questioning. Critical capacity is not well preserved. The content of delusions, not unexpectedly, reflects body image changes mixed with elements of the presenting life situations and stresses. They often have a mystical or religious flavor, suggesting the compensatory nature of the systematization. In this way, the frightening somatic experiences are rationalized.

In some instances, the seizure pattern or its associated behavior abnormalities will leave an imprint on the personality, which has been described as the epileptic personality.[10] Some of these patients have a very stereotyped way of conducting themselves in stressful situations, and their maneuvers often resemble those seen in sociopathic personality disorders. Nevertheless, such pseudosociopathic and manipulative acts are seen in other chronic illnesses where the patient perceives a somatic disturbance as a constant threat to his existence, and they do not seem to be specific for paroxysmal disorders. Not uncommonly, psychogenic factors will aggravate the seizure potentiality. Initially the patient may be able to exert a certain amount of control; in fact, it is known that some patients can abort seizures by distracting themselves or by strong afferent stimulations. A peculiar characteristic of epileptics with impaired impulse control is that once the emotionally precipitated outburst begins, the process becomes autonomous. Yet, while he may sometimes seem able to "turn it on," the patient is no longer able to "turn it off." In some instances, it is obvious that the seizures are "allowed" to occur, and they even may be self-induced. Fluctuations of awareness and the appearance of a strange sequence of physical and behavioral events will, over many years, become integrated into problem-solving techniques for the patient's adaptation. The ictal phenomena accompanied or followed by confusion reactions provide a guilt-free opportunity for the patient to express certain conflicts or drives which are a source of family concern. It is for these reasons that emergency admissions to medical and psychiatric settings limited to acute management of the disturbing behavior, or which offer custodial care, accomplish little and may even encourage regressive trends.

Once the "epileptic-symptom-complex"[7] has been identified in such patients, a combined therapeutic approach is warranted to take care of both epileptogenic and psychogenic factors. Improvement of behavioral manifestations and the suppression of motor discharges by drugs alone present no guarantee for over-all therapeutic success. Similarly, the presence of psychological disturbances is no indication that the patient will respond to psychotherapeutic intervention alone.

The pharmacological management of behavioral problems must be directed toward the stabilization of the "epileptogenic" mechanisms. Traditionally, the clinician's main concern has been to modify seizure threshold and treatment for the related behavior disorder and has been limited to the administration of ever-increasing amounts of diphenylhydantoin, phenobarbital, and primidone, often combined with physical restraints. The use of phenothiazine derivatives, although known to be effective in psychomotor excitement, has been rejected on the basis that these drugs may alter the EEG[11, 16] and are potentially epileptogenic in some individuals.[3, 4, 13] Among the few studies which have been published on the use of ataractics in epileptics, Bonafede[2] reported on 78 cases with episodic disturbance states, involving hyperactivity and destructiveness. Many of these patients required heavy doses of barbiturates; often increased confusion followed with this administration of large doses. The adjunctive use of chlorpromazine significantly decreased the severity of the behavioral disturbance. Pauig and his associates[15] studied a group of one hundred adults and children. Thioridazine combined with diphenylhydantoin and phenobarbital caused marked improvement in 61 of these patients. It is of particular interest that in 41 of those cases a decrease in the seizure frequency also occurred. Winkelmann[19] described a patient in whom psychomotor seizures occurred at least three times a day, while receiving diphenylhydantoin, methylphenylhydantoin, and phenobarbital therapy. The patient had no seizures at all during the two-month period during which chlorpromazine was added to the regimen. Similar results have been reported by Head.[8]

Central nervous system stimulants have been considered useful adjuncts to the anticonvulsant regimen in some cases of epilepsy.[1, 14] Logothetis[12] found a decrease in the seizure frequency of patients with sleep-activated epilepsy when they were receiving methamphetamine. It is of theoretical interest[5] that stimulation of the mesencephalic reticular formation may inhibit an acute or chronic epileptogenic focus and may prevent the spread of discharge at the onset of a seizure. Further experimental data are available[6] which show a relationship between the cortical arousal and seizure discharge. This is of special interest since it is known that behavioral manifestations become worse with increased drowsiness, and paradoxically the effect of a large dose of barbiturates may complicate the treatment of impulse-control disturbances. If these observations are correct, one may suspect that a drug which could cause a decrease in psychomotor excitement without causing drowsiness would be a valuable adjunct to the treatment of seizure states. Some investigators[9, 17] believe that phenothiazines with primarily alerting properties are very effective for acute confusional states. Fluphenazine (trifluoromethyl -3(hydroxy-ethyl-4' -piperazinyl)-3' propyl -10 phenothiazine) is such a compound, and in our experience is well suited for the treatment of behavior disturbances associated with seizure states.

A selected group of patients with mainly psychomotor-temporal lobe seizures admitted to the psychiatric division of the Yale–New Haven Medical Center received fluphenazine (Prolixin) under close observation along with anticonvulsant drugs (Table XV–1). In order to determine the safety and optimal therapeutic levels, a minimal daily dose of 3 mg. was administered. This was followed by gradual increases to 30 mg. per day. We have found the effective dose range to be usually between 6 and 20 mg. daily; increases above that level failed to produce further results. The presenting clinical picture included a wide variety of behavioral disturbances ranging from impulse disorder to psychotic manifestations. Initially, many were diagnosed schizophrenic or schizo-affective reactions. Of 16 patients who had prolonged observation and treatment, electroencephalographic changes compatible with seizure disorders were seen in 14. In 12 cases the past history included grand mal seizures as well. In no instance, however, did the simultaneous administration of fluphenazine and anticonvulsant drugs cause any increase in the seizure frequency. Obviously, the proper use for ataractics and the necessity for combined administration of anticonvulsant drugs must be experimentally approached. In some patients, for example, the institution of diphenylhydantoin therapy in adequate doses caused a diminution of confusion and the disappearance of psychotic behavior within three to five days. In others, the use of large amounts of diphenylhydantoin, phenobarbital, primidone, and paraldehyde had no effect on the behavioral disturbances, and it was only after fluphenazine replaced the conventional anticonvulsive regimen that the akinetic attacks and confusion disappeared.

Diagnostic and therapeutic problems presented by seizure patients often necessitate admission to the hospital. This is especially true when the patient is faced with a particularly difficult life situation and outpatient management is no longer possible. Many are admitted repeatedly and under dramatic circumstances; the medical and nursing personnel engage in heroic interventions to bring the patient "under control." At times, almost fantastic amounts of drugs are administered and a toxic brain syndrome may develop along with all sorts of other complications. The family usually responds to this by complaining about the extreme measures with the result that the institutions often become reluctant to admit this type of patient. The need for hospitalization, however, may also arise because rehabilitative efforts have failed despite over-all symptomatic improvement in the patient's social behavior. Such admissions do not represent an emergency but they can be a very helpful measure provided that the seizure patient be considered like any other psychiatric patient and his problem areas investigated accordingly. Whatever the circumstances surrounding the admission, most seizure patients benefit from a structured environment in combination with the appropriate drug treatment. As

Table XV-1

PATENT Sex Age	CLINICAL PICTURE	PAST HISTORY	EEG	DRUG THERAPY	FOLLOW-UP
P.M. F 16	Withdrawn, confused, bizarre behavior, depressed.	None	Spike discharges, seizure bursts. Ant. temporal, bilateral.	Prolixin Dilantin	Discharged to home and family. Returned to school.
R.S. F 37	Tonic spasms, bizarre body movts. unresponsive Akinetic spells 18 mos.	Head injury age 5	Slow wave bursts, temporal, right, left.	Prolixin Thorazine	Marked improvement in socializing on ward; no spells for 5 mos. with drugs.
K.R. F 28	Acute confusion, rambling speech, depressed.	Dreamy state at 12 and 15 yrs. Similar episode one yr. ago.	Right posterior temporal slow waves.	Prolixin Tofranil	Clearing and improvement on ward.
M.B. M 22	Paranoid, confused, visual and auditory hallucinations, periodic disorganization.	None	Right occipital seizure focus, esp. with photic stimulation.	Dilantin Trilafon	Return to work. No recurrence 10 mos.
S.M. M 17	Bizarre posturing, withdrawn, paranoid, periodic delusions, trembling, confusion.	None	Right ant. temporal slow spikes focus.	Dilantin	No recurrence of spells and no trembling episodes.
L.K. F 16	Agitated, hyperactive, confused, inability to concentrate.	Head injury age 10 yrs. Previous EEG abnormal.	Slow spikes, right temporal-parietal region.	Dilantin	Return to school on Dilantin; no recurrence in 10 months.

Patient	Clinical picture	History	EEG	Drugs	Outcome
F.D. F 20	Out of contact, confused bizarre behavior, disrobing.	None	Bilateral slow waves and spike waves.	Dilantin	No recurrence in 5 mos. on Dilantin.
P.P. M 18	Disorganized, memory impairment, withdrawn, somatic delusions.	None	Spikes and spike wave, bitemporally.	Prolixin Dilantin	No relapses for 9 mos. on these drugs.
M.T. F 31	Emotional lability, paranoid, confused, hallucinations.	Same symptoms 2 months and 1½ yrs. ago.	Right posterior temporal seizure focus.	Dilantin Mysoline Prolixin	No relapses for 6 months on Dilantin.
V.S. F 27	Withdrawn, confused, bizarre posturing.	Behavior problem child and previous abnormal EEG.	Post. temporal and occipital slow wave focus. Diffuse epileptiform pattern.	Dilantin Mysoline Prolixin	Cleared after dose of Dilantin reduced, with increased alertness and response to group therapy.
K.C. M 32	Progressive social deterioration. Paranoid ideas, hypomanic state.	Petit mal and grand mal, 14 yrs.	High-voltage atypical spike waves. Diffuse slow wave abnormality.	Celontin Prolixin	Marked decrease in paranoid ideas. Better socialization. Fewer petit mal attacks.
M.K. F 16	Agitated depression; many lapses of awareness and impulsive aggressiveness.	Similar recurrent episodes, 2 yrs.	Right temporal paroxysmal abnormality.	Trilafon Dilantin	Fewer episodes of confusion; no outbursts.
L.R. F 33	Frequent lapses, increased paranoid ideas, agitation.	Recurrences for 19 yrs.	Spike formations right temporal preponderance.	Dilantin Phenobarbital Prolixin	Decreased paranoid ideas; better adjustment with family.

confusion clears, the patient becomes socially better integrated. This kind of improvement, however, should not be the signal for discharge but rather an indication that the patient can now be considered ready for a thorough examination of his home situation and the transaction concerning his illness.

At times, the patient is prepared to view his illness only as an essentially exogenous interference in his psychological functioning. The family is frightened and in the course of patient's illness shows a complete lack of understanding of the problems involved. This confusion is a fertile ground for complicated and mutually destructive transactions between the patient and his closest relatives. Confusing role shifts may occur especially when the physician has attempted to overcome behavioral problems in the patient by ceaseless manipulations of complicated drug schedules and when a family member has to assume the role of special nurse. This not only heightens potential family pathology but increases the patient's passive dependence upon his home. Clarification of these problems is obviously a necessary step to free the family from an obligation to serve the patient's passive needs and to allow the reassignment of responsibility to the patient. It must be emphasized, however, that supportive measures in both areas, pharmacological and social, must continue over a long period of time. Maintenance drug treatment may be required indefinitely. The patient and the family must receive continued support to prevent the recurring need to resort to maladaptive techniques in stressful situations. Since the pattern of these maneuvers have an established tradition in the family's transactions, even after extensive rehabilitative efforts the necessity for rehospitalization may arise. This does not always indicate the failure of therapy but simply reflects the need for help and re-examination of issues in the midst of overwhelming stress.

Every institution must establish its own policies regarding the management of seizure patients, whether they are seen as out-patients or admitted to the hospital. But regardless of where the patient is admitted, the environment must be prepared to deal with complex psychosocial issues and offer the opportunity for the clarification of diagnostic and therapeutic problems.

SUMMARY

A large variety of behavior disorders may be associated with seizure states. These may include personality disorders, neurotic, and psychotic syndromes. The presence of psychological disturbances alone is no indication that the patient will respond to psychotherapeutic intervention, in spite of the fact that he "uses" his confusion to serve other ends. Fluctuation of awareness and appearances of a strange sequence of physical and behavioral events of many years' duration, so typical of epileptic disorders, lends itself to problem-solving techniques which may have dramatic effects on the patient's interpersonal relations. This will expose the family and other people in his environment to serious tests unless the over-all social integration is stable. A series of maladaptive events may take place with the development of peculiar family pathology. Such has been the case in several of our patients where it became clear that the ictal phenomena, accompanied or followed by confusional reactions, provided an opportunity for the patient to express certain drives which were a source of conflict within the family. Pharmacological intervention has a marked effect on the acute cloudy states and dysphoric moods, increasing the patient's awareness and ability to respond to psychotherapeutic measures. Emergency admission to medical or psychiatric settings, limited to custodial care of the crisis of the behavioral disturbances associated with seizures, accomplishes little and may even encourage regressive trends. It seems that, just as in other psychotic reactions, the behavioral disturbances in psychomotor seizures may require hospitalization. Ataractic agents alone or in combination with anticonvulsants may stabilize the patient and facilitate further rehabilitative efforts. The improvement of behavioral manifestations together with the suppression of epileptic discharges by drugs alone presents no guarantee for over-all therapeutic success. The acute management consists of fostering improved communications between the patient and his environment.

References

1. ALEXANDER, W. M. and WEAVER, L. C., "Anticonvulsant Evaluation of of D-Amphetamine Alone and Combined with Phenobarbital," *Arch. int. Pharmacodyn.*, 100:472, 1955.

2. BONAFEDE, V. I., "Chlorpromazine Treatment of Disturbed Epileptic Patients," *Arch. Neurol. Psychiat.*, *Chicago*, 77:243, 1957.

3. FABISCH, W., "The Effect of Chlorpromazine on the Electroencephalo-

gram of Epileptic Patients," *J. Neurol. Neurosurg. Psychiat.,* 20:185, 1957.

4. FAZEKAS, J. F., SHEA, J. G., EHRMANTRAUT, W. R., and ALEMAN, R. W., "Convulsant Action of the Phenothiazine Derivatives," *J. Amer. med. Ass.,* 165:1341, 1957.

5. GELLHORN, E., "Further Experiments on the Influence of Afferent Stimulation on Cortical Strychnine Discharges," *Electroenceph. clin. Neurophysiol.,* 12:613–619, 1960.

6. GUNN, C. G., GOGERTY, J., and WOLF, S., "Clinical Pharmacology of Anticonvulsant Compounds," *Clin. Pharmacol. Ther.,* 2:733–748, 1961.

7. HARTMANN, F. and DeGASPERO, H., "Epilepsie," in LANDOWSKY, M., *Handbuch der Neurologie,* vol. 5, Berlin, 1914, pp. 832–931.

8. HEAD, R. G., "The Use of Chlorpromazine as Adjunct in Treatment of Psychomotor Epilepsy," *Bull. Tulane med. Fac.,* 15:23–25, 1955.

9. HIMWICH, H. E., "Some Drugs in the Treatment of Mental Disorders," *Amer. J. Psychiat.,* 115:756, 1959.

10. KEATING, L. E., "Epilepsy and Behavior Disorder in School-Children," *J. ment. Sci.,* 107:161, 1961.

11. KILLAM, E. G., KILLAM, K. F., and SHAW, T., "The Effects of Psychotherapeutic Compounds on Central Afferent and Limbic Pathways," *Ann. N.Y. Acad. Sci.,* 66:784–805, 1957.

12. LOGOTHETIS, J., "Desoxyn Therapy for Nocturnal Seizures," *Neurology,* 5:236–241, 1955.

13. LOMAS, J., BOARDMAN, R. H., and MARKOWE, M., "Complications of Chlorpromazine Therapy in 800 Mental Hospital Patients," *Lancet,* 1:1144, 1955.

14. OTT, R. E. and McMASTER, R. H., "A Clinical Study of the Anticonvulsant Properties of Meratran," *Dis. nerv. Syst.,* 20:1, 1959.

15. PAUIG, P. M., DeLUCA, M. A., and CATERHELD, R. G., "Thioridazine in the Treatment of Behavior Disorders in Epileptics," *Amer. J. Psychiat.,* 117:832, 1961.

16. SHAGASS, C., "Effect of Intravenous Chlorpromazine on the Electroencephalogram," *Electroenceph. clin. Neurophysiol.,* 7:306, 1955.

17. SIGWALD, J., COMTE, C., and JUGE, D., "Neuroleptic Drugs," *World Neurol.,* 3:78, 1962.

18. STRAUSS, H., "Epileptic Disorders," *American Handbook of Psychiatry,* vol. 2, Basic Books, New York, 1959, Chap. 54.

19. WINKELMANN, N. W., "Chlorpromazine in the Treatment of Neuropsychiatric Disorders," *J. Amer. med. Ass.,* 155:18, 1954.

XVI

Closing Remarks, with Commentary on Depth Electroencephalography in Epilepsy and Schizophrenia

Robert G. Heath

More and more, as students of human behavior, we are directing our efforts toward the investigation of the brain as the organ of behavior. Much of the significant work today is being carried out by investigators trained in the use of introspective or reporting techniques for the study of behavior, as well as in the use of basic science methods. Employment of the inspective techniques—physiology, chemistry, anatomy, and so on—to study behavior has recently gained popularity after a rather extended period of dormancy. Earlier basic science techniques were inadequate. Only recently have sufficiently advanced methods of study and apparatus become available. Even now, however, this approach has not gained its desired and needed impetus.

As behavioral scientists, it behooves us to appraise the current status of our accomplishments in the light of other scientific and social developments. Technical advances in all areas of science have been extremely rapid, but possibly the most dramatic have been in the area of new weapons for destruction. These advances have served to emphasize our lagging progress in the understanding of human behavior and, particularly, our slow progress in evolving methods for treating disordered human behavior. Human emotion will be the factor determining whether or not weapons of ultimate destruction are employed. It is refreshing that during this meeting new and promising methods to study and ultimately to treat human behavior have been described. An appraisal of our current status and a look at what is required seem indicated.

The Introspective Method as a Treatment—Its Shortcomings

First, let us look at our current clinical approach to behavioral disorders. When a patient with disordered behavior, i.e., psychiatric illness, confronts us, our principal approach is to look into his background for incidents of undesirable or faulty learning experiences. These, of course, are considered against the possibility of a flaw in the patient's physical make-up but, for all practical purposes, we emphasize ontogeny. Similarly, in treatment, while we do employ some empirical somatic measures, our principal emphasis is on dynamic psychotherapy, which in essence is the use of interpersonal human influence to modify the patient's learned patterns of behavior to more effective ones. We emphasize the dynamic psychiatric approach in diagnosis and treatment, based on the techniques of reported introspection or psychoanalysis, wherein the patient reports his thoughts and feelings in detail. We study what is fed into the organ of behavior. By and large, however, very little attention in the everyday practice of psychiatry is directed toward study of the brain as the organ of behavior. This same situation has prevailed in regard to research. Major effort has gone into the study of what is fed into the organ with a disproportionate small amount of energy directed toward study of the brain itself. An appraisal of this generally accepted approach is in order.

On the therapeutic side, our results are not good. We cannot begin to handle adequately the population with overt psychiatric illness or to meet the sociological problem. I am not suggesting that we lessen our efforts to understand the effects of learning experience on behavior. However, we should do more to integrate and to correlate these findings with the organ that makes learning possible. The knowledge gained through the studies of psychodynamics should be more broadly applied. Education should be employed, wherever possible, to eliminate the sources of conflict which contribute to mental illness; but even under the most favorable conditions this method will fail to meet the challenge. Educational processes are slow, whereas the technical developments that have created the current sociological situation are rapid. We are faced with an urgent problem. It cannot be solved by treatment with the use of the techniques of introspection and education. The inspective methods, effectively directed and pursued with increased vigor, may offer an answer.

Psychodynamic data, on the other hand, should point the direction for our inspective studies.

Introspective Findings as a Guide for Inspective Studies

We note, from another viewpoint, that valuable data concerning human behavior have been gained through utilization of the introspective techniques. We have learned about hidden motivation in behavior—that man's irrational behavior is determined by emotion. This was noted near the turn of the century. It was then that evidence was accumulating to demonstrate that childhood experiences and family influences were important in determining ultimate behavioral patterns. Later, in 1926, Freud related all anxiety to realistic danger. He pointed up the importance of early memory experience on present behavior. Since then, basic findings have been somewhat elaborated; particularly pertinent was the clarification of the relationship of rage-aggression to danger. Nothing fundamentally new, however, has been forthcoming from the introspective approach.

It has been recognized for a considerable time that an inappropriate emergency response brought about by faulty learning experience is the key factor in disordered behavior. The descriptive symptoms of the various neurotic disorders represent ineffectual or inadequate patterns to neutralize the painful feelings of the emergency emotional state. It follows that if the inappropriate emergency response is eliminated, the reparative symptoms or clinical neuroses should disappear. Unrealistic, painful, emergency emotions lead groups of people to behave in maladaptive ways. These crucial observations, derived from the introspective methods, have not been adequately developed—partly because the psychoanalytic method has been overemphasized as a treatment; but the importance of psychoanalytic findings as a guide for further research employing a variety of techniques has been underemphasized. In my opinion, the single pathological entity crucial in all disordered behavior, as determined from the extensive introspective data, is inappropriate emergency emotion— fear and/or rage. Psychoanalytic data suggest that if effective and immediate measures could be developed for dealing with these emotions when they are pathological, immense strides could be made in treating disordered behavior in individuals and, as a result, in groups. This concept of disordered behavior is not universally accepted.

However, it is a useful approach since it provides something tangible for making a bridge between behavior, as we study it with psychiatric methods, and with physiological and chemical observations in animal and man.

Before relating this concept to the papers in this monograph, we should perhaps be reminded of the three fundamental processes by which disorders in emotional expression may occur. The first has been elaborated: namely, faulty learning experiences create inappropriate emergencies, thereby causing individuals to adapt to the here and now and anticipate the future in a faulty or maladaptive or neurotic way. The second process is exemplified in the schizophrenic who, seemingly, has defective machinery for the expression of emotion. Faulty learning experiences also can play a greater or lesser role in the schizophrenic, although a fundamental difference exists which is manifested by disturbances in the schizophrenic's affective and, particularly, pleasure-integrating machinery. The pleasure-integrating defect manifested in the schizophrenic adds to the predominance of the rage response. This relationship between pleasure and emergency emotion will be elaborated later. We believe that the cause of the defect in schizophrenics is a faulty metabolic pathway. This idea has been elaborated in a number of the Tulane publications[6, 7, 8, 11] and needs no further discussion here. The third process is that resulting from cellular damage seen in the so-called organic disorders—this needs no further elaboration.

Introspective Data Applied to Study of the Brain

Introspective data point up the importance of uncovering the neural mechanism for expression of emotion as well as the neural substrate for learning. A number of the papers presented attest to the importance of the two major themes. The papers by Flynn, Wasman and Egger, Eidelberg, Lesse and Gault dealt with the physiological substrate of emotion. Freedman pointed up the significance of biochemical phenomena with physiological changes. The importance of the interrelationship between learning and neural activity was stressed by Wells.

The unitary concept of mind and brain is widely accepted; the problem of relating the two is, and may always remain, a major one. There never can be a one-to-one relationship, as some of the earlier proponents of scientific monism postulated. Cross correlations, however, are altogether possible, and the data derived from psychoanalytic investigations are providing useful leads toward a bridge between mind and brain.

The complexity of interconnections between the parts of the brain is so great and feedback mechanisms are so complex as to make it unwise to attempt to attribute a particular function to a specific brain center, but some gross functions can be demonstrated to relate consistently to specific anatomical structures: for example, the correlation of disturbances in emotional expression with specific parts of the olfactory brain—this has been mentioned by several speakers during the meeting. An attempt at such a correlation was made by Papez. Some correlations have been demonstrated over many years in several laboratories, including Klüver's, Gibbs', MacLean's, and at Tulane. This is demonstrable with the conventional physiological techniques of stimulation, ablation, and recording. The anatomical structures demonstrated to be involved are the amygdala, parts of the hippocampus, and the septal region. In the Tulane studies, activity has been recorded in association with strong emotions in all of these regions. Marked reductions in, or absence of, emotional expression dramatically follows extensive lesions in the septal region. Our studies, particularly those in man, indicate that pleasure feelings are related to physiological activity in the septal region. Other investigators have demonstrated that the pleasure responses of lower animals apparently are widespread through this system. These are a few examples demonstrating a cross correlation between the psychological phenomenon of emotion-feeling and brain activity.

It is important to be cognizant of the limitation of animal studies. Because animals cannot talk, we are limited to objective data. We can know the meaning of the objective observation only when the subjective component is described to us through speech. Animal studies, therefore, take on considerably more meaning with the addition of human studies where the observable phenomena are complemented by the patient's descriptions of what he felt and thought in association with the observed phenomena. Combining inspective and introspective data enhances the value of both. Human studies, in which physiological studies of the brain are incorporated with psychiatric interviews, have demonstrated that physiological activity of different anatomical structures varies with the emotional disturbance. Feelings of strong emotion, whether the reaction be appropriately or inappropriately determined, create a typical response through the olfactory structures, whereas the physiological alteration in association with the psychotic schizophrenic clinical state is strikingly and consistently different. The same structures are affected, but in a different way. Figure XVI-1 is a baseline line recording from Patient J.H. Figure XVI—2 is a recording made when the patient was angry and

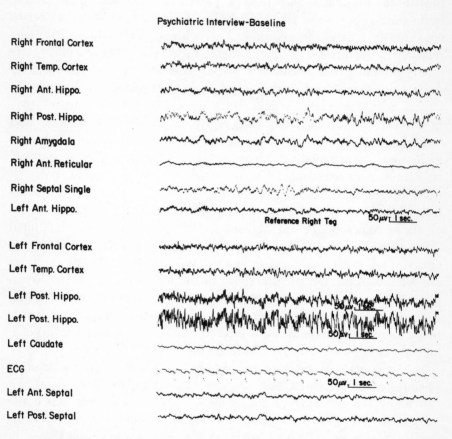

Pt. A-25 (J.H.) 2/19/57

Fig. XVI—1. *Cortical and subcortical recordings from schizophrenic patient A-25 during period of remission.*

complaining that the psychiatrist stirred up painful memories. Note, in association with the anger, the appearance of high-amplitude spindling in the hippocampus. These electrical changes consistently have appeared in a large number of patients in association with the expression of strong emotion. This observation was the background for Lesse's[14] exploration of the effects on recordings of the induction of emergency emotions in animals—a study referred to in Chapter X. Figure XVI—3 is a waking recording during remission from Patient A.D. Figure XVI—4, also a waking record, was obtained when the patient was grossly psychotic. The spiking and slow-wave activity in the

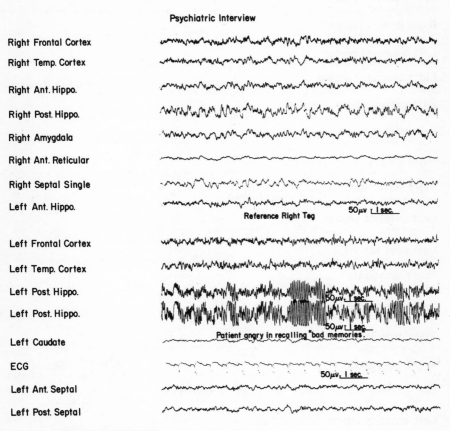

Psychiatric Interview

Right Frontal Cortex
Right Temp. Cortex
Right Ant. Hippo.
Right Post. Hippo.
Right Amygdala
Right Ant. Reticular
Right Septal Single
Left Ant. Hippo.

Reference Right Teg   50μv ⌐ I sec.

Left Frontal Cortex
Left Temp. Cortex
Left Post. Hippo.
Left Post. Hippo.

50μv, I sec.

Left Caudate

Patient angry in recalling "bad memories".

50μv, I sec.

ECG

50μv, I sec.

Left Ant. Septal
Left Post. Septal

Pt. A-25 (J.H.) 2/19/57

Fig. XVI—2. *Recordings from schizophrenic patient A-25 during period of anger.*

septal region is a consistent concomitant of the psychotic state. Spiking and slow-wave activity in the hippocampus and amygdala can be present or absent in association with this abnormality in the septal region when the patient is psychotic. However, spiking and slow-wave activity in the hippocampus and amygdala, without accompanying abnormalities in the septal region, is *not* associated with psychotic behavior. Note in these figures that the cortical recordings do not reflect the severe abnormalities appearing in the deep recordings. We have consistently seen that cortical and scalp recordings rarely reflect the marked fluctuations in electrical activity from the deep

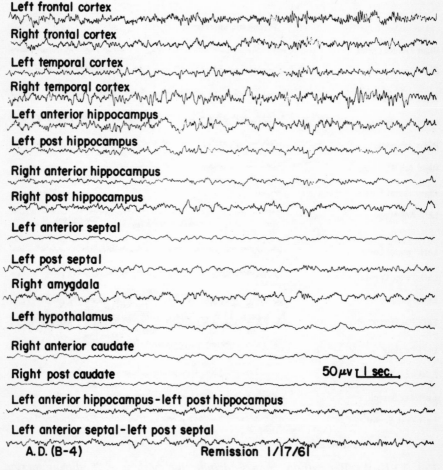

Fig. XVI—3. *Cortical and subcortical recordings of schizophrenic patient B-6 during period of remission.*

structures. Figure XVI–5 (Patient A. V.) demonstrates the marked difference between simultaneous recordings from the scalp, cortex (under the dura), and a wide variety of subcortical structures.

Flynn's presentation (Chapter V) of behavior during hippocampal discharge in lower animals was particularly interesting in the light of the findings we have obtained with human subjects. In our experience, there is no repeatable pattern of behavior associated with the hippocampal after-discharge. Sometimes there have been no behavioral changes in our human subjects; at other times the changes have been quite extreme. This is most frequently illustrated in our epileptic subjects where hippocampal discharges regularly occur. Figure XVI–6 is a recording obtained from epileptic Patient A. V. Note the high-

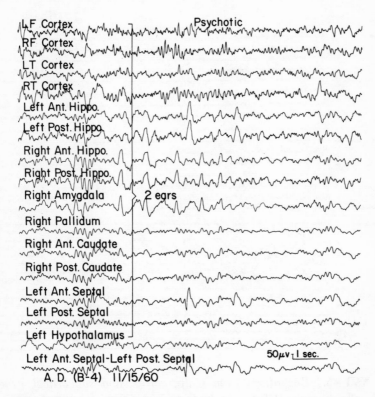

Fig. XVI—4. *Recordings from schizophrenic patient B-6 during period of gross psychosis.*

amplitude rhythmical activity in the amygdala and hippocampus of the type usually identified with seizures (also demonstrated in Figure XVI–5). This type of pattern is of frequent occurrence in epileptic patients. Patient A. V. did not display any behavioral changes either subjectively or objectively during the time of this recording. When the recording in Figure XVI–7 was obtained the patient was having what she described as a "scary spell." She was very anxious and thought she was about to see and converse with her long-deceased father. During the time of the recording, this was a fixed delusion. In reviewing our recordings, it appears that the important consideration is whether or not other structures are fired as a result of the hippocampal discharge. Figure XVI—7 shows the pattern of generalized slowing with occasional slow spikes in the septal recordings. Our experience suggests that one should be cautious in drawing conclusions concerning

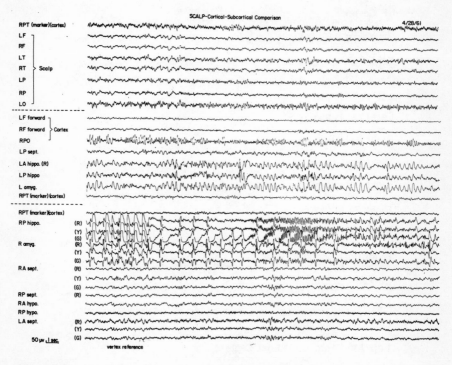

Fig. XVI—5. *Recordings from scalp, cortex, and subcortical structures of epileptic patient B-5 (see text).*

hippocampal function merely on the basis of electrical after-discharges. Sutin's studies (Chapter IX) with the ventromedial nucleus of the hypothalamus, demonstrating the interplay with the septal region and hypothalamus, were extremely interesting, particularly in view of the similarity in symptoms induced with stimulation or ablation of the septal region and the ventromedial hypothalamic nucleus. These findings further demonstrate the complex nature of the neural connections and overlapping functions within the brain.

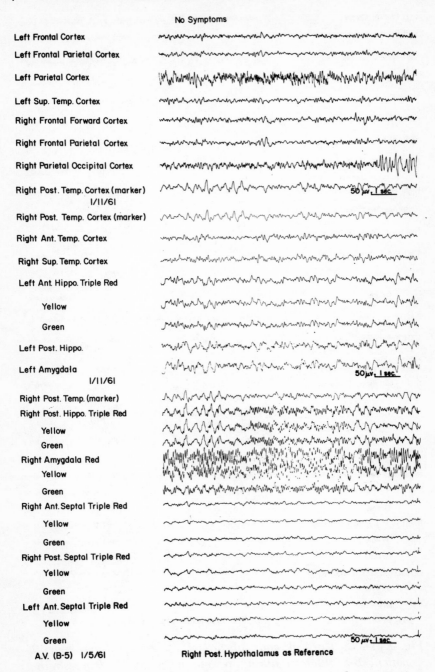

Fig. XVI—6. *Recordings of epileptic patient B-5 demonstrating hippocampal discharge.*

"Scary" Feelings

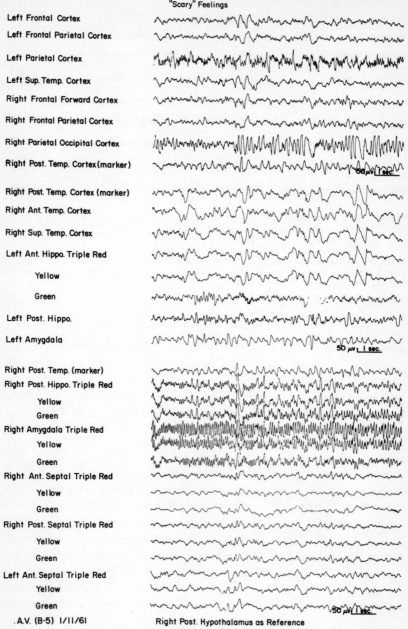

Left Frontal Cortex

Left Frontal Parietal Cortex

Left Parietal Cortex

Left Sup. Temp. Cortex

Right Frontal Forward Cortex

Right Frontal Parietal Cortex

Right Parietal Occipital Cortex

Right Post. Temp. Cortex (marker)

Right Post. Temp. Cortex (marker)

Right Ant. Temp. Cortex

Right Sup. Temp. Cortex

Left Ant. Hippo. Triple Red

Yellow

Green

Left Post. Hippo.

Left Amygdala

Right Post. Temp. (marker)

Right Post. Hippo. Triple Red

Yellow

Green

Right Amygdala Triple Red

Yellow

Green

Right Ant. Septal Triple Red

Yellow

Green

Right Post. Septal Triple Red

Yellow

Green

Left Ant. Septal Triple Red

Yellow

Green

.A.V. (B-5) 1/11/61   Right Post. Hypothalamus as Reference

Fig. XVI—7. *Cortical and subcortical recordings from epileptic patient B-5 obtained during period of "anxiety," demonstrating pattern of generalized slowing with occasional slow spikes in the septal recordings.*

The importance of diffuse brain-activating systems has been elaborated extensively in recent years and has been repeatedly referred to during this conference. It is noteworthy that the activating system apparently most consistently involved in the psychological phenomena with which we deal as clinicians is in these specific structures of the olfactory brain. Much attention has been directed toward the reticular activating system, but little concrete information has been forthcoming to implicate this system in emotional expression as related to clinical phenomena. It is proving to be a basic activating system tied in with sleep and wakefulness. Even the phenomenon of subjective pain is more convincingly related to the more rostral olfactory activating system.

The relationship between activity in these diffuse activating systems and clinical epilepsy has been the subject for important speculation in recent years and was discussed by both Goldensohn (Chapter XII) and Glaser *et al.* (Chapter XIV) in their presentations. Each referred to the midbrain or diencephalic origin for the abnormalities recorded in the scalp electroencephalograms in his psychomotor epileptic patients. This is in agreement with the concept advanced by Penfield and others. Since 1955, we have studied six epileptic patients with electrodes implanted into numerous specific subcortical nuclear masses as well as over the cortex and fixed so as to remain accurately in position for periods of up to two years. In each of these patients we have recorded preceding and during clinical seizures, during interictal periods when the patient was displaying a wide variety of clinical symptoms, and during periods of remission. All patients in this group had electrodes implanted into the specific olfactory structures referred to above. In addition, all six patients had two to nine electrodes in the hypothalamus; four of the six had two to six electrodes in the tegmentum of the mesencephalon. In no instance in this patient series did we ever obtain evidence that the seizure began or was generated in the midbrain or reticular activating system. We consistently found that the seizural activity began in the hippocampus or amygdala and that the recording change frequently appeared in these structures without accompanying clinical symptoms. It was only after the seizural activity spread to involve the septal region as well that it next involved all regions of the brain, and this generalized involvement was associated with the clinical seizure. Figure XVI–8, a recording from Patient A. V., illustrates the onset of a generalized seizure. It begins in the hippocampus and amygdala, spreads to the septal region and

then to all leads. In this group of patients, we have had an opportunity to record from subcortical, as well as cortical, scalp leads during
interictal periods of fluctuating behavioral states. When the patients
were psychotic during these interictal periods, the psychosis was
associated with severely abnormal recordings in the septal region. Thus,
again, there was a consistent relationship between recording abnormalities in the septal region and psychotic behavior.

In these temporal lobe or psychomotor epileptic patients with inter-

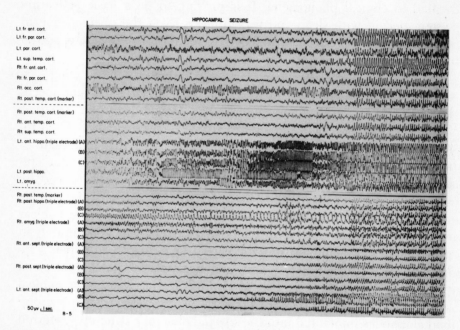

Fig. XVI—8. *Cortical and subcortical recording obtained from epileptic
patient B-5 during the onset of a generalized seizure.*

ictal psychotic behavior, the recording abnormalities, although in
the same anatomical structures, were strikingly different from those
obtained from our schizophrenic patients during episodes of psychotic period. Figures XVI—3 and XVI—4, the recordings obtained
from a schizophrenic patient, contrast quite sharply with those obtained from a psychomotor epileptic patient during psychosis. Our
studies on the relationship between psychomotor epilepsy and schizophrenia were presented at the 1961 meeting of the American Psychiatric Association.[9] The deep recordings of these two groups of

patients demonstrate that the areas from which the most abnormalities are recorded are the same in the schizophrenics and the epileptics. The type of recordings is so markedly different, however, and the contrasts in the over-all clinical pictures of the two groups are so striking that we see no reason for assuming that the two diseases are related. Those who have postulated a relationship between the two diseases have done so on the basis of the common denominator of psychotic behavior, but this is a weak point since implication of these same anatomical structures with pathological processes (e.g., paresis, trauma, tumors) of other types is associated with psychotic behavior. The relationship between epilepsy and the so-called functional psychoses has been frequently described in the literature since 1888[12] and since 1949 has been the subject of a number of studies in the Tulane Department.[5] These observations served as background for some of the animal studies that we conducted prior to embarking on our depth electrode studies in man.

At the time of the original presentation of our human studies in 1952[10] we reviewed some of the early literature which suggested involvement of deep olfactory structures in association with gross behavioral disorders and presented animal studies demonstrating functional connections between the septal region and the temporal and frontal cortex. Similar studies demonstrating these functional connections have been reported.[1] The clinical phenomena have been discussed by Gibbs at some length.[4] The effect of cellular lesions in these subcortical regions on the electroencephalogram as well as on behavior was discussed by Lennox and Brody.[13] Because there were many features in common between the interictal behavior of epileptic patients with electroencephalographic abnormalities and schizophrenic patients in whom we had demonstrated an electrical abnormality in the septal region, a study was conducted in the Tulane Department to evaluate the psychiatric and psychological status of a large group of patients who presented electroencephalographic abnormalities. These data were published by Ervin *et al.*[3] and Epstein *et al.*[2] It is gratifying that studies in this area are continuing since the problem is extensive as well as intriguing.

The neural basis for learning is being explored through conditioning experiments. This area of work, as presented by Pribram (Chapter VI), is similarly exciting and promising. Experiments concerning the mirror focus which continues to fire on its own after the original abnormal focus that set it into activity is removed are proving to be a most useful preparation for study. The finding by Morrell[15] that alterations in chemistry are present in the mirror focus opens many promising avenues.

References

1. AJMONE-MARSAN, C. and STOLL, J., "Subcortical Connections of the Temporal Pole in Relation to Temporal Lobe Seizures," *Arch. Neurol. Psychiat., Chicago, 66*:669, 1951.

2. EPSTEIN, A. W. and ERVIN, F., "Psychodynamic Significance of Seizure Content in Psychomotor Epilepsy," *Psychosom. Med., 18*:43–45, 1956.

3. ERVIN, F., EPSTEIN, A. W., and KING, H. E., "Behavior of Epileptic and Non-epileptic Patients with 'Temporal Spikes,'" *Arch. Neurol. Psychiat., Chicago, 74*:488, 1955.

4. GIBBS, F. A., "Ictal and Nonictal Psychiatric Disorders in Temporal Lobe Epilepsy," *J. nerv. ment. Dis., 113*:522, 1951.

5. HEATH, R. G., "Chronic Experiments with Animals," in HEATH, R. G. *et al., Studies in Schizophrenia,* Cambridge, Harvard University Press, 1954, p. 97.

6. HEATH, R. G., "Physiological and Biochemical Studies in Schizophrenia with Particular Emphasis on Mind-Brain Relationships," *Int. Rev. Neurobiol., 1*:299, 1959.

7. HEATH, R. G., "A Biochemical Hypothesis on the Etiology of Schizophrenia," in JACKSON, D. D. (ed.), *The Etiology of Schizophrenia,* Basic Books, New York, 1960, p. 146.

8. HEATH, R. G., "Reappraisal of Biological Aspects of Psychiatry," *J. Neuropsychiat., 3*:1, 1961.

9. HEATH, R. G., "Common Characteristics of Epilepsy and Schizophrenia: Clinical Observation and Depth Electrode Studies," *Amer. J. Psychiat., 118*:1013, 1962.

10. HEATH, R. G., BECKER, H. C. *et al., Studies in Schizophrenia,* Cambridge, Harvard University Press, 1954.

11. HEATH, R. G. and DE BALVIAN VERSTER, F., "Effects of Chemical Stimulation to Discrete Brain Areas," *Amer. J. Psychiat., 117*:980, 1961.

12. JACKSON, J. H., "On a Particular Variety of Epilepsy ('Intellectual Aura'); One Case with Symptoms of Organic Brain Disease," *Brain, 11*:179, 1888–1889.

13. LENNOX, M. and BRODY, B. S., "Paroxysmal Slow Waves in the Electro-encephalograms of Patients with Epilepsy and with Subcortical Lesions," *J. nerv. ment. Dis.*, 104:237, 1946.

14. LESSE, H., "Electrographic Recordings of Amygdaloid Activity During a Conditioned Response," *Fed. Proc.*, 16:79, 1957.

15. MORRELL, F., "Lasting Changes in Synaptic Organization Produced by Continuous Neuronal Bombardment," in *UNESCO Symposium—Brain Mechanisms and Learning*, Charles C Thomas, Springfield, Ill., 1961.

Name Index

395

Subject Index

References to illustrations and tables are in boldface.

abdominal epilepsy, 319, 320, 321, 323, 324

ablation: of cerebral structures, 88-89; flexion responses to in cat, 90; involving hypothalamus, 245; as physiological technique, 381, 386

"adrenergic" activity, transmission in brain stem, 278-279

affect: behavior and, 266; defense and, 141; disorders of, 16, 362; and responses, 10

after-discharges: in amygdala, 286; defined, 134; by electrical stimulation or drugs, 135, **288**, **289**; transition from propagated to reactive, **286**. *See also* hippocampal after-discharges

aggressive behavior: and amygdala, 246; EEG in, 15; and hypothalamus, 244, 245; and septal area, 246; spontaneous and evoked activity in, 317

alimentary reactions, inhibition of by amygdala stimulation, 287

alpha activity, in human subjects: in change of environment, 69; frequency variation of, 9; in paired sound-light stimulation, 28, 29, **35**, **36**, **42**; in photic stimulation, 49, **52**, **53**, 68; with psychopharmacological agents, 182, 187; in sensory deprivation states, 16; with single flashes, 41-44, **46**, **47**, **49**; with sound stimuli, **34**; in tension and anxiety, 9

alpha blocking response: in concentration, 62; conditioning of in animals, 71-82; conditioning of in man, 64-71; with cyclic stimulation, 70; following flash, **48**, 61, 62; following sound, 62, 70; in novel situation, 62

alpha rhythms (waves), in man: in behavioral disorders, 15; in brain-damaged and schizophrenic subjects, 44; with flickering light, 69; as measure of cerebral function, 44; metabolic setting of, 4; in photic stimulation, 10, 27-28, **34**; relation of personality to, 9; sensitivity of to stimuli, 4

Alzheimer-Pick presenile dementias, 18

amines, in brain: derivation of in mammals, 201; enzyme system in, 205, 207; inhibition of destruction of, 210; levels of, 203-204, 213, **216**, 220, 223, 227; mechanisms of, 218, 227-228; receptor sites of, 211-212; "release" of, 206-210; role of, 199-201, 217; in seizure activity, 220; storage form of, 204; in stress, 215; among subcellular elements, 205, 206, 217; synthesis of, 205-206; transport mechanisms of, 207. *See also* serotonin

amnesia: in rats, 151, 152; retrograde, in head injuries, 151; in seizures, 306, 345. *See also* memory

amygdala: effect of cocaine on, 279, 285; in emotion, 147, 381; excitability of, 225; modulating effect of on hypothalamus, 147; pattern of after-discharge of, **286**; responses arising in, 75, 76, 127; and sexual behavior, 246

amygdaloid-ventromedial evoked responses: decrease in with norepinephrine injection, 257, **258**, **259**; effect of glucose-saline on, **254**; effect of insulin on, **255**; effect of mesencephalic reticular formation stimulation on, **261**, **264**; recovery curve of, on injection with insulin, **256**

anesthesia: comparison of in monkey and man, **125**; effects of on evoked potentials, 113; in electrophysiological response, 120; in human evoked somatosensory responses, 122, **123**, **124**; in somatosensory evoked responses in monkey, 121

anticonvulsant drugs therapy, 316, 319, 320, 321, 324, 325, 346, 347, 366

anxiety: beta and alpha activity in, 15; in drug administration in seizure states, 345, 367; with photic stimulation, 16

aphagia, 244

aphasia, 367

arousal responses, 4, 7, 12, 63, 262

association cortex, 318

astroglia, 5

attentiveness, 11

auditory aura and hallucinations, 297, 299